Microprocessor System Design

A practical introduction

Michael J. Spinks

⊞ NEWNES

Newnes
An imprint of Butterworth-Heinemann Ltd
Linacre House, Jordan Hill, Oxford OX2 8DP

 PART OF REED INTERNATIONAL BOOKS

OXFORD   LONDON   BOSTON
MUNICH   NEW DELHI   SINGAPORE   SYDNEY
TOKYO   TORONTO   WELLINGTON

First published 1992

British Library Cataloguing in Publication Data

Spinks, Michael J.
   Microprocessor system design: a practical
   introduction.
   I. Title
   004.256

ISBN 0 7506 0279 1

Library of Congress Cataloguing in Publication Data

Spinks, Michael J.
   Microprocessor system design: a practical introduction/Michael
   J. Spinks
   p. cm.
   Includes bibliographical references and index.
   ISBN 0 7506 0283 X
   1. Microprocessors–Design and construction. 2. Electronic
   circuit design. I. Title.
   TK7895.M5S65   1992
   621.39'5–dc20   91-41074
                                                           CIP

Printed in Great Britain by
Thomson Litho Ltd, East Kilbride, Scotland
Composition by Scribe Design, Gillingham, Kent

Contents

Preface

This book has been written to introduce the reader to the concepts and techniques which go into the design of electronic circuits, especially microprocessor boards and their peripherals. No previous knowledge of electronics is assumed, and each time a new term or idea is introduced it is clearly explained. In addition, a glossary is provided for quick reference.

The book takes a different approach from that of many electronics books I have read, which take a very academic stand: they are full of unnecessary detail, jargon and often a lot of maths. It is easy to become lost or confused, and it is difficult to know which are the important points – if you understand them at all, that is! It is my experience that in reality design engineers rely on a few relatively simple techniques, and it is by combining such ideas that complex circuits are built up.

In my opinion an electronics book should foster the acquisition and understanding of these key techniques. I have written this text from a practical viewpoint to give the reader the essential knowledge that an engineer uses. I have kept the amount of maths to a minimum and have aimed to explain new concepts in plain English, rather than in terms of other pieces of jargon; this should make the contents accessible to readers of many backgrounds. Almost all the circuits and ideas have been used in real industrial situations, so the reader can study them in the knowledge that they will be of practical use, rather than of merely academic interest.

The book begins with the basic building blocks of electronic systems – digital and analog components – and is followed by the more advanced topics of operational amplifiers and programmable logic (PALs). The reader who masters these topics will be able to design many useful circuits and will have gained a solid grounding in electronics.

However, much of modern electronics is based on the flexibility of microprocessors, and anyone involved in electronics today must have a sound grasp of these devices. Here the 6809 is used to illustrate how a microprocessor works and the relationships between the hardware and software. The use of microprocessors is developed by considering how to expand a microprocessor system and the use of bus-based systems – *the* way to get a small control system working quickly. Some specialized circuits are then investigated – A/Ds, D/As, graphics and phase-locked loops. To conclude, some practical aspects of electronics design are examined.

Thus the book should be of interest to engineers and technicians who are involved in electronics, particularly microprocessor work. It should also provide useful reading for students on electronics engineering courses for HNC, HND and degree qualifications, and for anyone else who wishes to obtain a clear and concise working knowledge of electronics.

M.J.S.

Acknowledgements

I would like to thank the following for their assistance with this book:

Paul Cuthbert and Anthony Winter of Arcom Control Systems Ltd for permission to reproduce some of Arcom's circuit diagrams. I also thank the latter for many interesting discussions about various aspects of electronics.

One of the best ways to improve one's knowledge of electronics is to discuss ideas and circuits with fellow engineers. Amongst others the following have given unwitting tuition: Dave Albiston, Mike Cox, Paul Querelle and Peter Duffett-Smith.

Michael Tooley for his comments on the typescript.

All the staff at Butterworth-Heinemann who have worked on this book.

1 Digital logic

Logic levels

In digital electronics we are concerned with electrical signals which can have one of two values. These values are most easily referred to as one of the following pairs of names – HI and LO, TRUE and FALSE, or 1 and 0. Since confusion can arise as to whether a 'TRUE' signal is represented by a high or low electrical signal, here we shall use the HI and LO pair, and use them simply as a reflection of whether an electrical signal is in the high or low state. The exact voltage levels corresponding to the HI and LO states depend on the logic family (this book looks at TTL and CMOS) being used.

TTL

TTL (Transistor–Transistor Logic) operates off a +5 V supply and a TTL input will recognize a signal as a logic HI if the input voltage exceeds about 2.4 V. It will recognize a signal as a LO logic level if the input voltage is less than about 0.8 V. If the input voltage is between these figures, say 1.5 V, then the output is undefined (it could be in either the LO or the HI state); such a state will obviously occur momentarily when an input changes state between HI and LO or vice versa. Besides, if an input level is sitting at such a voltage then it means there is something wrong with your circuit, for example you might be trying to drive too many inputs from just one output. The output of a TTL gate is designed to satisfy another's input requirements, so if an output is in the HI state then it is guaranteed to have a voltage of at least 2.4 V (typically 3.4 V), and in the LO state a maximum voltage of 0.4 V (typically 0.2 V).

TTL comes in many varieties and the differences (mostly speed) are looked at later. The type in most common use at present is the 74LS series (LS stands for low-power Schottky) which can operate up to around 25 MHz. The 74 is the start of the part number and indicates the standard commercial series which operates over the temperature range 0 to 70°C, compared with the 54LS military series which can work from –55 to 125°C.

CMOS

The other logic family we shall look at is called CMOS (Complementary Metal Oxide Semiconductor). CMOS uses much less power than TTL (the power consumption increasing with frequency), so it is especially suitable for battery-powered operation. CMOS comes in two main varieties. The older 40xx series operates off a range of power supplies from 3 to 15 V (at 5 V it is nearly compatible with TTL), but is limited to speeds of a few megahertz; the higher the supply voltage the faster it can run. The newer high-speed CMOS families (74HC and 74AC), operating off 2 to 6 V, are pin compatible with the 74 TTL series and should be considered for new designs. For direct interfacing to TTL the 74HCT and 74ACT series are available, and can be used to replace TTL devices in existing circuits to reduce power consumption.

The output of a CMOS gate swings right to the supply rails and since the logic switching point is roughly midway between the supply rails CMOS has higher *noise immunity* than TTL. One disadvantage of CMOS chips is that they are susceptible to damage from static electricity before being inserted into a circuit, so correct handling procedures need to be adopted: do not touch the pins of ICs, work on a conducting surface and wear an earthed wrist-strap.

Simple gates and truth tables

In this section we shall look at simple logic gates and at how *truth tables* can be drawn up to show the relationship between the inputs and outputs of a logic circuit.

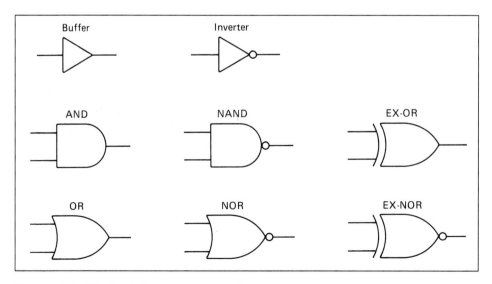

Figure 1.1 *The basic logic gate symbols*

The buffer

The simplest logic building block or gate is the *buffer*. The output of a buffer chip is simply a copy of its input. This is more useful than you might think – the output could have more drive than the input or a different type of driving circuitry, such as tri-state or open-collector, as we shall see later. The symbol for the buffer is shown in Figure 1.1. The logic equation for a buffer is written as $Y = A$, where Y is the output and A the input; both can have the value HI or LO.

The inverter and truth tables

The other single input gate is known as the *inverter*, see Figure 1.1. Here the output is the inverse, or opposite, of the input. The 74LS04 is an example of an inverter and has six inverters in one 14 pin package. In logic terminology the output is the negation or NOT of the input. The equation for the inverter is $Y = /A$ where the '/' means NOT. This can be written as a truth table as follows.

Input (A)	Output (Y)
LO	HI
HI	LO

A truth table contains all possible inputs of a logic circuit and the corresponding outputs arranged in a table. The name arises from the alternative labelling of the logic levels as TRUE and FALSE. Truth tables can be useful when trying to simplify logic problems, to minimize the number of chips required or for producing a list of inputs and outputs for coding into a programmable logic device (see Chapter 4).

The AND gate

The next simplest logic gates are those which have two inputs and produce one output. Firstly the AND gate (74LS08): here the output is HI if and only if the two inputs (A and B) are both HI. The symbol for an AND gate is shown in Figure 1.1. The logic equation (also known as the Boolean equation) for an AND gate is $Y = A \& B$, or alternatively A.B or A*B, and the truth table is given below.

A	B	Y
LO	LO	LO
LO	H I	LO
HI	LO	LO
HI	HI	HI

The OR gate

Secondly, the OR gate (74LS32; four in a package): the output is HI if either of the two inputs is HI. The symbol for an OR gate is given in Figure 1.1. Its equation is $Y = A + B$ and its truth table is as follows.

A	B	Y
LO	LO	LO
HI	LO	HI
LO	HI	HI
HI	HI	HI

The NAND gate

The NAND gate (74LS00), see Figure 1.1, is the negation of the AND gate and has the equation $Y = /(A \& B)$. Its truth table is shown below.

A	B	Y
LO	LO	HI
HI	LO	HI
LO	HI	HI
HI	HI	LO

De Morgan's theorem

The previous truth table is an example of *de Morgan's theorem* which states that $/(A \& B) = /A + /B$, and that $/(A + B) = /A \& /B$. In words: if you negate a logic term, then this is equal to the individual terms negated and with AND substituted for OR and vice versa. We can draw up a truth table to show this formula, as below.

A	/A	B	/B	A & B	/A + /B
LO	HI	LO	HI	LO	HI
LO	HI	HI	LO	LO	HI
HI	LO	LO	HI	LO	HI
HI	LO	HI	LO	HI	LO

In the days before programmable logic (PALs, EPLDs, etc.) de Morgan's theorem was quite important as a means of rewriting logic equations to minimize the number of gates required in a circuit. Nowadays gates are cheap and if you are using programmable logic the computer program which processes your equations implements de Morgan's theorem for you.

The NOR gate

The next two-input gate is the NOR gate – the negation of the OR gate. Its TTL part is the 74LS02, its symbol is shown in Figure 1.1 and its logic equation is $Y = /(A + B)$. By de Morgan's theorem, $Y = /A \ \& \ /B$. Its truth table is as follows.

A	B	Y
LO	LO	HI
LO	HI	LO
HI	LO	LO
HI	HI	LO

The exclusive-OR gate

There is one final two-input gate (and its negation), the exclusive-OR or EX-OR gate. In an EX-OR the output is HI if either input is HI but not if both are HI. The symbol for an EX-OR gate is given in Figure 1.1 and its equation is written as $Y = A \oplus B$. In terms of ANDs and ORs it is $Y = (A \ \& \ /B) + (/A \ \& \ B)$. Its truth table is given below.

A	B	Y
LO	LO	LO
LO	HI	HI
HI	LO	HI
HI	HI	LO

Multiple-input gates

With the exception of the EX-OR gate, multiple-input gates of the above logic block are available; for example, the 74LS30, an eight-input NAND gate. However, the advent of programmable logic means you only rarely need to use such gates.

Types of gate output circuitry

Tri-state logic

The gates we have looked at so far all drive their output pins either HI or LO (they are sometimes referred to as *totem-pole* outputs); two other types of output are available, the first of which is known as tri-state (a trademark of National Semiconductor) or 3-state. In tri-state logic the output of a gate can be in one of three states – the normal HI and LO levels and a third

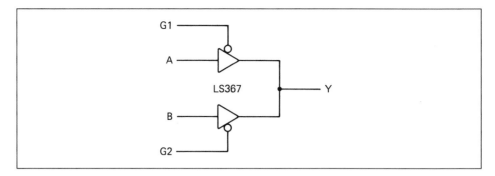

Figure 1.2   *A tri-state logic circuit*

state labelled Z. In the third state the gate is said to be tri-stated, and if so it will neither drive nor load the bus – it acts as though it is disconnected from the circuit. Gates which can be tri-stated have what are known as enable inputs – if the enable pin is in one state (usually HI) then the gate is tri-stated. The question then arises: what use is such a gate? The trick is that the tri-state facility allows you to connect together the outputs of different gates; provided all but one are tri-stated the circuit will act as though there is just one gate. Thus, at different times different chips can have control of the line (otherwise known as a *bus line*). This sort of arrangement is crucial to the construction of microprocessor circuits.

As an example consider the 74LS367 chip. This is a buffer chip which can be tri-stated and has two identical halves each controlled by an enable signal (G), see Figure 1.2. The corresponding truth table below shows how the enables can be used to select between two lines of data, A and B.

Gl	G2	Y	
HI	HI	Z	Both tri-state
LO	HI	A	Output follows input A
HI	LO	B	Output follows input B
LO	LO	?	Illegal

The state with both buffers enabled at the same time is illegal: if the two input signals are different the two LS367 outputs will fight one another; at best this will lead to misleading data being presented to the next gate along, at worst it will lead to the buffers becoming damaged. Thus, when designing a microprocessor (or any other) circuit it is essential to ensure that such an illegal state can never occur.

Examples of tri-state gates

The preponderance of 8-bit buses in microprocessor work means that most of the tri-state logic available is 8 bits wide; it consists of packs of eight buffers or inverters. For example, the 74LS240 is an 8-bit inverter, the

74LS244 is an 8-bit buffer. Both these chips have improved output drive over the standard LS-TTL of 24 mA of LO level drive. The 74LS245 transceiver chip, see Figure 1.3, is a very important IC. It has one tri-state enable pin and a *direction* pin. The direction pin decides which side of the IC is its input and which side is its output. This enables data to flow sometimes in one direction and sometimes in the other – precisely what is needed for a microprocessor data bus. Other tri-state devices include the 74LS374 which is a tri-stateable latch (see later), and the 74LS646, a 24 pin device which combines the facets of the 374 with those of the 245, again very useful for microprocessor data buses.

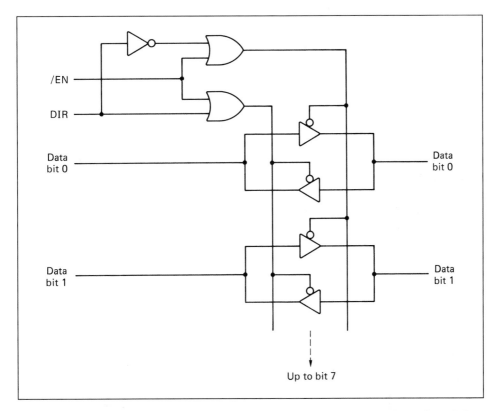

Figure 1.3 *The TTL 245 transceiver. When DIR is HI data flows from left to right, when LO from right to left. When /EN is HI the drivers are tri-stated*

Open-collector logic

In addition to tri-state logic there is also available a type of output known as *open-collector* logic. With this type of logic the output can be driven into the LO state but cannot be driven HI; instead it goes into a high-impedance state (or floats), just like a tri-stated gate does. A HI level can be obtained (and generally is) by connecting a *pull-up* resistor between the output pin and 5 V (a value of 4k7 is often used). This ensures that the input of the gate connected to the open-collector output sees a proper HI level. Like tri-state, the advantage of open-collector outputs is that many gates can be connected to the same line. A LO level from any of the chips produces a LO level output, and in this sense it acts like a 'wired-OR' gate. Note that because open-collector devices cannot drive a line HI two such outputs can never 'fight', so the gates do not have enable signals.

An open-collector line is often used in microprocessor interrupt request circuits (see Chapter 5). It works like this: many peripheral devices can generate an interrupt request (asking the microprocessor to perform some action), and they all use open-collector drivers on to the same line to do so; if any of them drives it LO then an interrupt is requested. Examples of open-collector devices are the 7406 and 7407; note the omission of the 'LS' – they are only available in the old 'standard' TTL series.

Practical considerations

Using CMOS

This section is concerned with the real-life problems of using CMOS and TTL. As a rule CMOS is easiest to use, and requires a power supply or battery of between 3 and 15 V (5 and 12 V are most common). One of the advantages of CMOS over TTL is that because of its high noise immunity – the difference between the voltage produced at the output of a gate and the point where the logic switches – the power supply does not have to be particularly stable. A few *decoupling* capacitors across the power rails are required, say one 100 nF for every five ICs. These smooth the power supplies and prevent noise generated by the logic chips from spreading through the circuit and affecting other chips. For CMOS chips driving other CMOS gates the *fanout* is very high – fanout is the number of gates an output can drive – here around 30. One important thing to remember when using CMOS is that all unused inputs (even on parts of the chip you are not using) must be tied to either 0 V or V_{DD} (V_{DD} is the symbol for the positive power rail on a CMOS chip, while V_{CC} is used for TTL). Failure to observe this rule can lead to excessive power dissipation problems and erratic circuit behaviour.

Using TTL

In contrast to CMOS, TTL requires a well-regulated supply of 5 ± 0.25 V. TTL generates more noise and uses more power than CMOS and so requires more decoupling capacitors: typically one 100 nF for every three ICs and a 22 μF tantalum capacitor for every 10. Decoupling becomes more important the faster the TTL family being employed. Table 1.1 lists the TTL families commonly available, plus the HCT and ACT CMOS families.

Table 1.1 Types of TTL compatible logic

Family	Speed (MHz)	Power consumption (mW)
74xx	15	80
74HCTxx	25	0.02
74LSxx	25	20
74ALSxx	35	15
74Sxx	75	150
74ASxx	105	50
74ACTxx	125	0.02

The figures in the second column of Table 1.1 are the guaranteed minimum speed that a 74 flip-flop can be clocked at, and the power consumption figures are typical values at 5 V. The power consumption figures of the CMOS families are their quiescent values and these will increase the faster the device is clocked.

The fanout of a typical TTL gate is about 10 and often this is insufficient, in which case the signal will have to be buffered with a driver chip, say an LS245, which can typically drive 20 loads. With TTL unused inputs do not have to be tied to 0 or 5 V, but it is good practice to do so.

Mixing TTL and CMOS

It is often useful to design a circuit using both TTL and CMOS, and therefore we need ways of interfacing the two families. How we achieve this depends on the voltage that the CMOS chips are running off. If they are using +5 V then to go from TTL to CMOS all that is required is a pull-up resistor (say 4k7) at the output of the TTL gate. This ensures that the signal rises high enough for the CMOS gate's input circuitry to see a HI

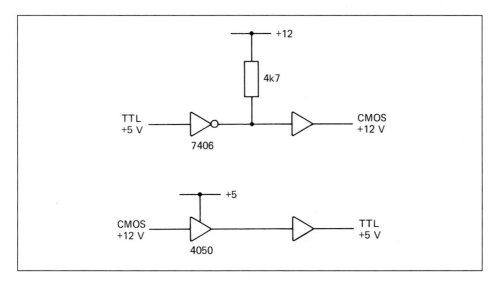

Figure 1.4 *Interfacing CMOS to TTL and vice versa*

9

level. Going from CMOS to TTL, one 40xx CMOS gate can drive up to two LS-TTL gates directly; if more drive is required then use a 4050 or 4049 driver IC.

If, however, the CMOS is running off a higher voltage, say +12 V, then to go from TTL to CMOS we use an open-collector 7406 or 7407 device with a pull-up resistor to +12 V. The outputs of a 7406 and a 7407 can be pulled to more than the chip's supply rail (note that this is not true of all TTL open-collector gates – the LS05's output voltage must not exceed 7 V). To go from CMOS at 12 V to TTL we use a 4050 or 4049 buffer powered off 5 V, for on these chips the input voltage can exceed the positive supply. Figure 1.4 illustrates how to interface TTL and CMOS chips when the CMOS is operating off a higher voltage than the TTL.

Flip-flops

The logic we have discussed so far has been combinational, by which we mean that if we know the input states we can deduce, perhaps using truth tables, what the output states will be. A second equally important type of logic is called *clocked logic*. In a clocked logic circuit block the outputs only change state on the rising or falling edge of a clock signal. Thus, knowing the inputs of a clocked circuit does not enable you to predict the outputs – you need to know what the inputs were before the last and previous clock edges.

The D flip-flop

The simplest clocked logic circuit building block is known as the D flip-flop (for example, the 74LS74). Figure 1.5 shows the symbol for this logic block. There are two outputs labelled Q and /Q, and four inputs labelled D, CLK, /R and /S. In normal operation the /R and /S inputs are held in

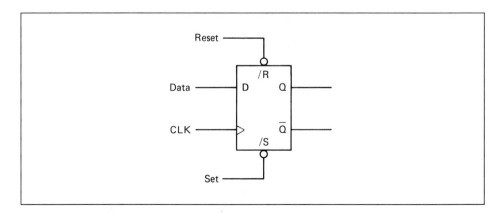

Figure 1.5 *The symbol for the D flip-flop*

the HI (inactive) state in which case the flip-flop's truth table is as follows.

CLK	D	Q	/Q
HI	X	Q	/Q
LO	X	Q	/Q
↑	LO	LO	HI
↑	HI	HI	LO

Here X means does not care, and the values of Q and /Q are given after the rising edge of the clock. Thus on a rising clock edge Q becomes equal to the value of D (the Data input). The other two inputs, /S (Set) and /R (Reset), act independently of (and override) the clock. /S puts the Q output into the HI state when /S is driven LO, and /R puts it into the LO state. The small circles in the figure on the /S and /R inputs, and the '/', indicate that the signals are *active-LO*, meaning their 'TRUE' state is LO. Finally /S and /R should not both be asserted (driven LO) at the same time, because this leads to unpredictable operation.

The ability of a flip-flop to remember the state of the system (the D input) at some earlier time (the last clock edge) means it can be used both for memory and for building circuits whose operation depends on what has happened before; without flip-flops it would be impossible to design almost all electronic circuits.

Clock division

A useful and simple application of a D flip-flop is clock division. If you have a clock at some high frequency and you want a lower frequency, a flip-flop lets you divide down the frequency in factors of two. To achieve a clock divider simply connect the /Q output to the D input. On each positive edge of the clock the output changes state. The output clock has half the

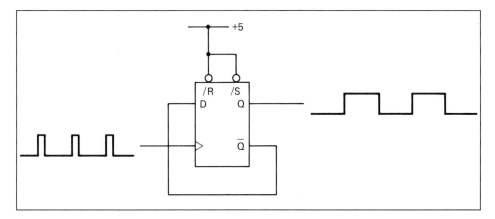

Figure 1.6 *Using a D flip-flop to divide an incoming clock by two*

frequency of the input clock and, as a bonus, a nice 50/50 duty cycle (the time in the HI state equals the time in the LO state), see Figure 1.6.

The JK flip-flop

Another type of flip-flop (less commonly used than the D-type) is the JK flip-flop (for example, the 74LS113). The JK flip-flop has two inputs, J and K, which are used to control the changes which take place on the active edge of the clock. The truth table for this device is shown below; note that the 74LS113 clocks on the falling edge.

CLK	J	K	Q	
HI	X	X	Q	
LO	X	X	Q	
↓	LO	LO	Q	No change
↓	LO	HI	LO	Go LO
↓	HI	LO	HI	Go HI
↓	HI	HI	/Q	Toggle

The 74LS113 also has an active-LO /Preset pin; if this pin is brought LO then Q goes into the HI state and /Q into the LO state. For an example of a circuit which uses a JK flip-flop refer to the microprocessor circuit in Chapter 5.

Flip-flop metastability

Before leaving flip-flops we will discuss the more advanced topic of *metastability*. When we drew up the truth table for the D flip-flop we made an assumption about the relationship between the D input and the clock. We assumed that the data was present before the clock edge arrived. The question is: what happens if the data input changes near to when the rising edge of the clock occurs? In fact for correct operation the D input must be valid for a certain time, known as the *setup time*, before the clock edge arrives. For a 74LS74 the setup time is 20 ns and for the faster 74S74 it is only 3 ns. Provided this setup time is satisfied the flip-flop is guaranteed to function correctly.

However, what happens if the parameter is violated? You might think that the flip-flop would go into either the HI or the LO state. If this was the case then most circuits would function quite happily. Unfortunately what can happen is that the flip-flop can go into a third so-called metastable state. In this state the output can hover between the logic levels (or even oscillate between them) for periods of up to microseconds before the flip-flop decides which state to go into. Such behaviour can obviously confuse the subsequent logic.

If metastability is likely to be a problem (it often is when you are trying to clock asynchronous signals) then a possible solution is to use faster logic,

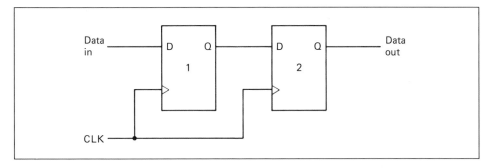

Figure 1.7 *Avoiding flip-flop metastability problems*

which reduces the probability of metastability. More reliably, the best solution is to clock the incoming signal twice, as shown in Figure 1.7. The first flip-flop may go into a metastable state, but this is missed by the second which is clocked at the same time as the first, so its data input is stable up to the clock edge, that is before the first goes metastable. Thus the output of the second does not suffer from metastability. Metastability also affects the flip-flops contained inside registered PALs – see the STE arbiter PAL in Chapter 4 for an example of a PAL avoiding metastable states, again by clocking the input signals twice.

Timing diagrams

We leave the discussion of logic for a moment to discuss *timing diagrams*. A timing diagram is the main tool an engineer uses when designing a digital circuit. As we saw in the previous section logic elements have certain timing parameters, like the setup time, which must be satisfied for a circuit to work correctly. Another timing parameter is the propagation delay, the time it takes the output to change following a change on an input; this can be different depending on whether the output is making a HI to LO or LO to HI transition. For the 74LS00 NAND gate the propagation delay is a maximum of 15 ns and is 'typically' 10 ns. Immediately we have a choice of values to choose from, and we can only use one when drawing up a design. The rule is always to use the worst case value, here 15 ns. The 'typical' value may not be true for all chips nor may it hold at all temperatures and range of working voltages; for a sound design you must use worst case values. Other timing parameters are tri-state time – how long it takes for a gate to go tri-state after its enable pin is driven inactive – and hold time – how long must you hold a signal for after a clock edge has occurred for correct operation.

Rather than trying to perform difficult addition and subtraction calculations the engineer produces a timing diagram as an illustration of how a circuit works; it shows which signals come in which order and what causes what. Cause and effect are shown by the use of curly arrows. The engineer then writes on timing parameters from a data book and checks that all parameters are satisfied. The conventions for timing diagrams are shown in Figure 1.8.

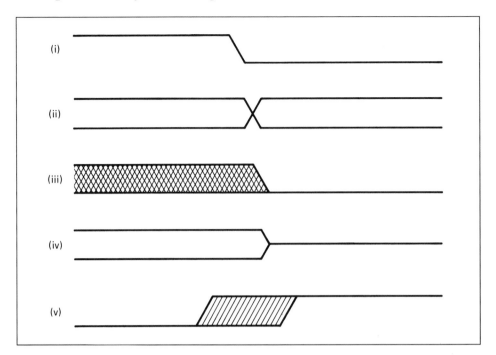

Figure 1.8   *Timing diagram conventions: (i) line changes state from HI to LO; (ii) line is valid before and after transition; (iii) don't care or unknown state becoming LO; (iv) line was driven with valid data then goes tri-state; (v) LO to HI transition some time during hatched region*

Using timing diagrams

As an example of a timing diagram consider the ('nonsense') circuit shown in Figure 1.9. t_{HL} is the propagation delay through the 74LS00, t_{SU} the setup time of the D input, t_{CQ} the time after clocking the flip-flop before the output changes state, t_{LZ} the disable or tri-state time of the LS367 and t_{ZL} the enable time. Here the only potential timing problem is the setup time for the D flip-flop which is satisfied if A rises $t_{HL} + t_{SU}$ before the clock edge.

Data sheets for LS-TTL do not give minimum propagation times, so what do you do if you have a potential timing problem if a signal changes too quickly? Again what you must not do is to use the 'typical' values. Instead you should assume a minimum propagation time of zero, which guarantees a sound design no matter how fast the chip actually switches state.

After you have drawn up the timing diagrams, the question of what to do about any problems arises. A possible solution is to use faster logic, though this means that if you are working in industry then additional stocking requirements are needed. Alternatively, and best of all, return to the initial design and look for ways to redesign parts of the circuit so as to satisfy the timing constraints; if it is a first try there will almost certainly be improvements to be made.

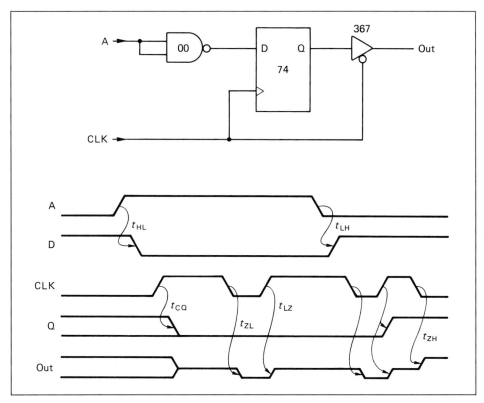

Figure 1.9 *An example timing diagram*

Logic building blocks

In this section we shall discuss the various types of logic functions used when designing a circuit. In principle these could all be built using the logic gates we have discussed, but in practice they are so commonly used that manufacturers produce chips to perform these functions.

Counters

Counters are a type of clocked logic. The outputs of a counter are usually labelled Q0–QN, and on a clock edge they change state so that the number represented by them either increments or decrements. Counters are available in various forms: BCD (Binary-coded Decimal) in which the count goes from 0 to 9 (the output being given in binary notation), and binary counters in which the count goes from 0 to some number 2^N-1 (for example, 15). Electronically, there are two types of counter – *synchronous* and *ripple*.

In a ripple counter each stage of the counter is clocked by the output of the preceding stage, and thus there is a propagation delay from the least significant stage to the most significant stage. For this reason it is inadvisable

15

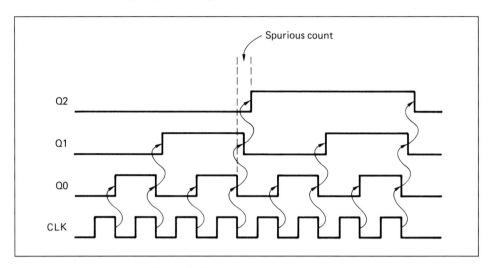

Figure 1.10 *A timing diagram for a binary ripple counter*

to decode the outputs of a ripple counter, for whilst the count is changing spurious transient states occur on the outputs. The 74LS393 is an example of a 4-bit binary ripple counter and the 74LS93 an example of a 4-bit BCD ripple counter. Figure 1.10 shows how the outputs of a ripple counter change one after the other.

In a synchronous counter all outputs are clocked simultaneously. This allows the outputs to be decoded, but it has the disadvantage of generating more noise, hence necessitating more decoupling.

For counters with many stages CMOS has a good selection; for example, the 4020 is a 14-bit binary counter and the 4040 a 12-bit counter. Counters can usually be cascaded to make larger ones. Note, however, that nowadays large counters, especially ones with odd counts (say, divide by 38), are normally calculated by software using a microprocessor.

Shift registers

In a *shift register* the logic levels at its outputs are shifted along 1 bit at a time on each clock edge. The 74LS164 is an example of an 8-bit, see Figure 1.11. The data input is labelled A (actually the 164 ANDs two inputs together but this is a minor detail) and the outputs QA–QH. On each clock edge QA becomes A, QB becomes what QA was before the clock edge, QC what QB was, and so on up to QH, which becomes what QG was. This type of shift register is known as a SIPO (Serial In Parallel Out). A SIPO shift register is easy to construct with flip-flops – Figure 1.12 shows how. In addition to the A input the 164 has a /CLEAR input, where holding /CLEAR LO causes all the outputs to go LO regardless of incoming clock pulses. The 4031 is a 64 stage SISO (Serial In Serial Out) shift register. A data bit is entered on a clock edge and 64 clock pulses later it emerges at the output pin. The 4021 is an 8 stage PISO (Parallel In Serial Out) shift register; 8 bits of data can be entered at once and on each clock edge they shift out 1 bit at a time.

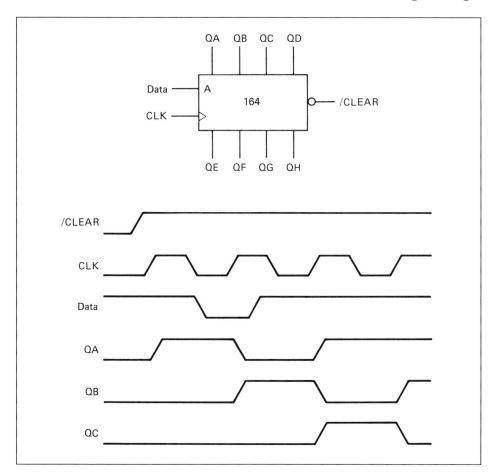

Figure 1.11   *The TTL 164 shift register chip and timing diagram*

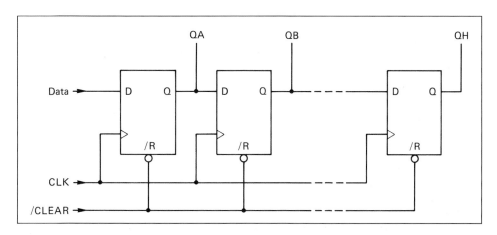

Figure 1.12   *Building a shift register out of D flip-flops*

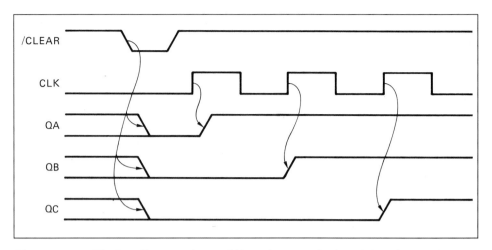

Figure 1.13 *Timing diagram for a shift register producing delayed signals*

One useful application of a shift register is as a timing generator, see Figure 1.13. With a 164 connect A to HI and assert the /CLEAR input. When you are ready to begin timing release the /CLEAR input; on each clock edge a HI will clock down the outputs. Thus for example when QD goes HI you know it is four clock edges since /CLEAR was released. This timing technique is used in almost all of the STEbus slave boards discussed in Chapter 6.

Latches

The 74LS374 is what is known as an octal *latch* which is edge triggered. It consists simply of eight D flip-flops, and on each clock edge a byte (8 bits) of information is stored. The outputs can be tri-stated for use in micropro-cessor systems.

There is another type of latch (74LS373) known as a *transparent* latch. In this type there is an ENABLE input instead of a clock. When the ENABLE input is HI the outputs follow the inputs, just like a buffer. However, when the ENABLE input goes LO the input data on the falling edge is latched or stored. Thus a transparent latch is a mixture of clocked and combinational logic. Both the 373 and 374 find many applications in microprocessor circuits; they are both byte wide and tri-stateable.

One point worth noting is that the 374 is more immune to noise on the clock-ing line than the 373. This is because the 374 can be left with its clock in the HI state, which for TTL is the state of most noise immunity, whereas the 373 must be left, after latching, with its 'clock' in the LO state, which can cause problems on noisy microprocessor boards. Thus, where timing constraints permit, it is better to use a 374, even if this means an extra gate to invert the clock line.

Decoders

A decoder chip looks at a number of inputs and *decodes* them to select one output. The 74LS42 is an example of a BCD decoder – a 4-bit binary input code (0000–1001) is used to select which of 10 outputs goes into the LO state. Of much greater practical importance is the 74LS138 chip. This is a one-of-eight decoder; three inputs A, B and C are used to select one of eight outputs (0–7). Table 1.2 gives the truth table for this device.

Table 1.2 Truth table for a one-of-eight decoder

A	B	C	0	1	2	3	4	5	6	7
LO	LO	LO	LO	HI	HI	HI	HI	HI	HI	HI
HI	LO	LO	HI	LO	HI	HI	HI	HI	HI	HI
LO	HI	LO	HI	HI	LO	HI	HI	HI	HI	HI
HI	HI	LO	HI	HI	HI	LO	HI	HI	HI	HI
LO	LO	HI	HI	HI	HI	HI	LO	HI	HI	HI
HI	LO	HI	HI	HI	HI	HI	HI	LO	HI	HI
LO	HI	HI	HI	HI	HI	HI	HI	HI	LO	HI
HI	HI	HI	HI	HI	HI	HI	HI	HI	HI	LO

In addition to the ABC decode shown in the truth table there are three enable signals, Gl, /G2A and /G2B, which must be HI, LO and LO respectively for the 138 to be enabled (if it is not then all the outputs go into the HI state regardless of the state of the ABC lines). The 138 is often used as an *address decoder* in a microprocessor system, see Chapter 5.

Multiplexers

Digital multiplexers

A *multiplexer* in contrast can almost be thought of as the inverse of a decoder. Here the select signals choose between N input pins and an output pin is driven with the state of the chosen input. The 74LS151 is an example of a digital multiplexer, with three select lines that encode which of the eight inputs to direct to the output pin. The 74LS157 contains four two-to-one multiplexers, with one control pin to select between two inputs. This chip is useful in DRAM ('Dynamic' memory) circuits, see Chapter 5. The truth table for one part of the 157 is given below.

A	B	SELECT	OUT
LO	LO	LO	LO
LO	HI	LO	LO
HI	LO	LO	HI
HI	HI	LO	HI
LO	LO	HI	LO
LO	HI	HI	HI
HI	LO	HI	LO
HI	HI	HI	HI

When SELECT is LO the output follows the A input, and when SELECT is HI it follows the B input. Thus, SELECT switches (or multiplexes) between A and B.

Analog multiplexers

Another class of multiplexer is the *analog* multiplexer. Here the data being selected is analog (the signal can be any voltage – it is not restricted to logic levels). The multiplexer is controlled digitally and selects which analog signal is transmitted to the output by means of FET (Field-effect Transitor) switches. An example of such a chip is the IH6216 multiplexer from Intersil, which is a sixteen-to-one multiplexer. A simple way of looking at it is to imagine that the multiplexer is a 16 way rotary switch, the digital inputs turning the switch to the required input signal. Such a device is ideal for an analog-to-digital converter system, see Chapter 7.

FIFOs

FIFO stands for 'First In First Out'. A FIFO chip is a type of temporary memory store. It works in the following way. A FIFO contains two clocking commands, CLOCKIN and CLOCKOUT: on a CLOCKIN command a *word* (a number of bits) is clocked into a queue of data inside the chip; on a CLOCKOUT command the data word which was put in the queue the earliest is clocked out onto the output pins of the chip. Thus the queue acts in the same way as a real queue – the first person in is the first person out, hence the name FIFO.

A good analogy is a vertical tube containing marbles: on a CLOCKIN command you drop one marble into the tube, and on a CLOCKOUT command you allow one marble to exit from the tube. The tube represents the FIFO and the marbles the data words. The 74LS225 is an example of a FIFO and is 16 words deep by 5 bits wide; to use the analogy, the number of marbles which can be fitted in the tube is 16 and each marble corresponds to five data bits. A FIFO chip will have two status pins – one indicates it is not full, so it can accept more data, and the second indicates whether it contains any data to be read out.

When might you want to use a FIFO? FIFOs are used mostly in systems where it is required to *buffer* (used in a different sense to a TTL buffer chip) information. Consider a system that is receiving data at a constant rate and is just about quick enough to cope with that rate. What happens if, for a brief time, the data rate is increased? Obviously the system will be unable to cope and so data will be lost. A way round this is to use a FIFO. The data is clocked into the FIFO as it arrives using the CLOCKIN command, and it is taken out of the FIFO using the CLOCKOUT command at the maximum rate the rest of the system can manage. Thus, if for a brief time the incoming data rate rises, then all that happens is that the FIFO fills up a bit; the data is not lost, it is simply read slightly later. Hence a FIFO enables a data receiving system to cope with data that arrives in bursts (the deeper the FIFO the longer the bursts may be).

Monostables

A monostable, or 'mono', is a device which in response to a clock edge produces a pulse of known duration (the length is set by a resistor and a capacitor). This sounds like a great IC. However, monostables can behave erratically, especially if there is noise from the power supply line. Thus, as a general rule, do not use a monostable unless your circuit can tolerate the odd missing or surplus pulse! There is almost always a better way of designing a circuit than with monostables, especially if you have a high-frequency clock signal available.

Monostables are available in two forms – retriggerable and non-retriggerable. If a monostable is retriggerable then it will remain in the triggered state as long as more clocking pulses come in. A non-retriggerable monostable can only be triggered if it is in the untriggered state. Hence a non-retriggerable mono always produces a pulse of the same duration. Retriggerable monostables are useful in timeout circuits. Here you want to detect the absence of pulses for a certain period of time. To do this you simply clock a retriggerable mono with the clocking waveform, and provided clock edges are received at intervals of less than the monostable pulse period the mono will stay in the triggered state. The 74LS221 is a non-retriggerable monostable, and the 74LS123 is retriggerable. Figure 1.14 shows timing waveforms for these two types of monostable.

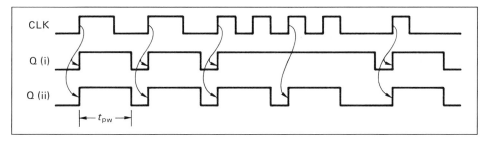

Figure 1.14 *Pulses produced by monostables in response to clock edges:* (i) *retriggerable type;* (ii) *non-retriggerable*

Clocking circuits

In an electronic circuit a source of clock pulses is often necessary. For instance, microprocessors require clock signals, as does clocked logic like counters and shift registers.

The 555 timer chip

For generating frequencies below about 1 MHz the 555 timer chip is a good choice. This chip requires just two resistors and one capacitor to set its frequency of oscillation, the time period being given by $T = 0.7(R_A + 2R_B)C$, see Figure 1. 15.

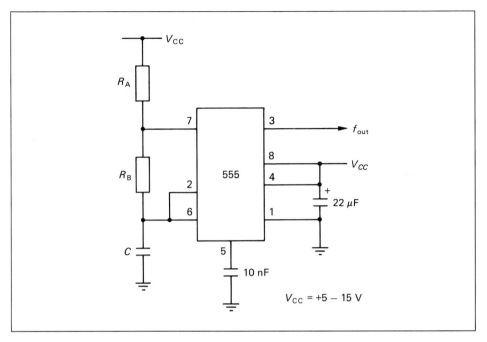

Figure 1.15 *Using the 555 timer chip to produce a clock waveform*

The 555 can also be used to produce a pulse of a given length in response to a trigger (just like a monostable).

A crystal oscillator

At higher frequencies a crystal oscillator circuit is recommended; one that works well is shown in Figure 1.16. The 16 MHz output can be divided down using a flip-flop to give lower frequencies and a 50/50 duty cycle too. At frequencies much above 20 MHz the oscillator of Figure 1.16 does not

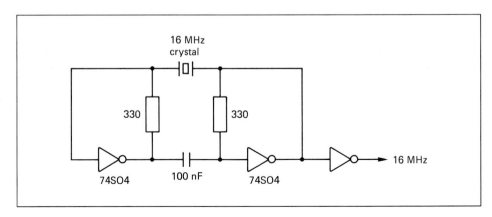

Figure 1.16 *A 16 MHz crystal oscillator circuit*

function well and it is best to use a ready-made crystal oscillator module. These modules produce TTL-compatible signals and only require a 5 V supply to operate.

Serial data transmission

Having designed a logic circuit we may wish to transfer data to and from it. One way of doing so is via a serial link. A full understanding of how this can be achieved requires a knowledge of microprocessors (see Chapter 5), but the basics are sufficiently important that the topic is discussed here. Various serial link protocols exist, but the most commonly used is called RS-232.

RS-232

RS-232 is a standard for communicating between serial (1 bit at a time) devices, for example between a computer and a VDU or terminal. Firstly, the logic levels are neither TTL nor CMOS. Instead logic HI is defined as +12 V and logic LO as –12 V. Thus for a TTL/CMOS microprocessor system to communicate using RS-232 these voltages must be available, and special transmitter and receiver chips must be used to convert the logic levels. The STE and VME buses which we look at in Chapter 6 do indeed provide ±12 V, admittedly at the expense of ±15 V lines which op-amps prefer.

The chips which take TTL signals and produce RS-232 levels or vice versa are the 1488 transmitter chip and the 1489 receiver chip, which also act as inverters. This inversion is very important when debugging an RS-232 system – if a signal is active-LO on the TTL side of the circuit then it is active-HI on the RS-232 wire. A useful chip is the MAX232C RS-232 transmitter/receiver chip, which generates its own RS-232 supplies – ideal if you only have 5 V available.

Protocol

The RS-232 specification permits the following serial data rates: 1200, 2400, 4800, 7200, 9600 or 19200 bits per second (slower rates are also allowed, but date back to the ages of slower technology). The bit rate is also known as the *baud* rate. The data is arranged in a small 'packet' which is sent as follows. Firstly a start bit indicates to the receiving device that data is about to arrive, then comes the data (7 or 8 bits) possibly followed by a *parity* bit, and lastly one or two stop bits which indicate that the transmission is complete.

Parity

The parity bit is an additional bit added to the data which can indicate whether a single data bit has been corrupted in transfer. Parity works like this:

the parity bit is made HI or LO such that the total number of bits which are HI is always odd or even. Hence if the receiving device gets, say, five HIs when it is expecting an even number it knows there has been a transfer error.

ASCII

RS-232 data is normally sent in a code known as ASCII (American Standard Code for Information Interchange). Computer terminals and serial printers understand this code and on receiving it they display or print the appropriate character. ASCII defines 128 characters with codes 0 to 127. In this code 'A' to 'Z' is 65–90 ($41–$5A in hexadecimal), 'a' to 'z' is 97–122 ($61–$7A) and '0' to '9' is 48–57 ($30–$39); the other codes are mostly control codes.

UARTs

To send data over an RS-232 link the first thing that must be checked is that the computer and terminal or printer agree on the data protocol (number of data, start, stop and parity bits) and the baud rate. An immediate problem here is that the computer operates on parallel words (8 bits for the 6809 discussed in Chapter 5) whereas RS-232 acts serially. To convert between the two arrangements we use a device known as a UART (Universal Asynchronous Receive and Transmit).

A UART works like this: when sending data the UART takes in 8 bits of parallel data and transmits it 1 bit at a time – it acts like a PISO shift register. When receiving data the UART takes in serial data and converts it to parallel form – it functions as a SIPO shift register. Examples of UARTs are the Motorola 6850 and 68681 and the Zilog Z8530. These chips are much more intelligent than simple shift registers, for example they can inform (by means of interrupts) the microprocessor when a byte of data has arrived or when it is free to send one.

RS-232 handshaking

Another facet of RS-232 is that of *handshaking*. Imagine that you have a computer using RS-232 to talk to a printer. The printer is a slow device, so if the computer churns out lots of data to print the printer will be unable to keep up and characters will be lost. To avoid this happening the printer must tell the computer to slow down, and it does this by a technique known as handshaking. There are two types of handshaking available, known as hardware and software handshaking.

Hardware handshaking

In hardware handshaking the printer, when it wants the computer to slow down, sends a logic signal along a piece of wire to the computer. This

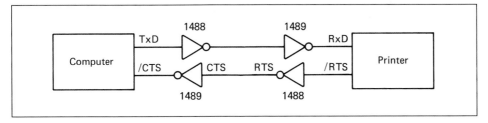

Figure 1.17 *RS-232 hardware handshaking connections*

indicates that the computer should stop sending data. This signal is known as RTS (Request To Send), and is part of the RS-232 standard; the wire goes down the same cable as the receive and transmit data lines. The computer, on seeing this signal, stops transmitting. At the computer end of things the RTS signal is fed into a pin called /CTS (Clear To Send), see Figure 1.17. The CTS line is connected into the UART on the computer, and as soon as the UART detects /CTS go HI (HI on its pin, −12 V on the RS-232 line – remember the RS-232 receivers invert the signals) it stops transmitting immediately, so no software or intervention by the microprocessor is required.

Software handshaking

In software handshaking the printer is able to send characters back to the computer via another RS-232 link. To stop transmission it sends an 'XOFF' character (often CTRL–S). On seeing this character the computer stops sending data. When the printer is ready for more data it sends an 'XON' character (often CTRL–Q) and the computer then starts to transmit again. The disadvantage of this method is that the software which controls the serial transmission is more complex than would be the case with hardware handshaking. On the other hand it is more flexible when a computer is hooked up to a terminal: if the user wants to stop the computer from transmitting, then it is only necessary to type CTRL–S.

Table of TTL gates

Table 1.3 lists a few of the most commonly used TTL gates available. For a complete list see a manufacturer's data book (for example, *The Texas Instruments TTL Data Book – Volume 1*).

Table 1.3 Some frequently used TTL gates

00	Quad NAND gate
02	Quad NOR gate
04	Hex inverter
06	Hex inverter open-collector

07	Hex buffer open-collector
08	Quad AND gate
14	Hex Schmitt trigger input inverter
32	Quad OR gate
74	Dual D flip-flop
86	Quad EX-OR gate
113	Dual JK flip-flop
123	Dual retriggerable monostable
124	Dual voltage-controlled oscillator
138	Three-to-eight decoder
157	Quad two-to-one multiplexer
163	Synchronous 4-bit binary counter
164	SIPO shift register
165	PISO shift register
174	Hex D flip-flop
175	Quad D flip-flop
221	Dual non-retriggerable monostable
225	16×5 FIFO
240	Octal inverter tri-state
244	Octal buffer tri-state
245	Octal transceiver tri-state
273	Octal D flip-flop with clear
374	Octal D flip-flop tri-state
393	Dual 4-bit binary ripple counter
646	Octal transceiver and register tri-state
688	8-bit comparator

2 | Analog Components

Resistors

In analog electronics we are concerned with voltages which can have a continuous range of values, in contrast to digital electronics where only two values are allowed. The simplest analog component is the *resistor*. The symbol for a resistor is shown in Figure 2.1. A resistor provides resistance to the flow of electrical charge. By Ohm's law, if a resistor of resistance R, measured in ohms (symbol Ω), has a voltage V in volts across it, then a current I, in amps, flows through the resistor and is given by:

$I = V/R$

An analogy which may be useful when looking at this relationship is that of water in a pipe. The amount of water flowing through the pipe corresponds to the current, the pressure on the water to the voltage and the diameter of the pipe to the resistance – the narrower the pipe the harder it is for the current to flow.

The power generated in a resistor is given by $V.I$, or applying Ohm's law V^2/R, and is measured in watts (symbol W). Each resistor has a power rating that must not be exceeded. Resistors used in digital work are

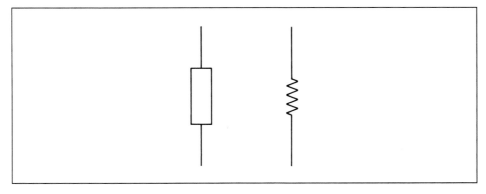

Figure 2.1 *Symbols for the resistor: left the modern one, right the older version*

normally 0.5 or 0.25 W. Higher-power resistors are sometimes needed for circuits running off 12 V, and are correspondingly larger in physical size.

Availability of resistors

Resistors are available in a series of values, see Table 2.1, and multiples of 10 thereof.

Table 2.1 Values of resistors

10	12	15	18
22	27	33	39
47	56	68	82

The above values are those produced for resistors with a tolerance of 10%, but additional values are available (for example, 75) for 1% and 5% resistors. It should be noted that if you want a resistor to be accurate to 1% then you do need to use a 1% resistor. You cannot simply take a group of 5% or 10% resistors and measure them till you find one that agrees with your required value. This is because the resistor is only guaranteed to 5% or 10% over its temperature range, so that as the temperature varies so will its value, away from what you selected!

The resistor colour code

The value of a resistor is labelled according to the 'resistor colour code', where a series of coloured bands around the resistor body are used to indicate its value. The encoding of these colours is given in Table 2.2.

Table 2.2 The resistor colour code

Colour	Value	Multiplier	
Silver	–	×0.01	Multiplier only
Gold	–	×0.1	Multiplier only
Black	0	×1	
Brown	1	×10	
Red	2	×100	
Orange	3	×1k	
Yellow	4	×10k	
Green	5	×100k	
Blue	6	×1M	
Violet	7	×10M	
Grey	8	–	
White	9	–	

The code works as follows. A series of four bands are drawn on the resistor: the first three bands are read as a number, thus yellow, violet and black equals 470, and the fourth band is the *multiplier*; it multiplies the

'470' by its multiplier value. So if the fourth band is red the value of the resistor is 470 × 100 = 47000 or 47 kΩ. Additional bands are often added to indicate the tolerance. One of the arts of reading resistor colour codes is in knowing which end of the resistor to start at, so it helps to remember the possible values a resistor can have!

Variable resistors

Variable resistors called *potentiometers* or 'pots' are also available. These allow you to vary their resistance from zero to a maximum value by turning a screw. They are available in two types: single-turn and multi-turn. In a single-turn pot one turn of the screw varies the resistance from its maximum to its minimum value, while in a multi-turn it takes typically 10 turns. Single-turns are preferred where you only need an approximate resistance and want to be able to adjust it quickly, and multi-turns let you set the resistance more accurately but are more fiddly to adjust. Figure 2.2 shows the physical appearance of single- and multi-turn pots, and their electronic symbols.

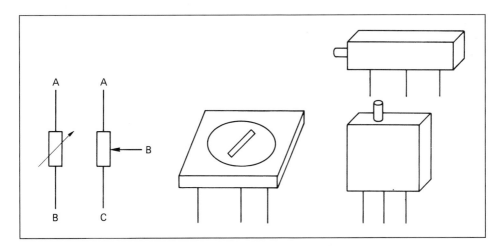

Figure 2.2 *Left, symbols for potentiometers: between AB and BC resistance is variable, between AC constant; centre, appearance of single-turn pot; right, multi-turn pots*

Resistor circuits

You often have a circuit with resistors in series or in parallel, and want to know their combined resistance. Figure 2.3 shows the rule for combining resistances: resistors in series add up; and in parallel the reciprocal of the total resistance equals the sum of the reciprocals of the individual resistances.

One of the most commonly used resistor circuits is the potential divider circuit, see Figure 2.4. R_1 and R_2 divide down the input voltage V_0. By

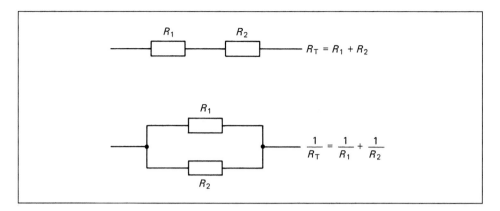

Figure 2.3 *The formulae for combining resistances*

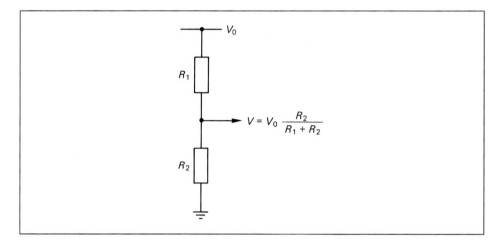

Figure 2.4 *The potential divider circuit*

Ohm's law, the current flowing through R_1 and R_2 is $V_0/(R_1 + R_2)$, hence the output voltage V is given by $V_0R_2/(R_1 + R_2)$.

Capacitors

A capacitor is a device which stores *charge*. Charge, measured in coulombs (symbol C), is the entity which constitutes the flow of electrical current (the water molecules in our water pipe analogy). Electrical current, in amps, is the rate of flow of charge per second. The value of a capacitor is measured in farads (symbol F) and is defined as follows. If a capacitor has a voltage V across it and is storing a charge Q coulombs, then it has a *capacitance* of Q/V farads, or mathematically:

$C = Q/V$

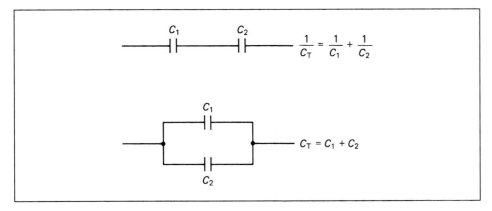

Figure 2.5 *The formulae for combining capacitors*

The rules for combining capacitors and their electronic symbol are shown in Figure 2.5. Thus, capacitors in parallel combine like resistors in series, and those in series like resistors in parallel.

Charging of a capacitor

We now want to consider how a capacitor accumulates charge. Figure 2.6 shows a simple circuit: at time $t = 0$ the switch is closed. What happens? When the switch is closed current will commence to flow, and thus charge will move round the circuit and be collected by the capacitor. We can calculate how quickly the charge accumulates as follows:

by definition $V = q/C$ and by Ohm's law $E - iR = V$

Since i, the current, is the rate of flow of charge $\mathrm{d}q/\mathrm{d}t$ we have:

$$E - V = R\frac{\mathrm{d}q}{\mathrm{d}t}$$

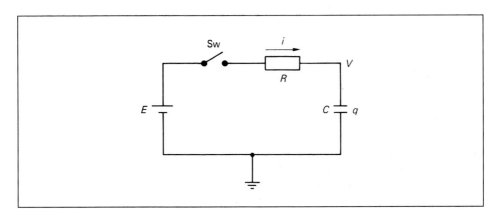

Figure 2.6 *The circuit used to analyse charging of a capacitor*

or

$$E - V = RC \ \frac{dV}{dt} \ \text{by the formula for } C$$

Now let $U = E - V$:

$$U = - RC \ \frac{dU}{dt}$$

Integrating

$$U = E \ \exp(-t/RC)$$

so

$$V = E \ [1 - \exp(-t/RC)]$$

A graph of this function is shown in Figure 2.7. It can be seen that the voltage, V, across the capacitor gradually increases until the capacitor is fully charged. RC is an important quantity which is known as the *time constant*; if you vary R and C but keep the time constant the same the circuit will behave as before. A similar calculation can be performed to show how quickly a charged-up capacitor loses charge when it is connected across a resistor. In this case the charge can be shown to die away exponentially, the discharge equation being given by $V = E \exp(-t/RC)$.

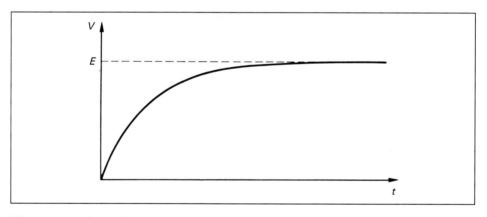

Figure 2.7 *A graph of voltage versus time for a charging capacitor*

Capacitors in digital circuits

In digital electronics capacitors appear most frequently as the decoupling capacitors mentioned earlier. You connect the capacitors across the two supply rails to prevent digital noise travelling round the circuit. You usually use a combination of two types – 100 nF disc ceramics sprinkled every four or five ICs, and 22 μF tantalum ones near large or noisy ICs. Another type occasionally used is electrolytic capacitors. Note that like 'tants' these are *polarized* and must be connected to the circuit the right way round, the lead marked '+' to the positive side of the circuit; failure to do so can lead to a small explosion!

Alternating current circuits

This section is somewhat mathematical, but the important thing is the results, so do not be put off if you are not mathematically minded!

In analog electronics we often have signals which are 'wavelike'; for example, if the current in a circuit varies as $I_0 \cos\omega t$ then it is said to be *alternating current* or a.c., compared to direct current (as in a logic circuit) or d.c. Since much of analog electronics consists of alternating signals we need a simple way of analysing a.c. circuits which use resistors, capacitors and *inductors* (which we discuss later).

Mathematical preliminaries

To derive a way of analysing a.c. circuits we proceed as follows. An a.c. voltage can be written as $V_0 \cos(\omega t + \phi)$, and is illustrated in Figure 2.8. V_0 is known as the amplitude of the signal, ω is its *angular* frequency and ϕ is called its phase. The angular frequency is measured in radians per second and is related to 'normal' frequency, f (in Hz), by $\omega = 2\pi f$. The phase is an angle and so is measured in either degrees or radians.

Handling cosines mathematically is tricky, so we now use a mathematical method called de Moivre's theorem to rewrite $\cos(\omega t + \phi)$ as the complex exponential $\text{Re}\{\exp[j(\omega t + \phi)]\}$, where Re means take the real part of, and j is $\sqrt{-1}$. We use 'j' to denote the square root of minus one rather than 'i', which mathematicians and scientists prefer, because 'i' could be confused with current. Hence we have changed a cosine into an exponential. The advantage of this is that exponentials are easier to handle mathematically. Let us now apply this bit of maths to a capacitor with a varying voltage across it.

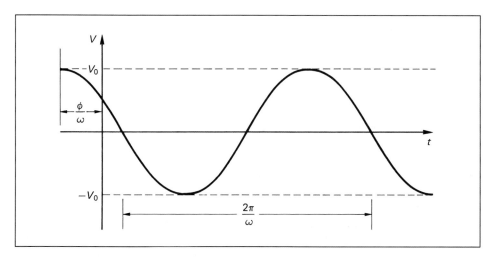

Figure 2.8 *An a.c. signal given by* $V_0 \cos(\omega t + \phi)$

Reactance of a capacitor

From the definition of capacitance ($C = Q/V$) we have the following expression for the current flowing through a capacitor:

$$I = \frac{dQ}{dt} = C\frac{dV}{dt}$$

Now

$$V = V_0 \exp[j(\omega t + \phi)]$$

so

$$\frac{dV}{dt} = j\omega V_0 \exp[j(\omega t + \phi)]$$

hence

$$I = j\omega CV$$

This looks similar to Ohm's law; it is as though the capacitor has a 'resistance' or *reactance* given by $X_c = 1/j\omega C$. Thus for an a.c. circuit you can simply pretend it is d.c. provided you use reactance instead of resistance.

For example, if a capacitor is in series with a resistor the combined (complex) 'resistance' is given by $Z = R + 1/j\omega C$. The combined 'resistance' is given the name *impedance*. Impedance is a general term that covers both resistance (a real number) and reactance (a purely imaginary 'j' number), so you will often hear people say that a capacitor has an impedance of $1/j\omega C$.

Reactance of an inductor

Another component used in a.c. circuits is the inductor. An inductor is a device which acts to oppose changes in current in it. Inductance is measured in henrys (symbol H). For an inductance of L henrys the voltage across it is given by $V = L\,dI/dt$. Hence we calculate its reactance as:

$$V = L\frac{dI}{dt}$$

so

$$LI = \int V_0 \exp[j(\omega t + \phi)]dt$$

and

$$LI = V_0 \exp[j(\omega t + \phi)]/j\omega$$

so

$$V = j\omega LI$$

Thus the reactance, X_L, of an inductor is given by $X_L = j\omega L$.

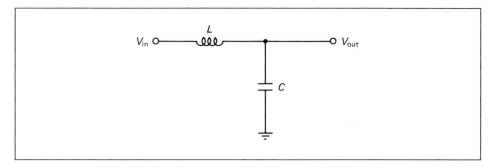

Figure 2.9 *An inductor capacitor circuit*

Use of reactances

Figure 2.9 shows an example of an a.c. circuit. To work out the net reactance of an a.c. circuit you simply use the same formulae for series and parallel resistances, only you apply them to reactances and impedances.

Figure 2.9 is like a potential divider circuit so we use that formula:

$$V_{out} = V_{in} \, X_C/(X_C + X_L)$$

$$= V_{in} \, \frac{1/j\omega C}{(1/j\omega C) + j\omega L}$$

$$= V_{in} \, \frac{1}{1 - \omega^2 LC}$$

Figure 2.10 shows the plot of voltage versus frequency. The response has a peak at $\omega = 1/\sqrt{(LC)}$, after which it acts as a low-pass filter with the amplitude falling as $1/\omega^2$. In practice all inductors have some finite resistance so the peak will not be infinite – try calculating the response if the impedance of the inductor is actually $R + j\omega L$.

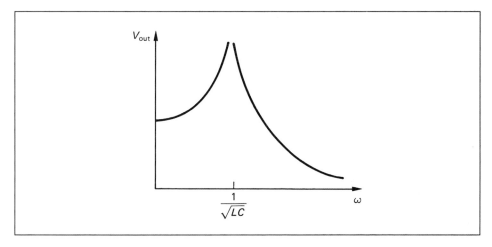

Figure 2.10 *The voltage versus frequency plot of the circuit shown in Figure 2.9*

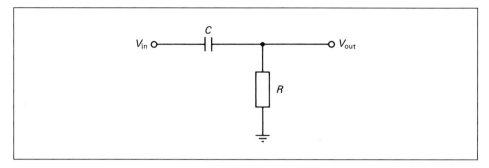

Figure 2.11 *A resistor capacitor circuit*

Figure 2.11 is also analysed by using the potential divider formula:

$$V_{out} = V_{in} \, R/(R + X_C)$$

$$= V_{in} \, \frac{R}{R + 1/j\omega C}$$

$$= V_{in} \, \frac{j\omega RC}{1 + j\omega RC}$$

$$= V_{in} \, \frac{\omega^2 R^2 C^2 + j\omega RC}{1 + \omega^2 R^2 C^2}$$

We can see that this is a high-pass filter – for small ω the numerator becomes small.

Calculating amplitudes and phases

Notice that V_{in} in the above equation is multiplied by a complex number. This means that the output signal has a different phase to the input. When this is the case the amplitude of the input signal is multiplied by the *modulus*, or 'size', of the complex number. The modulus of the complex number $(a + jb)$ is defined as follows:

$$\text{mod}(a + jb) \text{ or } |(a + jb)| = \sqrt{(a^2 + b^2)}$$

As an example, if $V_{out} = (1 + 2j)V_{in}$, then the output signal is $\sqrt{5}$ times larger than the input signal.

Occasionally you want to know the phase shift that the circuit has introduced. This is given by the *argument* of the complex number which is defined by:

$$\arg(a + jb) = \tan^{-1}(b/a) \text{ or } \arctan(b/a)$$

So if $V_{out} = (1 + 2j)V_{in}$, the phase difference between the input and output signals is $\tan^{-1}(2) \simeq 63°$.

Usefulness of reactances

We have seen in a.c. circuits (those with inputs like $V_0 \cos\omega t$) that by using the reactances of capacitors and inductors such circuits can be readily analysed. But what if you do not have a sinusoidal input? Fortunately, any waveform can be written as the sum of sinusoidal waveforms of different frequencies (known as Fourier's theorem). This means that you can work out, perhaps using a computer, what your circuit does to each individual frequency component, and then you can add the resultants back up to see what your circuit produces.

This technique is part of the subject of signal processing and is only mentioned here to give the reader an insight into the power of reactances.

Summary of key points

This section is much more mathematical than any other in this book. The reader should not worry if he or she finds the derivations hard to follow – the results are what matters. The key points are as follows: a.c. circuits can be analysed by using reactances, or impedances, of capacitors and inductors and then applying the standard rules for combining resistances. Having got a formula relating one voltage to another, the amplification factor is given by the modulus of the complex multiplying factor $(a + jb)$, and the phase difference by its argument. These results are summarized in Table 2.3.

Table 2.3 Summary of a.c. formulae

Component	Impedance
Resistor	R
Capacitor	$1/j\omega C$
Inductor	$j\omega L$
Modulus	$\sqrt{(a^2 + b^2)}$
Argument	$\tan^{-1}(b/a)$

Diodes

The diode is a *semiconductor* device and consequently it does not obey Ohm's law. Figure 2.12 shows the voltage–current characteristic of a diode. Notice that below about 0.6 V (the diode's forward drop) the current is small and that for negative voltages the current is very small – microamps to nanoamps. Thus current can only flow one way; it is blocked in the other direction. The equation for the voltage–current curve is in fact $I = I_0[\exp(V/V_T - 1)]$, where I_0 (about 10 nA for the 1N4148) is called the reverse leakage current, and V_T is about 50 mV. The symbol for the diode is also shown in Figure 2.12; note that current can flow in the direction anode to cathode.

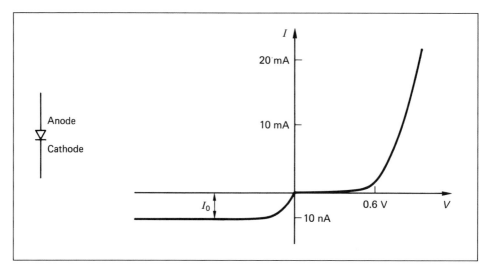

Figure 2.12 *Symbol for a diode and its voltage–current characteristic*

Diode applications

The diode as a protection device

Diodes are frequently used as protection devices. For example, you might have an analog circuit driving the input of a device operating off a 0–5 V supply. Figure 2.13 shows how two diodes can be used to constrain the signal to be between –0.6 and 5.6 V. When the signal is between these levels the output voltage equals the input voltage, and when it exceeds 5.6 V the top diode conducts current (acting as though it has no resistance) and the voltage is held at 5.6 V. Similarly if the voltage drops below –0.6 V then the lower diode conducts and the signal is clamped at –0.6 V.

Now consider the circuit shown in Figure 2.14. With the switch closed current I flows through the inductor. When the switch is opened the

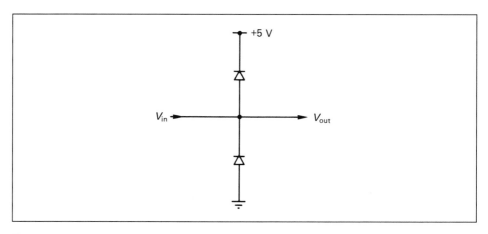

Figure 2.13 *Using two diodes to constrain a signal to TTL logic levels*

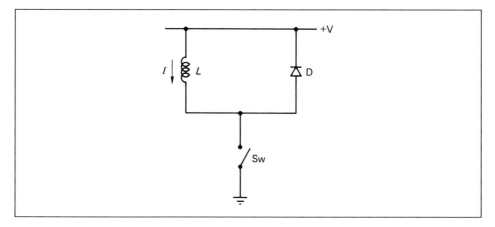

Figure 2.14 *Using a diode to protect a switch connected to an inductor*

current tries to fall to zero. However, because an inductor produces a voltage to oppose the change in current, a large voltage will build up on the switch. If the switch is an electronic one (say a transistor) it can be harmed. To avoid this damage a diode is placed across the inductor. Now when the voltage rises current simply flows through the diode, thus preventing a large voltage from building up.

The same circuit can be used with a *relay*, which is an electromechanical switch. Current flows through a coil which generates a magnetic field that causes a switch to close. The coil behaves like an inductor (an inductor is usually just a coil) so diode protection may be required.

Adding a d.c. offset to an a.c. signal

Figure 2.15 shows another example of the use of a diode. An a.c. signal comes into the capacitor, but it blocks d.c. signals (its reactance when ω

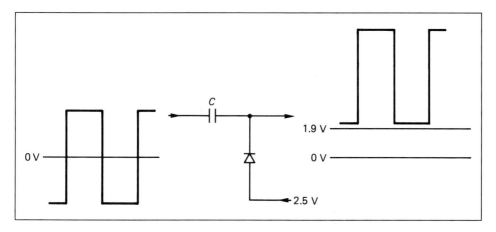

Figure 2.15 *Adding a d.c. offset to a capacitively coupled a.c. signal*

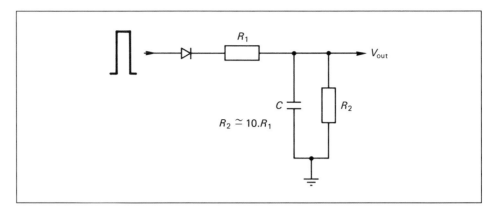

Figure 2.16 *A length of pulse detector*

= 0 is infinite), so without the diode the signal would be centred on zero volts. However, the diode acts to charge up the capacitor so that the signal is centred on 1.9 V (2.5 V minus the diode drop). This circuit is useful in video circuits and elsewhere where small signals must be handled – for an example see the SG84X circuit in Chapter 7.

A length of pulse detector

Figure 2.16 illustrates a way of using a diode and a capacitor to find the length of a pulse. For the circuit to function the pulses should have a duty cycle of less than about 10%. When the pulse is in the HI state the diode conducts and so the capacitor charges up through resistor R_1, the voltage being given by the charging formula $V[1-\exp(-t/R_1C)]$. If we choose R_1C to be large compared to t then this is approximately Vt/R_1C, which is linear with t. We sample the output voltage on the falling edge of the input pulse

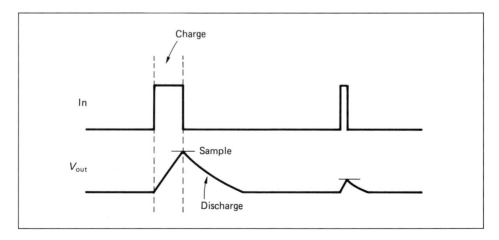

Figure 2.17 *Operation of the length of pulse detector*

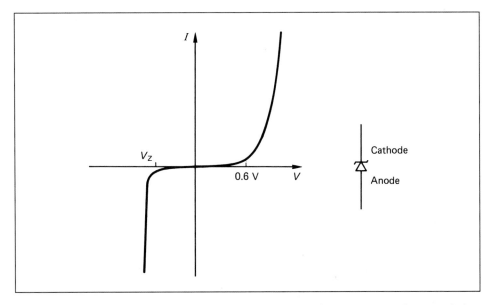

Figure 2.18 *Symbol for the zener diode and its voltage–current characteristic*

and, knowing V and R_1C, we can find t, the length of the pulse. We then need to reset the circuit in readiness for the next pulse. The input signal is in the LO state, so the diode does not conduct and hence the capacitor discharges through R_2 in preparation for the next cycle, see Figure 2.17.

The zener diode

The zener diode is like a normal diode except that it is almost always operated in the reverse bias state, that is with the cathode more positive than the anode. Its *V–I* characteristic is shown in Figure 2.18. As can be seen, for positive voltages the curve is the same as that of a normal diode. However, when a negative voltage is applied and slowly increased the zener suddenly begins to conduct very rapidly. The voltage at which it does this

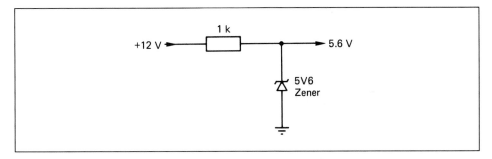

Figure 2.19 *Using a zener as a voltage reference*

Microprocessor System Design

is known as the zener voltage V_Z, where, theoretically, the conduction instantly becomes infinite. In practice there is a small bend called the knee. This sharp switch-on effect means that zeners are useful as voltage references – you simply bias a milliamp or so through one and the output voltage becomes V_Z, see Figure 2.19. Zeners are available in a range of values, the same as resistors, from about 2.7 V to around 100 V; note that the sharpest knees are for zener voltages of about 5 V.

The light-emitting diode or LED

An LED is a diode which, when current (around 10 mA) is passed through it, emits light of a given colour. The colours generally available are red, yellow and green. An LED has a forward voltage drop of about 1.4 V, the exact figure varying slightly with the colour of the diode. Figure 2.20 shows an LED being driven by an open-collector gate. The 330 Ω resistor sets the current through the diode as $(5–1.4)/330 = 11$ mA. The resistor also acts as a protection device; if it was not there a massive current would flow through the LED promptly blowing it up.

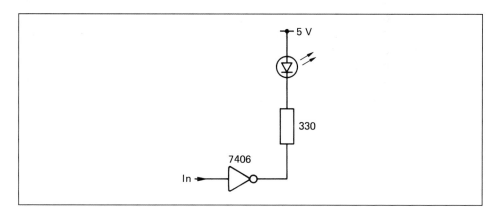

Figure 2.20 *Driving an LED with a logic gate – In equals HI switches the LED on*

Figure 2.21 shows a variation of the LED, where two diodes are used in parallel, one red and one green. Thus when current flows in one direction the LED is green, and in the other it is red. This sort of LED is

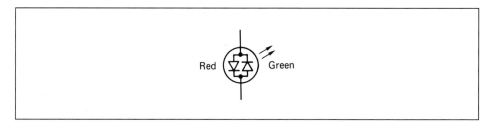

Figure 2.21 *A bicolour LED*

useful on equipment indicator panels. Some manufacturers also make bicolour flashing LEDs! These have two colours and flash at a rate of about once or twice a second.

Seven-segment displays

A seven-segment display consists of seven rectangular-shaped LEDs arranged in the shape of a numeral. By lighting the correct segments the numerals 0–9 and letters A–F can be made to appear. Seven-segment displays are available in two types – common anode and common cathode. In the common anode type the seven anodes of the LEDs are joined together, and similarly for the common cathode type. There are two ways of driving seven-segment displays – multiplexed and non-multiplexed.

Non-multiplexed display driving

In a non-multiplexed display a driver chip decodes four binary-weighted input lines, corresponding to 0–F, and produces seven active-LO outputs to drive directly one common anode seven-segment display. The 74LS48 is an example of a seven-segment display driver, see also Chapter 4 for an example of a driver made out of a PAL. A disadvantage of non-multiplexed display driving is that one driver chip is required for each seven-segment display, which in turn requires a set of seven current-limiting resistors; there are an awful lot of wires to connect. For these reasons, where you have a large number of seven-segment displays, say more than three, the technique of multiplexed driving is used.

Multiplexed display driving

In a multiplexed display each seven-segment display is lit in turn with its appropriate value. This is done by outputting the appropriate lines with one part of the driver chip, whilst another part of the logic enables the common cathode connection of the selected seven-segment display, see Figure 2.22. Then a small time later the common cathode of the next display is activated and lit with its required number. Thus if you could look at the display in slow motion you would see each of the seven-segment displays light then go out sequentially. The trick is that if the displays are strobed sufficiently rapidly (say a few hundred times a second) the eye is deceived into thinking they are on all the time, just like a television set.

The advantages of multiplexed displays are as follows: only one set of current-limiting resistors is required, fewer wiring connections need be made and power consumption is less since only one seven-segment display is lit at any given time. Also, since multiplexed display chips are available from manufacturers you do not have to design and build one yourself.

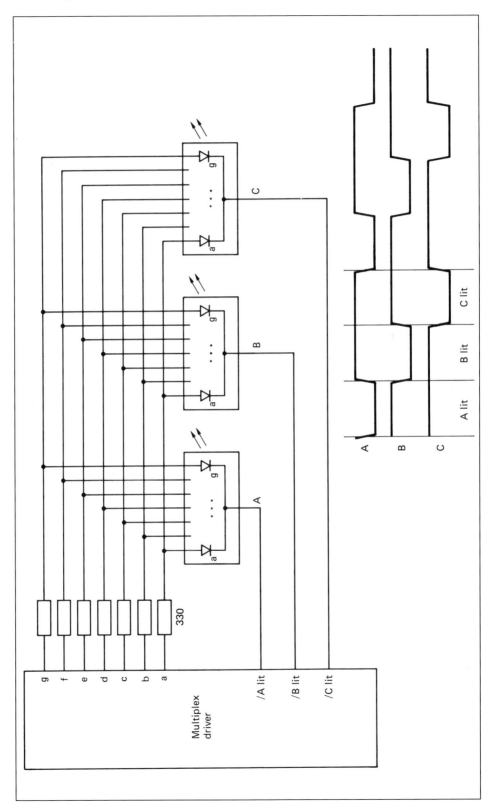

Figure 2.22 Multiplexed driving of seven-segment displays

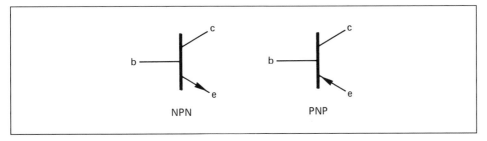

Figure 2.23 *The symbols for transistors*

Transistors

Transistor are, like diodes, semiconductor devices; they are usually made from silicon or germanium. They are available in two types called NPN and PNP. Transistors can be used for a variety of purposes, for example as switches, mixers, current sources and amplifiers. Unless you are working at very high frequencies (above around 50 MHz) an op-amp (see Chapter 3) is used more commonly than a transistor for amplifying signals. We shall therefore not look at transistor amplifiers; the interested reader is referred to the chapter on further reading.

A transistor has three terminals known as the base, collector and emitter, see Figure 2.23. For an NPN transistor the following points can be made. When the base-emitter voltage is greater than about 0.6 V the transistor is said to be switched on and current flows into the collector. The magnitude of the current is controlled by the current flowing into the base, the relationship being $I_C = \beta I_B$, where β is known as the current gain of the transistor (another symbol for the same thing is h_{fe}). β varies for each type of transistor but is typically about a hundred. We are now in a position to look at some transistor circuits.

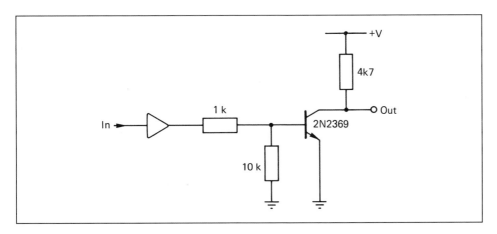

Figure 2.24 *A transistor in the open-collector configuration – when In is HI Out is LO*

Microprocessor System Design

Transistor circuits

The open-collector configuration

The open-collector or transistor switch circuit is shown in Figure 2.24. In this circuit when the logic gate is at a HI level the base-emitter voltage is greater than 0.6 V, so the transistor is switched on and current flows into the collector (technically the collector *sinks* current), and the collector goes to about 0.2 V – a TTL logic LO. In this state the transistor is said to be *saturated*. When the logic input goes LO the base–emitter voltage is less than 0.6 V, the transistor is said to be switched off and no current flows into the collector, and because of the presence of the 4k7 pull-up resistor the output goes into the HI state. Note that the transistor acts just like an inverting open-collector logic gate – a 7406 would do the same job.

A transistor mixer circuit

Figure 2.25 illustrates a transistor mixer circuit. Three logic levels representing red, green and blue come out of some sort of video circuit. We do not have a colour monitor so we want to produce a grey-scale picture. The three colour signals are fed into the base of the transistor via a set of binary-weighted resistor values. The voltage at the base is arranged always to be greater than 0.6 V so that the transistor is switched on. Since it is switched on, then one way of looking at the circuit is to imagine that the base–emitter is a forward-biased diode with a 0.6 V drop. Thus the emitter follows the base minus a diode drop – the circuit is known as an *emitter follower*.

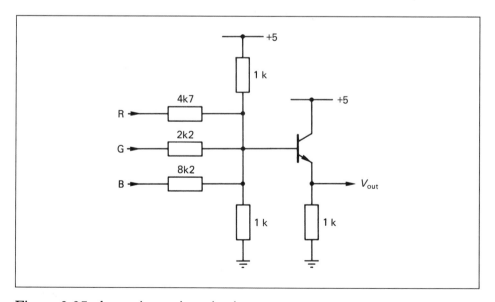

Figure 2.25 *A transistor mixer circuit*

A similar circuit is used on the SG84X genlock board (see Chapter 7) with the addition of a 'Schottky' diode to enable the transistor to be switched off under the control of a logic signal, see TR2 on Figure 7.10(c). The Schottky diode has a forward drop of only 0.2 V, so when the logic line 'I' is LO the base is pulled to 0.2 V, thus ensuring the transistor is switched off. When the logic level is HI the diode's cathode is at 5 V and so does not affect the video signals, which are around a volt.

Transistor current sources

It is often desirable to have a source of constant current, which means that if the load changes the same current flows through it. Such a current source can be easily designed using transistors. Figure 2.26 shows the

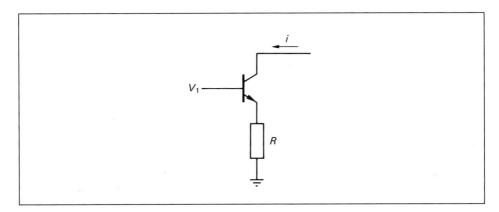

Figure 2.26 *A simple transistor current source*

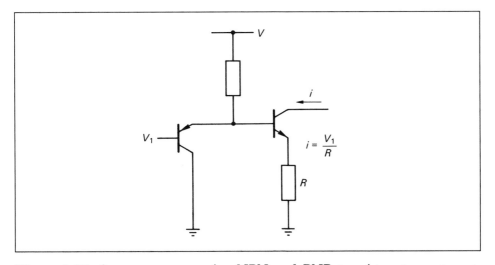

Figure 2.27 *A current source using NPN and PNP transistors to compensate for temperature effects*

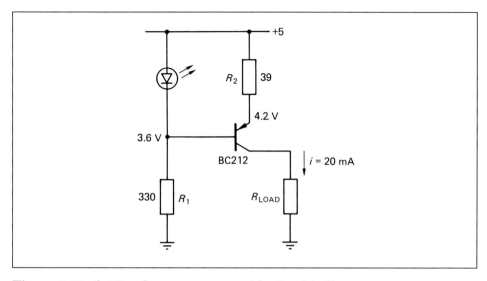

Figure 2.28 *A 20 mA current source with visual indicator*

simplest arrangement: $V_e = V_1 - V_{be}$ and $i = V_e/R$. This circuit assumes that the drop V_{be} remains constant with temperature, but in fact it varies with temperature. A better circuit is shown in Figure 2.27 where the base–emitter drops of the two transistors cancel out; such a circuit is used on the SG84 circuit, see Chapter 7.

A nice current source circuit is shown in Figure 2.28, where an LED is used to hold the base at $5 - 1.4 = 3.6$ V. Hence the emitter sits at 4.2 V. Thus, there is 0.8 V across resistor R_2 so 20 mA flows through it. Much industrial control around factories is done using 20 mA current sources: to transmit a bit of information the device simply interrupts the flow of

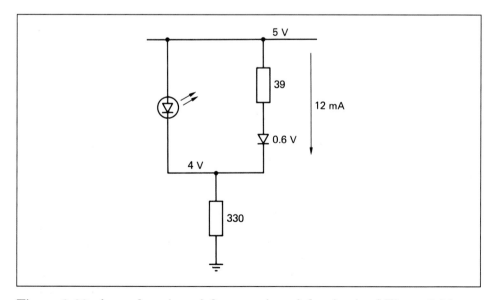

Figure 2.29 *An explanation of the operation of the circuit of Figure 2.28*

the 20 mA current. The neat part of the circuit is that if for any reason the current loop (the wire) is broken then the LED goes out, and thus you have a visual indication of a fault in the current path. Figure 2.29 explains why: with the collector disconnected current flows through the base raising the cathode of the LED to 4 V, or 1 V across it which is below its turn-on voltage (1.4 V); hence the LED goes out.

Voltage regulators

A voltage regulator is a device for converting an input voltage to a different output voltage. The one most commonly used in logic circuits is the 7805. This device takes a high input voltage, say 12 V, and regulates it down to give a 5 V output. The 7805 also removes any ripple or noise on the input line, and thus it is not just simply a potential divider circuit. Figure 2.30 shows a 7805 in operation. The input and output capacitors (22 µF 'tants' are often used) are present to smooth the supplies. The only limitation on a 7805 is the amount of power it can supply – for the 7805 it is a maximum of about 1.75 W. If you do not need as much power as this then you can use a 78L05 which has a limitation of 0.6 W and comes in a smaller package.

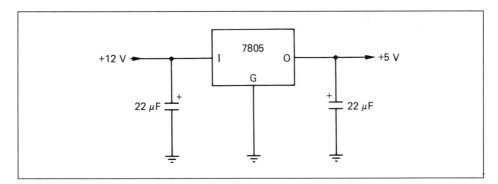

Figure 2.30 *The 7805 voltage regulator*

Figure 2.31 shows a useful variant of the basic 7805 circuit. Here the ground pin is not connected directly to ground, but instead via a resistor or transistor. When the CNTR input is HI the transistor is switched on, so current flows through the collector and emitter, just as if it shorts resistor R_1 out. Thus the ground pin is connected to earth and so the 7805 produces 5 V, just like our previous circuit. Now consider what happens when CNTR is LO: the transistor is switched off and so it is as though the transistor is not there. Hence current will flow through R_1 raising the voltage of the ground pin. Consequently, since the regulator is maintaining 5 V between the ground and output pin, the output voltage will rise. We can calculate by how much as follows.

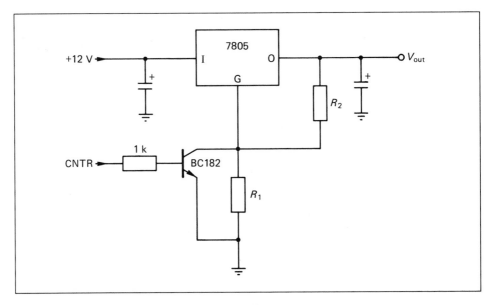

Figure 2.31 *A selectable 5 or 6 V supply*

Let the current flowing through the resistors be i. Then:

$$V_G = iR_1$$

and

$$5 = iR_2$$

and the output voltage is given by $i(R_1 + R_2)$. Using the last two equations to eliminate i gives:

$$V_{out} = 5(R_1 + R_2)/R_2$$

$$= 5(1 + R_1/R_2)$$

Hence by choosing appropriate values for the resistors we can get a second output voltage, which can be selected under the control of a logic level. If we choose R_1/R_2 to be equal to 0.2 then the second voltage is 6 V. This is precisely the pair of voltages we require for an *EPROM* programming circuit – modern EPROMs (memory chips) can be programmed to store data in two modes, fast and slow; for fast programming the EPROM's power pin needs to be supplied with +6 V, and then when programming is complete it has to be returned to the standard TTL power supply voltage of 5 V. Thus the circuit shown in Figure 2.31 achieves this task.

Other types of voltage regulator are available. For example, the LM317 is adjustable in the way shown above using two resistors to set the output voltage. Also, there exist devices which take an input voltage and convert it to a higher output voltage. At first sight this might sound impossible! The way they work is this: the device produces a high-frequency square wave which it uses to excite an external inductor; the inductor then releases its stored energy into a capacitor which therefore builds up a high voltage. Such chips (such as the MAX733) are useful when you want to produce ±15 V for powering op-amps and you only have ±12 V for RS-232 interfacing available, as with the STE and VME buses discussed in Chapter 6.

Opto-isolators

Opto-isolators are a neat and cheap method for connecting computers to equipment in a factory or 'plant'. The problem with connecting a computer to equipment on the factory floor is that although the computer has a nice clean power supply (or certainly should have) in general the rest of the factory does not. There can be large spikes and other noise on factory equipment, and down the length of a factory there can arise large potential differences. If you connect such equipment to your computer system there is a danger of damage.

One solution to this problem is the use of *opto-isolators*. These give isolation or protection of around 1000 V and above by using a beam of light to convey the signals instead of making an electrical connection between the computer and the factory equipment. Figure 2.32 shows the symbol for an opto-isolator. On the one side of the 'opto' is an LED which, when current flows through it, produces a beam of light that excites the receiving photo-transistor, which then acts iust like an open-collector transistor. Notice how the two grounds are given different symbols to indicate they are isolated. Opto-isolators come in standard dual-in-line packages and are available in a range of speeds and current-sinking capabilities. For example, if you want to transmit fast logic signals then the 6N137 is capable of handling a data rate of up to 10 MHz and is a possible choice.

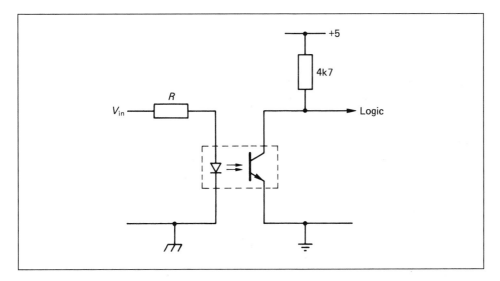

Figure 2.32 *An opto-isolator*

3 Operational amplifiers

Negative feedback

The operational amplifier (op-amp for short) is a very important analog circuit building block. An ideal op-amp has a very large gain, A, over a wide range of frequencies. However, because it is difficult to build an amplifier with a large and stable gain, a technique known as *negative feedback* is used. In a negative feedback circuit a fraction of the output voltage is fed back and subtracted from the input. By this technique many of the parameters of the op-amp are improved. Consider the block diagram in Figure 3.1. The op-amp multiplies the difference between the two input signals to give an output voltage of $V_{out} = A(V_+ - V_-)$. The '+' and '−' terminals are called the non-inverting and inverting inputs respectively. 'B' is the feedback network and feeds back a voltage $B.V_{out}$ to the input.
Hence:

$$V_{out} = A(V_{in} - BV_{out})$$

Rearranging

$$V_{out} = V_{in}A/(1 + AB) \approx V_{in}/B$$

where we have used the fact that A is very large, so AB, known as the loop gain, is also very large. Hence the overall gain of the circuit is just

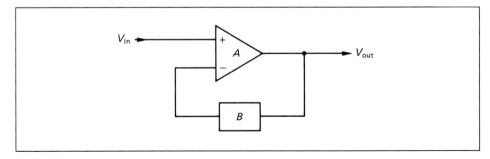

Figure 3.1   *Op-amp feedback*

$1/B$. This gain is independent of A, so by making 'B' out of resistors a stable circuit can be built. To show this mathematically we evaluate how the gain, G, varies with changes in A. To do this we differentiate G with respect to A:

$$G = \frac{A}{1 + AB}$$

so

$$\frac{dG}{dA} = \frac{1 + AB - AB}{(1 + AB)^2}$$

or

$$\frac{\Delta G}{\Delta A} = \frac{1}{(1 + AB)^2}$$

and

$$\frac{\Delta G}{G} = \frac{\Delta A}{A} \cdot \frac{1}{1 + AB}$$

$\Delta A/A$ is the fractional change in the open-loop gain, A. This causes a fractional change in the overall gain of $\Delta G/G$, but the change in A is divided by $(1 + AB)$ which, since A is very large, means that G is hardly affected by variations in the gain of the op-amp.

Two fundamental op-amp rules

Before analysing 'real' op-amp circuits the following two simple rules are needed:

1 The op-amp inputs source or sink no current.
2 The negative feedback ensures that the two inputs are at the same voltage.

Rule 1 is a result of the design of op-amp chips, but is a very good approximation. For example, the 741 op-amp has input currents of a few hundred nanoamps.

Rule 2 follows from the fact that if the op-amp is not *saturated* (its output is not at one supply rail or the other) then, because $V_{out} = A(V_+ - V_-)$ and A is around 10^5, the two inputs must be at very nearly equal voltages.

Example op-amp circuits

The inverting amplifier

The simplest op-amp circuit is the inverting amplifier. Two resistors are used to provide the feedback to the input, see Figure 3.2. Notice that

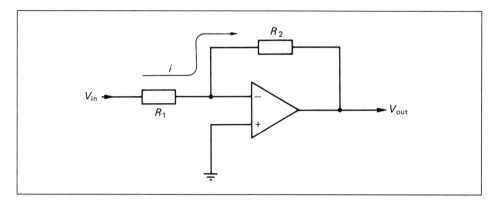

Figure 3.2 *The inverting amplifier*

conventionally we do not show the op-amp's power supply connections (they generally use ±15 V), nor the power supply decoupling capacitors, which are typically 100 nF. To analyse the circuit we note that by rule 2 V_- is at 0 V; this is also known as the virtual earth approximation. Applying Ohm's law to the current flowing in the two resistors:

$$V_{in} = iR_1 \text{ and } V_{out} = -iR_2$$

hence

$$V_{out}/V_{in} = \text{Gain} = -iR_2/iR_1 = -R_2/R_1$$

Thus the circuit has a gain given by the ratio of the two resistors, and the minus sign means the output signal is of opposite polarity to the input. 'Sensible' values for the resistors are in the range 1 kΩ to 1 MΩ.

The follower

Figure 3.3 illustrates the op-amp follower. Feedback is taken directly to the inverting input. By rule 2 we have $V_{out} = V_{in}$. The advantage of this circuit is that the input impedance is very high and the output impedance very low (see the later section on the effect of feedback on these two parameters). These two characteristics mean that the follower acts as a very good buffer IC.

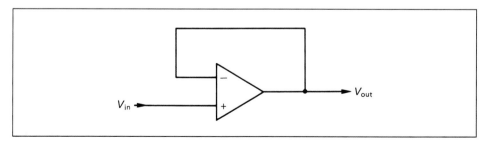

Figure 3.3 *The op-amp follower*

The non-inverting amplifier

It is often useful to amplify a signal without inverting it. Figure 3.4 shows how an op-amp can do this. To evaluate the gain we again apply Ohm's law to the resistor network:

$$V_{out} = i(R_1 + R_2) \text{ and } V_- = V_{in} = iR_2$$

Eliminating i

$$G = V_{out}/V_{in} = (R_1 + R_2)/R_2$$

$$= 1 + R_1/R_2$$

Thus the minimum gain which can be produced from a non-inverting op-amp is unity. This restriction is irritating when you want a gain of less than one. One solution is to use two inverting configurations and a dual op-amp chip.

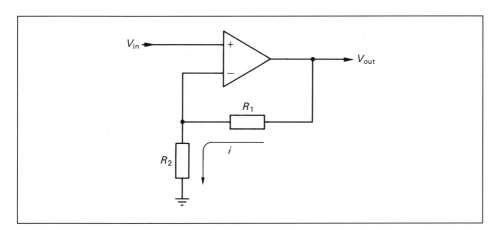

Figure 3.4 *The non-inverting amplifier*

The adder

Figure 3.5 shows an op-amp adder where resistors are used to connect more than one input voltage to the op-amp input. Again we apply the usual technique of using Ohm's law to give the input and output voltages in terms of the resistors and currents, and then eliminating the currents:

$$i_1 = V_1/R_1 \text{ etc. and } i_t = i_1 + i_2 + i_3 = - V_{out}/R_4$$

hence

$$V_{out} = - R_4(V_1/R_1 + V_2/R_2 + V_3/R_3)$$

Thus we have a weighted adder network: to add the voltages just make the resistors equal. An example of this circuit is shown in the SG84X circuit in Chapter 7. In the SG84X two monochrome video signals and a

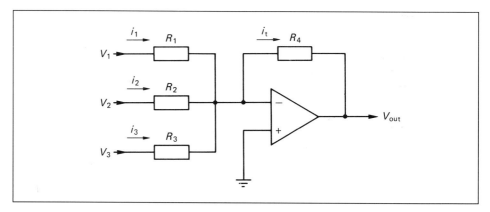

Figure 3.5 *An op-amp adder*

'composite sync' signal are mixed together in a fast op-amp adder like this. Another application of this circuit is as a simple digital-to-analog converter. The input digital number is fed into an adder with resistors in the ratio 1:2:4:8:16 etc.; the output voltage will then be proportional to the inputted binary number. Obviously your resistors must be well matched for such a circuit to work accurately.

The differentiator

Figure 3.6 shows the 'differentiator' circuit. To evaluate its gain we simply use the reactance of the capacitor in the normal gain equation of the inverting op-amp:

$$G = - R/(1/j\omega C)$$
$$= - j\omega RC$$

So if $V_{in} = V_0\cos\omega t$ then the factor of ω in the gain means that the output voltage is proportional to the differential of the input voltage, dV/dt. The

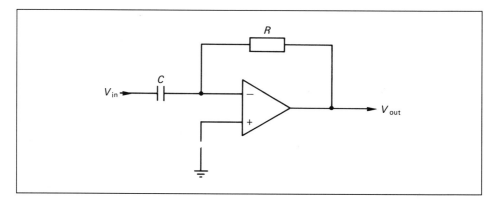

Figure 3.6 *The differentiator circuit*

fact that the output is proportional to frequency also means that the circuit acts as a high-pass filter, letting through higher-frequency signals whilst attenuating lower-frequency signals.

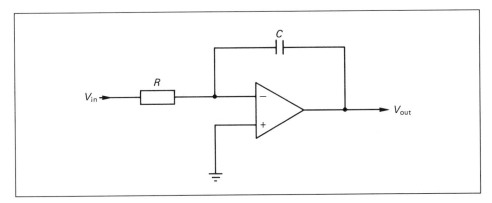

Figure 3.7 *The integrator circuit*

The integrator

The integrator is the opposite of the differentiator, as can be seen by the reversal of the resistor and capacitor in Figure 3.7. Now we have:

$$G = - (1/j\omega C)/R$$

$$= - 1/j\omega RC$$

Now signals are integrated:

$$\int V_0 \exp(j\omega t)dt = V_0 \exp(j\omega t)/j\omega$$

The factor of $1/\omega$ means that high-frequency signals are attenuated, so the circuit acts as a low-pass filter. One problem not obvious from the circuit diagram is that there is no d.c. feedback path from the output to the input (the capacitor blocks d.c. signals). This can result in the integrator slowly drifting, and the solution to this problem is to put a high-value (say 1 MΩ) resistor across the capacitor.

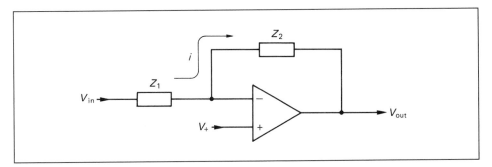

Figure 3.8 *Inverting amplifier with offset*

Inverting amplifier with offset

Figure 3.8 shows another configuration where instead of tying the non-inverting input to ground it is connected to a voltage V_+.
Hence

$$V_{in} = iZ_1 + V_+$$

and

$$V_{out} = V_+ - iZ_2$$

Eliminating i:

$$V_{out} = V_+ - (V_{in} - V_+)Z_2/Z_1$$

This expression shows that the offset voltage is multiplied by the d.c. gain. We shall see this is important when we consider later the inherent offset voltage of an op-amp.

An active clamp

Figure 3.9 shows an op-amp circuit which uses a diode. The circuit acts to prevent the output voltage from going below V_+, and if it is above V_+ then it follows the input. The circuit works as follows: if V_{in} is less than V_+ the op-amp's output is positive and the diode conducts, thus closing the feedback loop. The circuit then looks like an op-amp follower with an output voltage equal to V_+, since by the virtual earth approximation the two inputs are equal. When V_{in} rises above V_+ the op-amp's output becomes negative and the diode ceases to conduct. The feedback connection is now broken and so the op-amp saturates (at around −13 V) and the output becomes V_{in}.

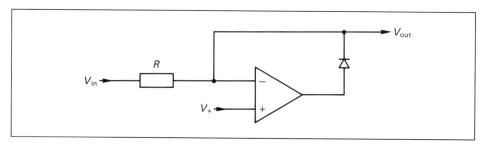

Figure 3.9 *An op-amp clamp circuit*

If you want to constrain the output signal to be below V_+ and to follow the input when V_{in} is less than V_+ then simply reverse the diode. Check that the circuit then functions as stated.

A peak detector

Figure 3.10 illustrates a voltage peak detector. As the input varies, then provided the diode is conducting the op-amp will charge up the capacitor,

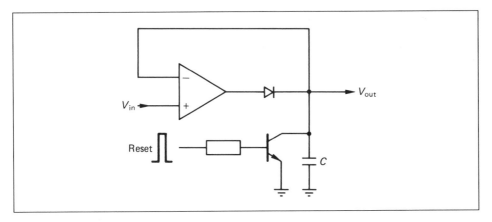

Figure 3.10 *A voltage peak detector circuit*

which will store the op-amp's output voltage. However, when the input voltage drops the voltage on the op-amp's output will go negative, since the voltage stored on the capacitor is greater than the input voltage. Hence the diode will not conduct and the feedback network will be broken. Consequently the output voltage will be that stored on the capacitor. In order for the output voltage to change the input must exceed that stored on the capacitor. Hence the output represents the maximum or peak input voltage to date.

In fact, because of the finite input current of the inverting input of the op-amp the capacitor will slowly discharge, and leakage in the capacitor itself will cause the voltage to fall slowly. For similar reasons the subsequent stage should be buffered by an op-amp follower to prevent the capacitor discharging into the following circuit. To reset the circuit a switch is needed across the capacitor; this could be a transistor, low-leakage FET or relay.

A power booster

The output current of a typical op-amp is about 20 mA. Sometimes it is necessary to drive a load which requires more current than this. One way

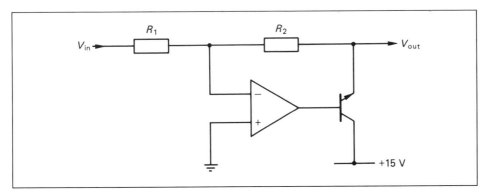

Figure 3.11 *Using a transistor to increase an op-amp's output drive*

of boosting the output power is by connecting a transistor to the op-amp's output, see Figure 3.11. The transistor multiplies the op-amp's current by its current gain factor β. Using an NPN transistor allows current to be sourced to the load, but if you want to sink current then a PNP transistor should be used with its collector tied to –15 V.

If you only want to drive a high current load into an on or off state then an op-amp can be used to drive an NPN transistor in the open-collector configuration. The only additional requirement is a protection diode connected with its anode to ground and its cathode to the transistor's base. This prevents the transistor's base going more negative than its emitter.

A logarithmic amplifier

Figure 3.12 shows an interesting circuit which acts as a logarithmic amplifier – the output voltage is the logarithm of the input voltage. The circuit is analysed as follows: by the virtual earth approximation the inverting terminal is at 0 V and hence the current flowing through the resistor is given by $i = V_{in}/R$. This current flows into the diode. Now the transfer characteristic of a diode is $i = I_0[\exp(V/V_T) - 1]$ where V is the voltage across the diode, here V_{out}, so:

$$V_{in} = RI_0[\exp(V_{out}/V_T) - 1]$$

We now assume that the output voltage is much greater than V_T.
Hence:

$$V_{in} \approx RI_0\exp(V_{out}/V_T)$$

Taking the natural logarithm of each side yields:

$$V_{out} = V_T \log_e[V_{in}/RI_0]$$

The circuit is not ideal since V_T depends on temperature. However, if you are working over a relatively small range of input voltages then it will function satisfactorily.

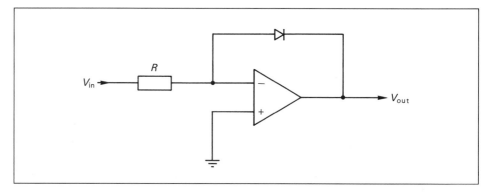

Figure 3.12 *A logarithmic amplifier*

Real op-amp behaviour

So far we have assumed that all our op-amps have perfect characteristics. In real life this is not the case. Table 3.1 lists some op-amp characteristics and their ideal values.

Table 3.1 Op-amp characteristics

Characteristic	Ideal value
Input bias current	Zero
Input offset current	Zero
Input offset voltage	Zero
Open-loop gain (A)	Infinite
CMRR (Common Mode Rejection Ratio)	Infinite
PSRR (Power Supply Rejection Ratio)	Infinite
Slew rate	Infinite
Settling time	Zero
Noise	Zero
Bandwidth	Infinite
Cost(!)	Zero

Many hundreds of op-amps are available, in each case offering a trade-off of some or all of the above factors. We shall now investigate some of these characteristics.

Input offset voltage

Input offset voltage is the voltage between the two inputs which gives zero volts output. Ideally this parameter should be zero, the same voltage on the two input pins giving zero volts output. The offset voltage (given the symbol V_{OS}) is multiplied by the d.c. gain of the op-amp circuit; see the inverting amplifier with offset example. Since the d.c. gain can be quite high a large offset, or error, can be produced at the output. To overcome this problem manufacturers enable this offset to be trimmed out by means of a pot connected across two of the op-amp's pins. If the use of a pot is inconvenient then you can always use an op-amp with a lower value of V_{OS}.

Input offset and bias current

Input bias current is the current flowing into each input terminal. This current is small (rule 1 in the first section), but if you have large resistors then the currents can generate offset voltages at the output. Input bias currents can be countered by ensuring that each input 'sees' the same impedance, and thus any voltages built up cancel out. Figure 3.13 shows how to balance the inputs for an inverting op-amp. Alternatively an op-amp can be used with low bias currents; for example, the CA3140

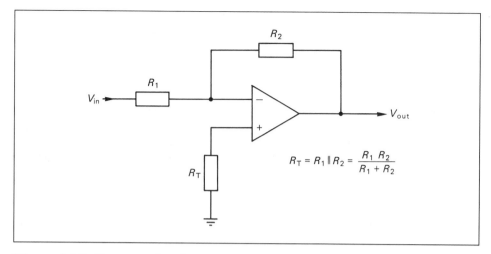

Figure 3.13 *Compensating for an op-amp's input bias currents*

MOSFET op-amp has a bias current of only 5 pA compared to 100 nA for the 741.

The input offset current is the difference between the two input bias currents. If this is too large then you have to use either lower feedback resistors or, preferably, an op-amp with lower input currents.

Slew rate

Slew rate is a measure of how quickly an op-amp's output can respond to changes in the input voltage. The slew rate is measured in V/μs, and is the maximum rate at which the op-amp's output can change. The 741 op-amp has a slew rate of 0.5 V/μs. This means that if the output of the 741 has to change by 10 V then it will take 20 μs to do so. Thus for signals with 10 V swings the maximum frequency a 741 can cope with is about 50 kHz. This may be too slow for your application, in which case you have to use a faster op-amp, for example the LM318 which has a slew rate of 70 V/μs.

Settling time

Settling time indicates how long it takes an op-amp's output voltage to reach 0.1%, or some other quoted figure, of its final value. Note that the settling time to 0.1% does not imply anything about how long the op-amp will take to reach 0.01%. Settling time and slew rate are particularly important for analog-to-digital converter circuits (A/Ds). Here analog inputs are sampled by op-amps before being passed to the A/D converter, which takes the analog input voltage and converts it to a digital representation of the voltage. If the input signal is changing then it is important that the input op-amps settle quickly to their final values. Also, in an A/D the front end of the circuit often consists of a multiplexer which selects between different analog signals.

These signals could be widely separated in voltage, so high slew rate op-amps are required to acquire the new voltage after switching channels.

Rejection ratios

Common mode rejection ratio (CMRR) is a measure of the response to common mode signals on the input terminals. In theory if the inputs are 10.0 and 10.1 V then the output should be the same as if the inputs were 0.0 and 0.1 V, so the op-amp should only respond to differences, not the common part of the signals. The CMRR is quoted in decibels (dB), the decibel being defined as 20 log (V_1/V_2). Thus, if the CMRR is stated at 60 dB, it means that common mode signals are reduced by a factor of 1000.

Power supply rejection ratio (PSRR), again quoted in decibels, measures the op-amp's immunity to noise on its power supply lines; generally speaking, for well-bypassed supplies this parameter is unimportant.

Effect of feedback on op-amp parameters

We have already seen how feedback improves the stability of op-amps to changes in their open-loop gain A. We now consider how it affects their bandwidth, input impedance and output impedance.

Bandwidth

The bandwidth of an op-amp can be defined as the range of input frequency before the output voltage is diminished by $1/\sqrt{2}$. In decibels this is $20 \log(1/\sqrt{2}) = 3$ dB. In terms of power, since power is proportional to the square of voltage, it corresponds to the half-power point. Figure 3.14 shows a plot of the frequency response of a typical op-amp. With no feedback the gain is A up to a frequency of ω_0, after which the gain falls off as $A/(1 + j\omega/\omega_0)$. This fall-off is due to capacitance inside the op-amp. As we have seen, with feedback the closed loop gain is $A/(1 + AB)$. If we denote the bandwidth with feedback as ω_b, then the gain with feedback is given by:

$$\text{Gain} = \frac{A/(1 + j\omega/\omega_0)}{1 + AB/(1 + j\omega/\omega_0)}$$

$$= \frac{A}{1 + AB + j\omega/\omega_0}$$

Dividing the numerator and denominator by $1 + AB$ gives:

$$\text{Gain} = \frac{A}{1 + AB} \cdot \frac{1}{1 + j\omega/\omega_b}$$

where $\omega_b = \omega_0 (1 + AB)$.

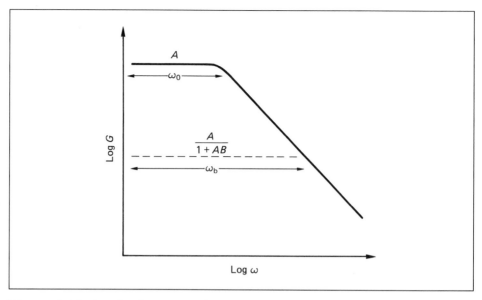

Figure 3.14 *A gain–frequency plot of an op-amp*

So the bandwidth has been increased by the factor of $(1 + AB)$. It is also interesting to note that the product of the gain and the bandwidth is a constant. Thus given the bandwidth at any particular gain, the bandwidth at another gain is easily calculated.

Input impedance

Ideally the input impedance of an op-amp stage should be infinite, and the output impedance zero. Figure 3.15 explains why. An input voltage is applied through a resistor R, and if the op-amp has an input impedance of R_{in} then we have a voltage divider circuit and the op-amp's input is at $V.R_{in}/(R + R_{in})$. To see the 'correct' voltage, the input impedance needs to be infinite so that no current flows into the input resistance. Similarly, to avoid a voltage drop at the output we require zero output impedance.

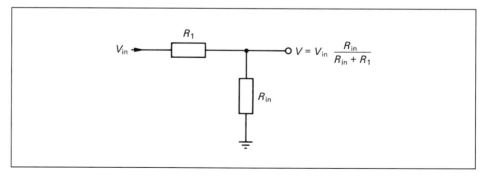

Figure 3.15 *Effect of finite input impedance on input voltage*

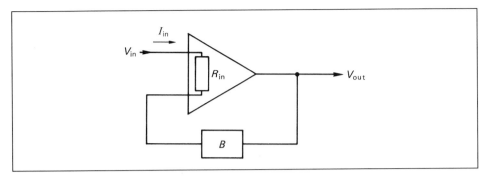

Figure 3.16 *Analysing the effect of feedback on the input impedance of an op-amp*

Figure 3.16 shows the effect of feedback on an op-amp's input impedance. The feedback gives a voltage BV_{out} on the negative input terminal. Hence the input current is $(V_{in} - BV_{out})/R_{in}$. Using the equation for the gain, $G = V_{out}/V_{in} = A/(1 + AB)$, yields:

$$I_{in} = V_{in}/[R_{in}(1 + AB)]$$

Hence the input impedance has been increased by the (large) factor $(1 + AB)$.

Output impedance

The output impedance with feedback can be calculated with reference to Figure 3.17. Here V_{out} is measured after the output impedance, R_{out}. Hence we have:

$$V_{out} = A(V_{in} - BV_{out}) - I_{out}R_{out}$$

Rearranging:

$$V_{out} = V_{in}.A/(1 + AB) - I_{out}R_{out}/(1 + AB)$$

Thus the output impedance is reduced by the factor $(1 + AB)$. For low-frequency signals this means the output impedance is negligible, but for

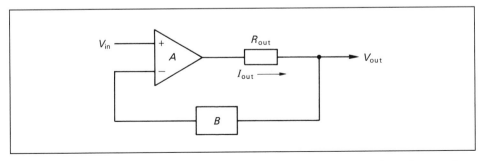

Figure 3.17 *Analysing the effect of feedback on the output impedance of an op-amp*

high frequencies where A falls off it can become appreciable (around 10–100 Ω for a typical op-amp).

The instrumentation amplifier

An instrumentation amplifier takes in two signals and produces their difference as the output voltage. Usually the difference can be multiplied by some factor, typically $\times 10$, $\times 100$ or $\times 1000$. An instrumentation amplifier can be made with standard op-amps and accurately matched resistors; Figure 3.18 shows how. The circuit is straightforward but lengthy to analyse:

$$V_+ = V_2 R_4 / (R_3 + R_4)$$

$$V_{out} = V_1 - i(R_1 + R_2)$$

but the two input terminals are at the same potential so:

$$V_1 - V_2 R_4 / (R_3 + R_4) = iR_1$$

Eliminating i:

$$V_{out} = V_1 - (R_1 + R_2) [V_1/R_1 - V_2.R_4/R_1(R_3 + R_4)]$$
$$= -V_1.R_2/R_1 + V_2[R_4(R_1 + R_2)/R_1(R_3 + R_4)]$$

To simplify this expression we set $R_2 = R_4$ and $R_1 = R_3$. We then get:

$$V_{out} = -V_1.R_2/R_1 + V_2.R_2/R_1$$
$$= [V_2 - V_1]R_2/R_1$$

So, as required, we have an output voltage proportional to the difference of the two input signals. It is useful to see how accurately matched our

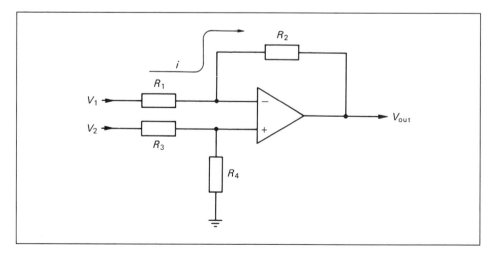

Figure 3.18 *An instrumentation amplifier*

resistors must be for tolerable performance. To evaluate this let us assume $R_4 = (1 + \alpha)R_2$ and $R_3 = (1 + \beta)R_1$, where α and β represent the (small) matching errors. To simplify the maths let us also assume we want a gain of 1 for this we need $R_2 = R_1$. Then:

$$V_{out} = -V_1 + V_2[(1 + \alpha)R_2(R_1 + R_2)/R_1(R_1 + R_2 + \alpha R_2 + \beta R_1)]$$
$$= -V_1 + V_2[(1 + \alpha)2/(2 + \alpha + \beta)]$$
$$\approx -V_1 + V_2[1 + (\alpha - \beta)/2]$$

Thus if the resistors are mismatched by 1% and if both V_1 and V_2 are set to, say, 10 V, then the output voltage could be as much as 1% of 10 V, but for a perfect instrumentation amplifier the output should be zero if both inputs are at the same voltage. We can see that the circuit has a poor common mode rejection ratio if the resistors are not accurately matched.

In practice instrumentation amplifiers are commercially available as a package with accurately trimmed internal resistors, and thus you would usually buy one off the shelf rather than try to make your own. Since instrumentation amplifiers are generally used to magnify small differences between signals (as with a strain gauge) the most important parameters to look for are the CMRR, the slew rate and the settling time. The gain is either programmed by logic pins on the device or by shorting pins together. In order to allow the gain to be changed under software control the shorting can be done using relays. Figure 3.19 shows the symbol for an instrumentation amplifier.

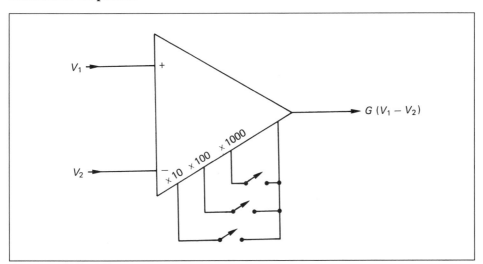

Figure 3.19 *Symbol for an instrumentation amplifier*

The sample and hold amplifier

A sample and hold amplifier (sometimes written S/H) has two modes of working. In the sample mode it behaves just like a normal op-amp, but by changing a logic input it can be put into the hold mode. Figure 3.20

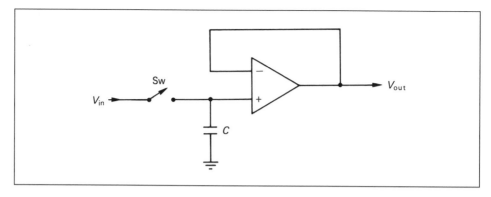

Figure 3.20 *Principle of the sample and hold amplifier*

illustrates how it achieves these two modes of operation. In the hold mode it holds the value of the signal at the output, regardless of what the input is doing. The hold voltage is held on a capacitor, which may be internal to the device. Two parameters of a sample and hold are of practical value – the *aperture* time and the *acquisition* time. The aperture time is how long the switch takes to respond to a change on the logic input. The acquisition time is how long the capacitor takes to charge up to the input voltage after the switch is closed; obviously the larger the capacitor the longer it takes to charge up. Figure 3.21 shows how the output of an S/H varies with the input voltage in the two modes. One way of thinking of an S/H is as an analog equivalent of a digital transparent latch, which if you recall either stores or follows a logic signal depending on the state of its ENABLE input.

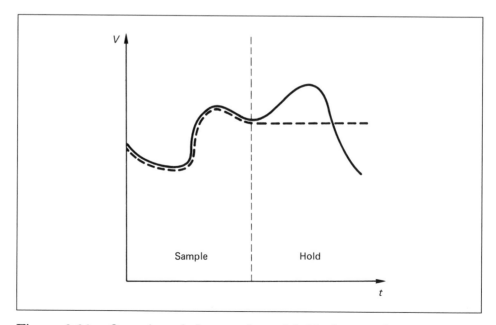

Figure 3.21   *Operation of the sample and hold. Input voltage, solid line; output voltage, dashed line*

The S/H is ideal for an A/D converter circuit. The A/D takes time to convert the analog input to a digital number, during which time (the conversion time) the input voltage must be stable. Thus you use the conversion in progress signal from the A/D to put the S/H into the hold state. The AD585Q is a good choice of sample and hold being both fast and cheap.

Comparators

A comparator is used when you want to know if a signal is above or below a certain level, that is you need to make a comparison. The comparator circuit is unusual since it uses positive feedback. Figure 3.22 shows such a circuit; notice that the feedback is to the non-inverting input and so is positive. Since there is no negative feedback the op-amp will be saturated and so its output voltage will be at −10 or +10 V, if the op-amp is operating off ±10 V supplies. The effect of the feedback is shown in Figure 3.23. There is a range of input voltages where the output voltage depends on the history of the system. Let us assume the input voltage starts off at −10 V and is slowly increased; when it reaches +0.4 V the output will change state. However, if it is then reduced it has to fall to −0.4 V (not +0.4 V) before the output switches back to its previous state. This type of behaviour, where the switching point depends on what has happened before, is called a Schmitt trigger, or hysteresis.

The advantage of hysteresis is that if you have a noisy input waveform which is slowly changing its voltage, then as the switching threshold is crossed the output voltage only changes state once and does not duplicate the incoming noise. You can use a normal op-amp as a comparator, but

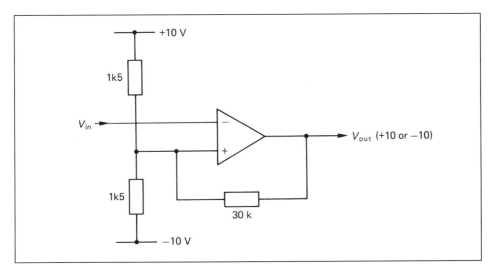

Figure 3.22 *A comparator with positive feedback*

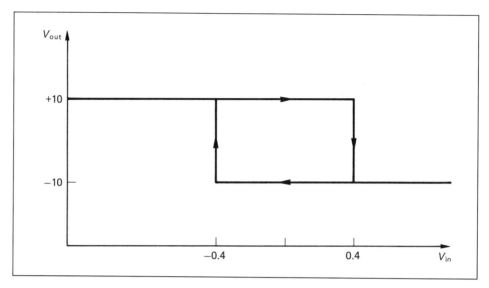

Figure 3.23 *Input to output voltage of comparator showing hysteresis*

it is usual to use a specially designed comparator chip. These chips have very high slew rates and open-collector outputs to simplify logic interfacing.

Schmitt triggers are also used on the inputs of some TTL logic gates for the same reason (better noise immunity), for example the 74LS14, LS244 and LS245.

4 Programmable logic

Introduction to programmable array logic

PALs (a trademark of Advanced Micro Devices Inc.) are a logic family which can be used to replace standard discrete TTL and CMOS gates in circuits. As its name suggests, a PAL can be programmed, or configured, to match the requirement of a given circuit. This means that since a PAL can be tailored for a given design, chips and hence space can be saved. Typically this space saving means that a given TTL circuit can be replaced by about a fifth as many PAL chips. PALs are especially efficient when replacing combinational or state-machine logic. In addition, by designing from square 1 with PALs, many circuits are possible which would be unthinkable with standard TTL.

We shall look at the following PAL types – 16L8, 16R4, 16R6, 16R8 and 22V10. The inside of these chips contains an array of *fuses*. These fuses connect input signals to the internal logic of the PAL. To make the PAL conform to the required logic function some of the fuses are *blown* by a special PAL programmer. Figure 4.1 shows the arrangement of fuses for a 16L8 PAL; all PALs have much the same arrangement. Each input (a 16L8 has 10) and its inverse is routed into the fuses array. For a 16L8 there are eight rows of fuses per output, each row being routed into an AND gate. Thus with no fuses blown all the inputs and their inverses are ANDed together. Each row of fuses is known as a 'product term', and the number of product terms varies from PAL to PAL – the 22V10 has two outputs with 16 product terms. Seven of the AND gate outputs form the inputs to a seven-input OR gate. The fuses can be thought of as a wired-OR type of logic. The output of the OR gate on the 16L8 is inverted to produce an active-LO (hence the 'L' in 16L8) output, and the output of the pin is fed back to the fuses array (actually only six out of the eight outputs on a 16L8 have this feedback facility).

Encoding logic functions

To see how a PAL can be made to encode a logic function a good place to start is with what it produces in the unprogrammed state. With no fuses

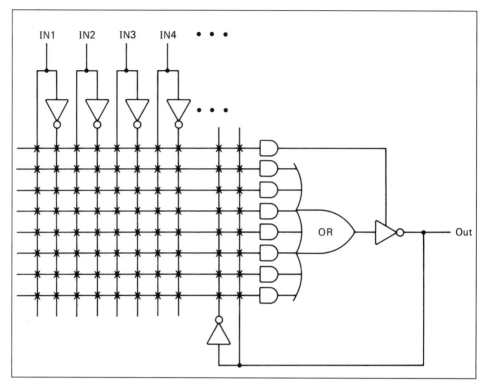

Figure 4.1 *The internal structure of a PAL16L8. The matrix of crosses repre-sents the PAL's fuses*

blown all the inputs and their inverses are connected to the AND gates, so the output is given by:

/OUT1 = IN1 & /IN1 & IN2 & /IN2 & IN3 & /IN3 & ...
    + IN1 & /IN1 & IN2 & /IN2 & IN3 & /IN3 & ...
    + IN1 & /IN1 & IN2 & /IN2 & IN3 & /IN3 & ...
    + IN1 & /IN1 & IN2 & /IN2 & IN3 & /IN3 & ...
    + IN1 & /IN1 & IN2 & /IN2 & IN3 & /IN3 & ...
    + IN1 & /IN1 & IN2 & /IN2 & IN3 & /IN3 & ...
    + IN1 & /IN1 & IN2 & /IN2 & IN3 & /IN3 & ...;

This is not a very useful logic equation. To construct something more worthwhile we blow out fuses to disconnect selected inputs from the AND gates. For example, a simple OR gate, active-LO because of the output inversion, has the equation:

/OUT2 = IN1
    + IN2
    + /IN3;

OUT2 will be LO if IN1 is HI OR IN2 is HI OR IN3 is LO. Note that if we want an active-HI output then we need to apply de Morgan's theorem to get:

/OUT3 = /IN1 & /IN2 & IN3

We can check this with a truth table, as follows.

IN1	IN2	IN3	/OUT3
LO	LO	LO	HI
HI	LO	LO	HI
LO	HI	LO	HI
HI	HI	LO	HI
LO	LO	HI	LO
HI	LO	HI	HI
LO	HI	HI	HI
HI	HI	HI	HI

/OUT3 is HI if IN3 is LO or if IN2 is HI or if IN1 is HI, as required. With most PAL *compilers* (the computer program which takes your PAL equations and produces the code for programming a PAL), there is no need to perform de Morgan's theorem manually, the compiler does it for you. A point to watch for is if you have a long AND term, say IN1 & IN2 & /IN3 & /IN4 & OUT2 & IN7 & OUT3 & /OUT4, and you want to invert this term. By de Morgan's theorem this will become a set of OR terms; in fact there will be eight of them, one for each AND term. However, the 16L8 only contains seven product terms so it is impossible to construct such a PAL; of course the PAL compiler will tell you this, at which point you have to redesign your equations.

We can also obviously construct an AND gate, for example:

/OUT4 = IN1 & /IN2 & IN3 & /IN4 & IN5;

OUT4 is LO if IN1 is HI, IN2 is LO, IN3 is HI, IN4 is LO AND IN5 is HI.

Notice that if, having programmed the PAL, you decide that you do not want the IN5 term in the equation then this can be arranged by simply blowing out the corresponding fuse inside the PAL. However, if you decide you need to add an additional IN6 term to the PAL equation, then because this cannot be done by blowing a fuse (you cannot unblow fuses) the previously programmed PAL would be wasted, and a new one would have to be blown.

Producing a functioning PAL

Assuming that you have decided to use a PAL for some logic part, what do you have to do to get a functioning device? There are three steps: firstly, write out a set of PAL equations and enter them onto a computer; secondly compile the equations; and lastly download the compiled codes into a PAL programmer.

Writing PAL equations

Firstly, the writing of PAL equations. The equations representing the

PAL's logic must be written out in a format which the compiler can understand. We shall base our format on the CUPL compiler (from Logical Devices Inc.), but to avoid confusion stick to the logical symbols '/', '&' and '+' for NOT, AND and OR respectively. The first thing that you have to supply is a *pin list*, that is a list of names corresponding to each input or output pin, and whether it is active-LO or HI. The pin list is followed by the equations for each output pin.

Active-HI and active-LO equations

A note should be made here about the use of active-HI and LO pins. If you want a pin to be active-LO there are two ways of achieving this: firstly, in the pin list you can designate the output, say OUT2, as active-LO by the definition Pin 12 = /OUT2. Later in the program there will be an equation like OUT2 = ...; if the right-hand side of this equation is TRUE then the output pin will be in the LO state, since the pin list has defined the signal as active-LO – it is LO if TRUE. Where the active state of the signals is given in the pin list the PAL equations are best read as 'TRUE or FALSE' statements.

The alternative way of handling signals is to designate the pin as Pin 12 = OUT2; and put the active-LO part in the equations, that is /OUT2 = ...; The advantage of this method is that all the information is contained in the equations (you do not need to refer to the pin list to find out whether a signal is active-HI or LO), and the signal levels correspond to the voltages measured at the inputs and outputs, so it is easy to check with a logic probe to see if the PAL is functioning as you expect. The merit of the first method is that the equation, when read as a true or false statement, gives an indication of how the PAL works, which means it is better for documentation purposes. As an example of the two methods consider the following fragments of a PAL:

Pin 1 = /BR;	Pin 1 = BR;
Pin 2 = /BUSAK0;	Pin 2 = BUSAK0;
Pin 15 = /BUSRQ0;	Pin 15 = BUSRQ0;
BUSRQ0 = BR & /BUSAK0	/BUSRQ0 = /BR & BUSAK0
+ BR & BUSRQ0;	+ /BR & /BUSRQ0;

These are the equations necessary to request use of the STEbus (see Chapter 6). BR is a signal that indicates that a microprocessor wishes to use the bus – if it is LO then the processor wants to use the bus. BUSRQ0 is the output of the PAL which, if LO, requests the bus; the input BUSAK0 is LO if the processor has been granted control of the bus. The two sets of equations are electrically identical, so a PAL compiled from either set will function identically.

The equation on the left puts the active-LO terms in the pin list, so the equation is best read as: BUSRQ0 is TRUE if BR is TRUE and BUSAK0 is FALSE, OR is TRUE if both BR and BUSRQ0 are TRUE. The equation on the right would be read as BUSRQ0 is LO if BR is LO AND BUSAK0 is HI, OR if BR is LO AND BUSRQ0 is LO. Some designers prefer one form, some the other. It is a good idea to use only one form for programming, but you should be able to read both, though having to invert everything for the form you are not used to can be confusing. Here we shall use the right-hand form: the active-LO states are indicated in the equations rather than the pin list.

Compiling PAL equations

Having written your equations and typed them into a computer, in say CUPL format, the next thing you have to do is compile them. With CUPL the appropriate command is:

    cupl -uj libcupl pl6r8 vt1.pld

'vt1.pld' is the name of the file containing your PAL equations (here for a 16R8 PAL). This command line causes the computer to check your equations file for syntax or logic errors, for example too many OR terms when performing de Morgan's theorem. The computer will then compile the equations and produce a file named 'vt1.jed', known as a 'JEDEC' file. This JEDEC file contains a list of numbers in a specified format which define the fuse map of the PAL corresponding to your equations. This file can now be downloaded (transmitted) via a serial link to a PAL programmer (such as a Stag ZL30).

Programming a PAL

Having downloaded the PAL JEDEC file you can now program your PAL. Firstly enter into the programmer the device's code number, which varies with the type of PAL and its manufacturer. Then place the PAL in the appropriate socket and press a button to check that it is in the empty unprogrammed state. You then press the 'program' button, and if all is well within a few seconds the programmer will beep and you will have a correctly programmed device. If the PAL fails to program there are a few possible causes of this. Firstly, somewhat less than about 1% will fail because of manufacturing defects. Secondly, you may have entered the wrong device code number or have downloaded the wrong file. Once blown fuses cannot be 'unblown' (except in the case of UV erasable PALs), so if you have worked out a logic design incorrectly then you will have wasted a PAL for nothing.

Types of PALs and simple applications

Combinational PALs

Now let us have a look in more detail at the inside of some PALs, and some simple applications. Firstly, the 16L8. The 16L8 is a 20 pin device with eight outputs, 10 inputs and two power pins. Each output can be optionally tri-stated by one product term, as shown in Figure 4.1. The actual output is a seven-input OR gate, each input to the OR gate being a product term and the whole output being inverted to create an active-LO pin. Six of the eight outputs have a feedback line which feeds back the voltage at the output pin (and its inverse) into the fuses array. This feedback term allows the user to implement a transparent latch in a combinational PAL, that is:

```
/OUT2 = /IN2 & LAT
      + /OUT2 & /LAT;
```

When LAT is HI the output follows the input IN2. When LAT is LO the output is a copy of itself. Thus on the falling edge of LAT the value of IN2 is stored on the output pin (just like an LS373). If we want the latch to store data on the rising edge then we simply invert LAT:

```
/OUT2 = /IN2 & /LAT
      + /OUT2 & LAT;
```

There is a slight difference between this PAL emulation of a 373 and the 373 itself – a 373 can be tri-stated and still remember latched data. However, the PAL cannot do this, because the feedback is taken from the output pin and not from just after the OR gate. Hence when the latch is tri-stated the indeterminate (actually it will probably float HI) logic output will be fed back.

Registered PALs

The 16L8 is a combinational PAL, the other type is the registered PALs such as the 16R4, 16R6 and 16R8. These are PALs containing four, six and eight registers, or D flip-flops, respectively. Each has a total of eight output pins, the ones not used for register outputs being used for combinational outputs with feedback as on the 16L8. Figure 4.2 illustrates one of the register outputs. The registers consist of D flip-flops, the clock inputs of which are connected to Pin 1 of the PAL. The output of the register goes to an output buffer which can be optionally tri-stated by driving Pin 11 of the PAL HI. The /Q output of the flip-flop is used as the feedback term (plus its inverse). The fact that the feedback is not from the output pin itself means that tri-stating the PAL does not affect logic equations which are using the feedback terms. The D input is driven by an eight-input OR gate, its inputs being the product terms from the fuses array.

Example of a registered PAL

Let us show a simple example using a registered PAL. We want to produce two 'quadrature' clocks (E and Q) for driving a 6809E microprocessor. Figure 4.3 shows the relationship between the two clock signals. For a

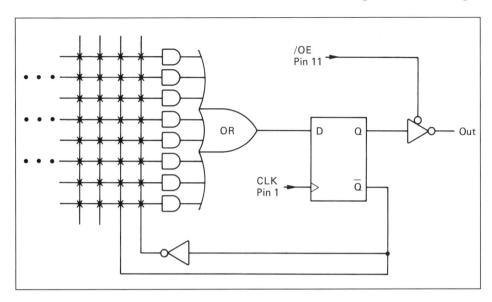

Figure 4.2 *The output structure of a registered PAL*

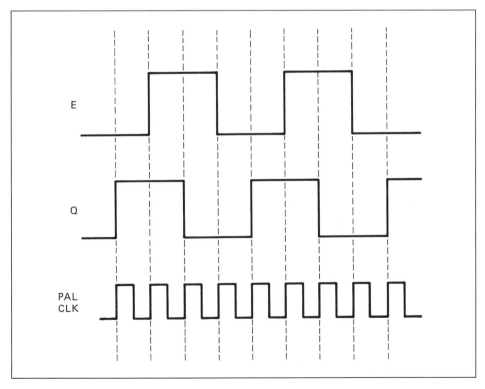

Figure 4.3 *The E and Q clocks of the 6809E*

registered PAL the equations are written as OUT1.D = ...; if the equation on the right hand side is TRUE then the output goes HI after the next clock edge. Thus here we examine the state of the E and Q signals prior to each clock edge, then if we want E or Q to go LO after the clock edge we encode the state of the logic before the clock edge into the equation. Hence, for Q we can say 'Q becomes LO if E AND Q are both HI OR if E is HI AND Q is LO before the clock edge'. In equations this is:

Pin 14 = E;
Pin 15 = Q;

/Q.D   = E & Q
        + E & /Q;

/E.D   = E & /Q
        + /E & /Q;

Where '.D' indicates a registered output.

The E and Q clocks are at a quarter of the input clock frequency applied to Pin 1 of the PAL. Thus for a 68B09E running at 2 MHz we need to input an 8 MHz clock.

The PAL22V10

The PAL22V10 is a 'deluxe' version of the 16R and 16L series of PALs. It has 10 outputs instead of eight and occupies a 24 pin 0.3 inch pitch DIL package. With one clock line (Pin 1) this leaves two power pins and 11 inputs. What makes the PAL22V10 'deluxe' is its much more flexible output structure.

Each output pin can be either combinational or registered, which is determined by how you program it. The outputs have more product terms than the 16R and 16L series – on two of the outputs there are 16 product terms into the OR gate. The output enables are not controlled by a single pin, as on the 16R series, but in each case by a product term. Two other useful additions are included in the registered outputs – an asynchronous reset and a synchronous preset. The asynchronous reset is a product term (labelled .ar), which when asserted resets all the register outputs to their inactive states. The synchronous preset product term (symbol .sp), when asserted, causes the flip-flops to go into their active states on the next rising edge of the clock.

Equations for a 22V10 can get quite complicated, and these PALs are also more expensive than other PALs. For this reason it is a good idea to invest in some UV erasable PALs. These can be programmed as normal but, when no longer required or (more likely!) found to be wrong, can be erased under UV light and then reused.

General considerations

In general, as far as hardware considerations are concerned the following points can be made. PALs are TTL compatible and are available in a range of speeds, from propagation delays of 35 ns for the older standard type to 5 ns for the AMD -5s series. The drive capability of the 16R and 16L series is 24 mA LO level, the same as a TTL bus driver chip and enough to drive 'standard' bus lines; note, however, that the 22V10 has only 16 mA of drive which is insufficient to satisfy the STE or VME bus specifications.

PAL examples

We shall now look at some examples showing the use of PALs for a variety of purposes.

BCD counter

We want to design a 4-bit BCD counter. We proceed by listing the states the counter will pass through, as follows.

Q3	Q2	Ql	Q0
0	0	0	0
0	0	0	1
0	0	1	0
0	0	1	1
0	1	0	0
0	1	0	1
0	1	1	0
0	1	1	1
1	0	0	0
1	0	0	1

After the last state (9) the counter is to return to zero. The equation for Q0 is simple – on each clock edge it changes state:

/Q0.D = Q0;

From the state table Q1 becomes (or stays) LO if Q1 AND Q0 were both LO OR both HI OR if Q3 was HI. Thus:

/Q1.D = /Q1 & /Q0
      + Q1 & Q0
      + Q3;

Similarly the equations for Q2 and Q3 are:

/Q2.D = /Q2 & /Q1
      + /Q2 & Q1 & /Q0
      + Q2 & Q1 & Q0
      + Q3;

$$/Q3.D = /Q3 \ \& \ /Q2$$
$$+ \ /Q3 \ \& \ /Q1$$
$$+ \ /Q3 \ \& \ /Q0$$
$$+ \ Q3 \ \& \ /Q2 \ \& \ /Q1 \ \& \ Q0;$$

One final word of caution is now required: we have not looked at the states 1010–1111 (counts 10–15). It is important to check that if the counter gets into one of these states, perhaps on power up, then it returns to the required counting region 0–9 and does not get 'stuck'. In fact states 10, 12 and 14 go to state 9, and 11, 13 and 15 to state 8. Since this PAL requires only four registers a 16R4 could be used, leaving its combinational outputs for other pieces of logic.

An LS 138 emulator

The last example was a registered design, but for a combinational design we shall emulate an LS138 chip. Normally this would not be necessary so we will add in the additional facility that the outputs are to be tri-stated if the EN signal is HI. Recall that the 138 has three input pins A, B and C which select which of eight outputs go LO, A being the least significant bit, see Table 1.2. It also has three enable pins Gl, /G2A and /G2B which must be HI, LO and LO for the output to be driven LO. The PAL equations for this are straightforward to produce:

```
/OUT0 = /C & /B & /A & G1 & /G2A & /G2B;
OUT0.OE = /EN; /* enable output if EN LO */

/OUT1 = /C & /B & A & G1 & /G2A & /G2B;
OUT1.OE =  /EN;

/OUT2 = /C & B & /A & G1 & /G2A & /G2B;
OUT2.OE = /EN;

/OUT3 = /C & B & A & G1 & /G2A & /G2B;
OUT3.OE = /EN;

/OUT4 = C & /B & /A & G1 & /G2A & /G2B;
OUT4.OE = /EN;

/OUT5 = C & /B & A & G1 & /G2A & /G2B;
OUT5.OE = /EN;

/OUT6 = C & B & /A & G1 & /G2A & /G2B;
OUT6.OE = /EN;

/OUT7 = C & B & A & G1 & /G2A & /G2B;
OUT7.OE = /EN;
```

Thus we have a tri-statable LS138. We shall now look at some PALs with more practical value.

STEbus master control PAL

This example shows a PAL which uses both registered and combinational outputs. The aim of this PAL design is to produce an interface for a processor which wants to interface to the STEbus (see Chapter 6 for more details). Before the processor can use the bus it must obtain permission to use it. It does this by asserting a bus request signal, called BUSRQ, but it is only allowed to assert this signal if BUSAK is HI. When the PAL detects BUSAK in the LO state it knows it has permission to use the bus, though it must still keep asserting BUSRQ until it no longer wishes to use the bus. The PAL equation to achieve these requirements is:

/BUSRQ.D = /REQ & BUSAK
+ /BUSRQ & /REQ;

/REQ is the signal which indicates that the processor wishes to use the bus. The first product term is the condition that must be satisfied for BUSRQ to go LO. Once it has gone LO the second product term keeps it LO as long as /REQ stays LO. When the processor has received permission to use the bus it can drive address and data onto it by enabling the bus driver chips (typically LS245s). However, before it does this it must check that a signal called DATACK is in the HI state; this ensures that the previous bus cycle, or operation, has finished. The equation for the enable, EN, signal is:

/EN.D = /BUSRQ & /BUSAK & DATACK;

The '/BUSRQ & /BUSAK' term ensures that the processor has control of the bus, and the DATACK term makes the equation satisfy our last condition. Actually we do not connect EN into the enable input of the LS245s. The reason for this is that DATACK can change at any time, so it may not satisfy the setup time of the D flip-flop in the PAL, and hence the register may go into a metastable state. To avoid this we clock the signal again, and use this signal, SEN, to drive the EN pin of the LS245s:

/SEN.D = /EN;

We have now enabled the address and data bus driver chips. To complete the interface we have to generate two remaining signals: ADRSTB and DATSTB. These indicate, to the device which the processor is talking to, that correct address and data signals are present on the bus. These signals should be asserted in the order ADRSTB followed by DATSTB, and be driven at least 35 ns after the address and data is valid on the bus, which will be the LS245 enable time after SEN goes LO (or 40 ns worst case). So if we clock the PAL at 12.5 MHz one clock cycle is 80 ns. Hence, if we produce a signal (DDEN) which is activated one clock cycle after SEN we can use it to produce the ADRSTB and DATSTB signals. The equations for ADRSTB and DATSTB become:

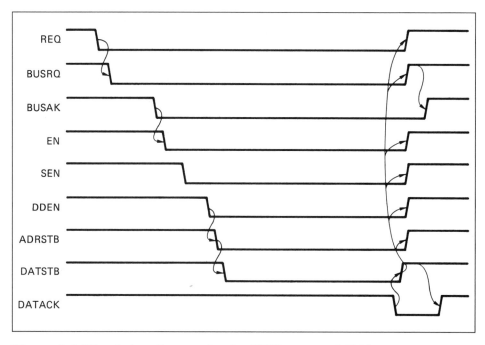

Figure 4.4 *The timing diagram for the STEbus control PAL*

/DDEN.D = /SEN;

/ADRSTB = /DDEN & DATACK
         + /DATSTB;

/DATSTB = /ADRSTB & DATACK;

Thus when DATACK goes LO, indicating the end of the cycle, first DATSTB goes HI then ADRSTB. Finally, at the end of a bus cycle we need to reset all the registered outputs. To do this we use the asynchronous reset facility on the 22V10:

FIELD = [BUSRQ, EN, SEN, DDEN];

FIELD.AR = DATSTB & /DATACK & /SEN;

The FIELD term is just a list of the registered outputs – it saves you having to write out .AR for each register. Figure 4.4 shows the timing diagram corresponding to the working of this PAL.

A video shift register

This example is quite complicated, yet it shows the power of PALs quite well. In a video display circuit picture information is stored in memory. This data is read out from the memory and sent to the video monitor. Memory data is stored in a parallel form and has to be converted to a serial data stream for transmission to the monitor. Thus we need a PISO shift register, which is known as a video shift register. For a full description of a video system refer to Chapter 7. Here we shall just define how our PAL should respond to incoming signals, and not be too concerned with why it performs certain actions.

The first set of inputs to our PAL is eight data bits, labelled D0–7, corresponding to the data read out from memory which must be turned into serial form. The bits are loaded into the shift register when the LOAD input is HI. Shifting is not permitted when the EN input is LO, which means that the outputs are frozen so that pixels on the screen are repeated; this is what is required for 'horizontal zooming'. If the CURSOR input is LO the outputs should be tri-stated, which allows the video board to produce a cursor on the screen.

So far it is relatively straightforward, but we now come to the final input bit, called B4. If B4 is LO then we are said to be working in '8-bits per pixel mode'. In this mode we want the PAL to look like two 4-bit PISO shift registers working in parallel, with two outputs Q6 and Q7. If B4 is HI then we are working in '4-bits per pixel mode', and we want the bits to be shifted out in a single 8-bit PISO shift register, with one output Q7. Firstly we define the pin list for completeness:

```
PAL22V10
Inputs                  Outputs
Pin 1 = CLK;            Pin 15 = Q0;
Pin 2 = D0 ;            Pin 16 = Q1;
Pin 3 = D1;             Pin 17 = Q2;
Pin 4 = D2;             Pin 18 = Q3;
Pin 5 = D3;             Pin 19 = Q4;
Pin 6 = D4;             Pin 20 = Q5;
Pin 7 = D5;             Pin 21 = Q6;
Pin 8 = D6;             Pin 22 = Q7;
Pin 9 = D7;
Pin 10 = LOAD;
Pin 11 = EN;
Pin 13 = B4;
Pin 14 = CURSOR;
```

The required equations for Q7 are:

```
Q7.D    = D7 & LOAD
        + EN & B4 & /LOAD & Q6
        + EN & /B4 & /LOAD & Q5
        + /EN & /LOAD & Q7;
Q7.OE   = CURSOR;
```

The first term is the 'load' term: if LOAD is HI then Q7 is loaded with the input data D7. Notice that the other three terms all contain /LOAD and hence they are only considered if a load operation is not in progress. The last term, in which /EN occurs, corresponds to no shifting – Q7 is reloaded with Q7. The other two terms correspond to the two modes of operation of the shift register: the first to a shift register which shifts bits in the order Q0–7, the second to two shift registers with outputs Q0, 2, 4, 6 and Q1, 3, 5, 7. The equations for the outputs down to Q4 are:

```
Q6.D   = D6 & LOAD
       + EN & B4 & /LOAD & Q5
       + EN & /B4 & /LOAD & Q4
       + /EN & /LOAD & Q6;
Q6.OE = CURSOR;

Q5.D   = D5 & LOAD
       + EN & B4 & /LOAD & Q4
       + EN & /B4 & /LOAD & Q3
       + /EN & /LOAD & Q5;
Q5.OE = CURSOR;

Q4.D   = D4 & LOAD
       + EN & B4 & /LOAD & Q3
       + EN & /B4 & /LOAD & Q2
       + /EN & /LOAD & Q4;
Q4.OE = CURSOR;
```

The equations for Q0–3 are similar. The SG84 graphics board discussed in Chapter 7 uses PALs similar to this. In fact it uses an extra input (Pin 23) to cause the outputs to 'flash': if this flashing input bit is asserted the outputs become their inverses. It is left as an exercise to the reader to see how this enhancement might be achieved. The ability of the PAL to switch, under the control of one signal, between two different modes of operation – single or dual shift register – would be difficult to emulate with standard TTL, even using four or five ICs.

A seven-segment display driver

We wish to design a PAL for driving a seven-segment display. It should take in four binary-weighted inputs (D0–3) and produce seven outputs, A–G. The outputs, A–G, drive the individual LEDs of the seven-segment

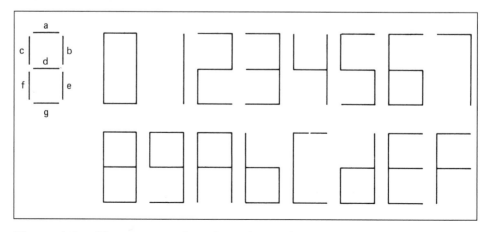

Figure 4.5 *The representation of numbers using a seven-segment display*

display. Figure 4.5 shows which LEDs are lit to represent the numerals 0–9 and the letters A–F corresponding to the inputs 0–15. With 16 possible numbers it might be thought that our PAL would require 16 product terms to do all of the necessary decoding, which even a 22V10 could not cope with. In fact a maximum of eight product terms are needed. To see that this is the case consider what happens if exactly eight terms are required, and you now need to add in another term, making nine; then this additional term must lie next to one already in use – the only difference between the two terms is that one has 'D0' and the other '/D0'. Thus, the two terms can be paired off by removing the 'D0' variable which is redundant, and hence the number of required terms remains at eight. Consequently we can use a 16R8 PAL which has eight product terms for each OR gate. Our PAL becomes:

```
PAL16R8
Inputs          Outputs
Pin 1 = CLK;    Pin 12 = A;
Pin 2 = D0;     Pin 13 = B;
Pin 3 = D1;     Pin 14 = C;
Pin 4 = D2;     Pin 15 = D;
Pin 5 = D3;     Pin 16 = E;
                Pin 17 = F;
Pin 11 = /OE;   Pin 18 = G;

/A.D = /D3 & /D2 & /D1 & /D0    /* '0' */
     + /D3 & /D2 & D1           /* '2' and '3' */
     + /D3 & D2 & /D1 & D0      /* '5' */
     + /D3 & D2 & D1            /* '6' and '7' */
     + D3 & /D2 & /D1           /* '8' and '9' */
     + D3 & /D2 & D1 & /D0      /* 'A' */
     + D3 & D2 & /D1 & /D0      /* 'C' */
     + D3 & D2 & D1;            /* 'E' and 'F' */
```

We can see that 12 inputs (0, 2, 3, 5, 6, 7, 8, 9, A, C, E and F) have only required eight product terms. In fact the above could be simplified further by noting that the term for '2 and 3' is the same as that for '6 and 7' except for a redundant D2 term, so /D3 & D1 would encode '2, 3, 6 and 7'. Since the PAL produces a LO signal when the LED should be lit, this driver should be used with a common anode type of display. The PAL could be used either directly in a non-multiplexed fashion, or by producing appropriate strobe signals fed into the /OE pins it could be used in parallel for multiplexed driving.

Rather than encode all of the PAL equations for this device we leave this as an exercise for the reader, and give each segment output in terms of the inputs only:

```
B = 0,1,2,3,4,7,8,9,A,D        C = 0,4,5,6,8,9,A,B,C,E,F
D = 2,3,4,5,6,8,9,A,B,D,E,F    E = 0,1,3,4,5,6,7,8,9,A,B,D
F = 0,2,6,8,A,B,C,D,E,F        G = 0,2,3,5,6,8,9,B,C,D,E
```

Thus the first term for 'B' would be /D3 & /D2 /* 0–3 */

STEbus arbiter PAL

The STEbus is discussed fully in Chapter 6, but here we are concerned with one small part of the protocol – bus *arbitration*. An arbiter is a device (the PAL we are about to design) that decides which of three possible microprocessors, or masters, is allowed to use the bus at any given time. The arbiter produces three bus acknowledge signals – BAK, BUSAK0 and BUSAK1 – which when asserted (LO) indicate that the selected master can use the bus. Corresponding to the three acknowledge signals are three request inputs – BR, BUSRQ0 and BUSRQ1 – which are asserted (LO) by a master requiring use of the bus.

The rules for the arbiter are fairly straightforward. Firstly, if it is asserting a bus acknowledge line and the master keeps asserting the corresponding bus request signal, then the arbiter likewise continues to assert that bus acknowledge, regardless of whether the other bus request lines are asserted. Secondly, if the arbiter has to choose which bus acknowledge to assert, then the order, or priority, it uses is firstly BUSAK0, BUSAK1 and then BAK. The PAL equations for this design are as follows:

```
PAL 16R6
SBR.D = BR; /* Latch bus request to avoid metastability */
SBRQ0.D = BUSRQ0;
SBRQ1.D = BUSRQ1;
/BUSAK0.D = /SBRQ0 & BUSAK1 & BAK
          + /BUSAK0 & /SBRQ0;
```

The first term drives BUSAK0 LO if there is a request and the arbiter has not granted the bus to one of the other levels. The second term keeps granting the bus whilst the bus request is asserted.

```
/BUSAK1.D = /SBRQ1 & BUSAK0 & BAK & SBRQ0
          + /BUSAK1 & /SBRQ1;
```

The SBRQ0 term ensures that if both BUSRQ0 and BUSRQ1 are asserted simultaneously then only BUSAK0 is asserted.

```
/BAK.D = /SBR & BUSAK0 & BUSAK1 & SBRQ0 & SBRQ1
       + /BAK & /SBR;
```

BAK can only go active if neither of the other bus requests are being asserted; it then stays active whilst SBR is asserted (LO).

We could also write these equations in the form where the active-LO state is put in the pin list. The equations are then perhaps easier to read, but do not of course correspond to the voltages you would see on the PAL. For example, the equation for BUSAK0 would become:

```
BUSAK0.D = SBRQ0 & /BUSAK1 & /BAK
         + BUSAK0 & SBRQ0;
```

We read this as: assert BUSAK0 if synchronized BUSRQ0 (SBRQ0) is TRUE and both BUSAK1 and BAK are not asserted OR keep asserting if SBRQ0 is TRUE. As we have already said, whether you prefer to think in terms of voltages or TRUE/FALSE statements is a matter of taste.

A priority interrupt encoder

We want to produce a PAL which acts as a priority interrupt encoder. Interrupts are discussed in Chapter 5; here all we need to know is that an interrupt causes a microprocessor to stop executing its main program and do something else instead. The STEbus contains eight interrupt lines called ATNRQ*0–7, ATNRQ0* being the highest-priority line. We want our PAL to examine the states of these eight lines and produce a 3-bit output, IRQ0–2, that encodes which is the highest-priority interrupt present. Thus if ATNRQ4* and ATNRQ7* are both asserted then the output should be HI, LO, LO or 100, binary for the number 4. We also want to be able to make the PAL ignore, or mask off, selected interrupt lines. This is achieved by having eight mask bits, MASK0–7, which if set disable that interrupt level from causing the IRQ bits to be asserted. If we ignore the mask bits then we can draw up a truth table for the IRQ0–2 lines dependent on the input ATNRQ* lines, as follows.

ATNRQ*	IRQ2	IRQ1	IRQ0
0	LO	LO	LO
1	LO	LO	HI
2	LO	HI	LO
3	LO	HI	HI
4	HI	LO	LO
5	HI	LO	HI
6	HI	HI	LO
7	HI	HI	HI

To use the table you find the highest-priority ATNRQ* and read off the IRQ0–2 levels. We can now write the pin list for our PAL:

PAL22V10

Inputs	Outputs
Pin 1 = CLK;	Pin 18 = IRQ0;
Pin 2 = ATN0;	Pin 19 = IRQ1;
Pin 3 = ATN1;	Pin 20 = IRQ2;
Pin 4 = ATN2;	
Pin 5 = ATN3;	
Pin 6 = ATN4;	
Pin 7 = ATN5;	
Pin 8 = ATN6;	
Pin 9 = ATN7;	
Pin 10 = MASK0;	
Pin 11 = MASK1;	
Pin 13 = MASK2;	
Pin 14 = MASK3;	
Pin 15 = MASK4;	
Pin 16 = MASK5;	
Pin 17 = MASK6;	
Pin 21 = MASK7;	

Notice how many of the output pins have been reconfigured, using the feedback, as inputs; this is not possible on the registered outputs of standard '16R' PALs.

Referring to the truth table above, the equation for IRQ2 is straightforward:

```
/IRQ2 = /ATN0 & /MASK0
      + /ATN1 & /MASK1
      + /ATN2 & /MASK2
      + /ATN3 & /MASK3;
```

IRQ2, the most significant bit, is LO if any of the four highest-priority ATNRQ*s are asserted and they are not masked off.

The equation for IRQ1 is more complicated: it should be driven LO if ATNRQ0* or ATNRQ1* are LO and not masked off as before, or if ATNRQ4* or ATNRQ5* are asserted and ATNRQ2* and ATNRQ3* are not asserted or they are masked off. This leads to the following expression for IRQ1:

```
/IRQ1 = /ATN0 & /MASK0
      + /ATN1 & /MASK1
      + /ATN4 & /MASK4 & ATN2 & ATN3
      + /ATN4 & /MASK4 & MASK2 & ATN3
      + /ATN4 & /MASK4 & ATN2 & MASK3
      + /ATN4 & /MASK4 & MASK2 & MASK3
      + /ATN5 & /MASK5 & ATN2 & ATN3
      + /ATN5 & /MASK5 & MASK2 & ATN3
      + /ATN5 & /MASK5 & ATN2 & MASK3
      + /ATN5 & /MASK5 & MASK2 & MASK3;
```

The equation for IRQ0 is more involved still, but follows the same pattern. IRQ0 should be asserted if ATNRQ0* ATNRQ2*, ATNRQ4* or ATNRQ6* are active and not masked off. AND higher-priority interrupts are either not active or are masked off. This gives:

```
/IRQ0 = /ATN0 & MASK0
      + /ATN2 & /MASK2 & ATN1
      + /ATN2 & /MASK2 & MASK1
      + /ATN4 & /MASK4 & ATN1 & ATN3
      + /ATN4 & /MASK4 & MASK1 & ATN3
      + /ATN4 & /MASK4 & ATN1 & MASK3
      + /ATN4 & /MASK4 & MASK1 & MASK3
      + /ATN6 & /MASK6 & ATN1 & ATN3 & ATN5
      + /ATN6 & /MASK6 & MASK1& ATN3 & ATN5
      + /ATN6 & /MASK6 & ATN1 & MASK3 & ATN5
      + /ATN6 & /MASK6 & ATN1 & ATN3 & MASK5
      + /ATN6 & /MASK6 & MASK1 & MASK3 & ATN5
      + /ATN6 & /MASK6 & MASK1 & ATN3 & MASK5
      + /ATN6 & /MASK6 & ATN1 & MASK3 & MASK5
      + /ATN6 & /MASK6 & MASK1 & MASK3 & MASK5;
```

A minor problem with this set of equations is what happens when there is no ATNRQ* being asserted; then IRQ0–2 all go HI, which is the same as if ATNRQ7* was active. To overcome this we can add an output to the PAL which detects whether or not an unmasked interrupt is present, its equation being

/INT = /ATN0 & /MASK0
    + /ATN1 & /MASK1
    + /ATN2 & /MASK2
    + /ATN3 & /MASK3
    + /ATN4 & /MASK4
    + /ATN5 & /MASK5
    + /ATN6 & /MASK6
    + /ATN7 & /MASK7;

INT is LO if a permitted interrupt is present. This signal could go to the interrupt pin of the processor.

This PAL is of the combinational type, and shows once again how one PAL can replace many many TTL gates. The best way to learn how to use PALs is, as with all electronics, actually to sit down and use them; nevertheless it is good practice to take some TTL designs and write down the PAL equations which replace the TTL gates, an exercise which can be done on paper.

Erasable programmable logic devices (EPLDs)

Although PALs are the first programmable devices that the reader new to the industry is likely to encounter, there are other programmable devices available. Generally speaking the larger and more flexible the device the more you have to pay for it. For example, ASICs (Application Specific Integrated Circuits) give great flexibility but are expensive, so are only used for mass production quantities. In order to give the reader a flavour of these larger devices we shall briefly discuss the logic family called EPLDs (Erasable Programmable Logic Devices).

EPLDs have a similar architecture to PALs, but at the time of writing are somewhat slower. Figure 4.6 illustrates the internal layout of the EP1800 EPLD. It can be seen that the device is divided into four equal sections. Each section consists of 12 *macrocells*, which are input/output blocks. The outputs are more flexible than a 22V10 – they can be combinational, D flip-flop, JK flip-flop or toggle flip-flop, all with optional feedback. The four blocks of macrocells are connected by the 'global' bus, which consists of signals from the chip's input pins plus signals from the global macrocells. Thus the four global macrocells in each segment can communicate with the other three blocks, whereas the enhanced (meaning faster) and standard macrocells can only send signals between macrocells in the same block.

The arrangement means that the EPLD effectively splits into four PAL-sized chunks. One very useful feature of the EP1800 is the way its clocking circuitry is designed. All PALs have only one clock pin, but an EPLD

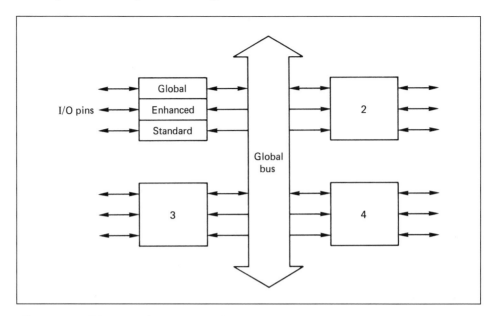

Figure 4.6 *The overall structure of the EP1800 EPLD*

macrocell can use any input or even a product term as its clock. When using the EP1800 a good design philosophy is to split the design into four parts. An example of this is its use on the Arcom VSAD12/32 board, which is an intelligent analog-to-digital converter board (see Chapter 7 for more discussions on A/Ds). One-quarter of the EP1800 was used to generate incrementing addresses for an on-board memory, another controlled how quickly the A/D took samples, the third selected between different channels on an analog multiplexer and the last quarter was used for miscellaneous logic.

EPLDs cost more than PALs, as does the software and hardware required to program them. However, in certain conditions their size and flexibility means they can surpass PALs for particular applications. For further details the reader is referred to the data books of Altera, the manufacturer of EPLDs.

5 | Microprocessors

This chapter is concerned with the subject of *microprocessors*. A simple definition of a microprocessor would be an electronic device which inputs data from the outside world, manipulates or processes that data and then outputs new data back to the outside world. We shall look firstly at how a microprocessor, or CPU, counts and then at how a small microprocessor circuit enables programs to be run.

Computer number systems

Binary

Microprocessors and computers are built using digital logic. Each element of a digital circuit (say a flip-flop) can be in either the HI or LO state. Thus one flip-flop can count to two, represented by the states HI or LO, or 0 and 1. Two flip-flops can store four numbers – 00, 01, 10 and 11 – and each additional storage element increases the possible count by a factor of two. This counting system is known as *binary* and is used by all microprocessors. In a binary number the rightmost digit (Bit 0) is worth one, the next to the left two and so on. Thus, the binary number 100110 has the value:

weighting	32	16	8	4	2	1
	1	0	0	1	1	0
equals	32 + 4 + 2 = 38 in decimal					

In computer terminology each binary digit is called a *bit*, 4 bits are a *nibble*, and 8 bits a *byte*. Large numbers of bytes and bits are expressed in terms of 'kilo' and 'mega' bytes and bits. A 'kilo' is 1024, and a 'mega' 1024 × 1024 = 1048576. They are abbreviated to K (or Kb) and M (or Mb) respectively. Usually when someone refers to 32K of something it is implicitly assumed they mean 32K bytes not bits (an exception is DRAM memory where if its size is quoted at 256K manufacturers generally mean 256K bits or 32K bytes).

Hexadecimal

For humans, manipulating binary numbers is slow and prone to error. For this reason a related counting scheme, called hexadecimal (hex), is used. Computers handle data in byte-wide chunks (or 2 or 4 byte chunks) and we therefore use a counting sytem based on taking 4 bits at a time. With 4 bits we store $4^2 = 16$ numbers (a count from 0 to 15). We can then use a base 16 number system (hexadecimal) which counts from 0 to 15, and in which each more significant digit is worth 16 times a much as the one to its immediate right.

We use the letters A–F to represent the numbers 10–15 respectively. To distinguish a hex number from decimal we either put a '$' sign in front or an 'H' at the end of the number (here we shall use the '$' convention). Thus, for example, $BA5 is

```
weighting      256   16    1
hex              B    A     5
decimal         11   10     5
number = (11 × 256) + (10 × 16) + 5 = 2981 in decimal
```

Many scientific calculators can interconvert hex, binary and decimal and if you do a lot of microprocessor work one of these is a good investment.

Two's complement notation

As stated above, microprocessors use binary arithmetic, but we need to enhance our counting scheme somewhat. To simplify the discussion of this section let us assume we have a 4-bit microprocessor; with 4 bits we can count from 0000 to 1111 in binary, or 0–15 in decimal. The problem with 'straight' binary is that it does not leave any room for negative numbers. To allow for negative numbers we use what is called two's complement notation.

The rule for writing a negative number in two's complement is as follows: firstly write down the number you want in positive notation, for example –4 is 0100 (just +4), and then invert or complement all the bits, so 0100 becomes 1011. This is known as one's complement. To get two's complement you add one to this figure, so 1011 + 1 = 1100. The fact that the top or most significant bit, also known as the sign bit, is set indicates that you have a negative number. With 4 bits you can count from –8 to +7. Table 5.1 shows the two's complement representation for 4-bit integers.

Table 5.1 Two's complement representation

7	0111	–8	1000
6	0110	–7	1001
5	0101	–6	1010
4	0100	–5	1011
3	0011	–4	1100
2	0010	–3	1101
1	0001	–2	1110
0	0000	–1	1111

By extending this to 8 bits the count can range from 127 to −128. You are probably wondering why we have chosen such a complicated scheme. After all it would be so much simpler just to indicate a number as negative by setting the most significant bit, like −6 = 1110. The reason for using two's complement notation is that with it numbers add up correctly! For example, what is 5 − 3? In two's complement it is the following sum:

```
    0101
    1101 +
  ─────────
  1 0010
  ─────────
```

that is, 5 + (−3) = (8) + 2.

The '8' is what is known as a *carry bit*, an overflow beyond the 4-bit range of our adder. If we only look at the last 4 bits, ignoring the carry, then we have the answer 2 as required. Microprocessors often work on 8-bit (byte) wide numbers, but they too can generate carries; what you do with the carry depends on the calculation you are performing. The carry is saved for you in the carry *flag*, a 1-bit piece of temporary data store.

On a microprocessor two's complement notation is most obvious when the CPU is calculating the destination for a *branch* (an instruction which causes the processor to move to a different part of its program). If the branch is forwards then the sign bit is clear; if it is backwards then the sign bit is set and the branch is a negative number.

Two's complement overflow

How in fact does a microprocessor add up? Inside the CPU is a device called the arithmetic logic unit or ALU, which takes in two incoming bytes and adds or subtracts them. After doing so it sets a number of flags – carry, zero, overflow and negative, which are labelled C, Z, V and N, depending on what happened whilst the calculation was being performed. The zero flag is easy to understand: if the answer of the arithmetical operation was zero then this flag is set. The negative flag is set if the answer was negative, so Bit 7 was set. The carry flag was seen above and is set if the 8-bit answer cannot hold the result. The overflow flag is more difficult to understand. It indicates that a two's complement number has overflowed, so if you are using that notation you have to adjust your answer. An example should make this clear. The following sum is the binary addition for 100 + 80:

```
  0110 0100
  0101 0000 +
  ───────────
  1011 0100
  ───────────
```

In two's complement the answer is the representation for −76, and not the 180 we expected. Thus the two's complement notation has overflowed and the CPU will set the V flag to warn us of this. A solution is to *clear* the top bit by means of a microprocessor instruction, and to put that bit into a byte which represents a more significant part of the number. So we would have 128, from the more significant byte, plus 52 (00110100) from the lower byte with its most significant bit cleared, giving a total of 128 + 52 = 180 as required. Fortunately most microprocessor work does not require the use of negative numbers, so you can get away without having to use the V flag – you simply treat all numbers as 'straight' binary.

Memory chips

A microprocessor spends much of its time transferring data to and from *memory*. In this section we look at the different types of memory used in microprocessor systems. The two types commonly used are known as RAM and ROM.

Read-only memory

ROM stands for Read-only Memory, that is memory which can be read from but not written to by the microprocessor. To use an analogy, a musical LP or record is a read-only memory – you can play it but cannot store sound on it. ROMs do not forget their contents when the power is switched off. This means that you can use a ROM to store the microprocessor start-up or *boot* code, which indicates what it should do when you first switch it on. ROMs are actually expensive to buy and cannot be changed by the user. They are only used where you require a mass-produced quantity and are quite sure you will not want to change its contents. For this reason devices called EPROMs are available.

EPROMs

The 'EP' stands for Electrically Programmable. EPROMs can be programmed, or filled, with the required data by using a cheap programming module that supplies the +12 to +25 V needed. The second useful facet of EPROMs is that they can be *erased*, that is reset to their unprogrammed state. You do this by exposing the EPROM's glass window, on the top of the chip, to ultraviolet light for about 30 minutes. Thus incorrectly programmed EPROMs can be used again and again. You can tell when an EPROM is erased by reading its data bytes – an erased EPROM is filled with $FF in each memory location. Because EPROMs can be erased by light, when you have a working system you should cover the window of your EPROMs with an opaque label, often with the serial or version number of the EPROM written on this label. The size of EPROMs (the number of bytes of information they can store) keeps increasing; at present it is 256K.

Figure 5.1 shows the pinout of the 27512 EPROM, a device which can hold 64K. To select which byte you are reading 16 *address* lines, labelled A0–15, are used. These address lines are provided by the microprocessor

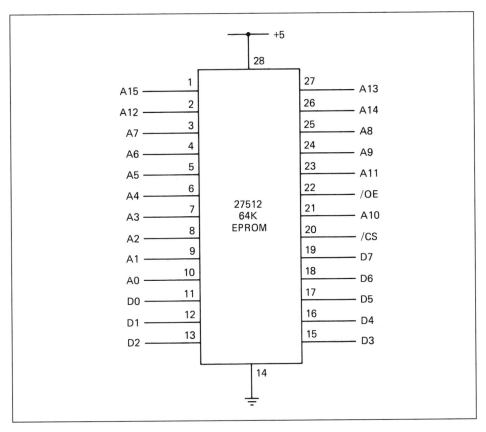

Figure 5.1 *The pinout of a 27512 64K EPROM*

and the EPROM decodes them to select which byte of memory to output – the byte is output on the *data* lines D0–7. Smaller EPROMs will have fewer address lines. Thus, the 2764 is an 8K device and has only 13 (A0–12).

EPROMs have two other signals: a *chip select*, /CS pin, and an *output enable*, /OE pin. In order to access the EPROM both of these lines must be driven LO. Usually the /OE line will go to a microprocessor read signal which indicates that the microprocessor is trying to read or transfer data into itself. The /CS will be driven by the output of an *address decoder* chip. For example, consider the 6809 CPU which has 16 address lines, A0–15, and so can access 64K locations. Now if we use a 2764 EPROM this only occupies 8K locations, so in order to allocate the microprocessor address space we decode A13–15 in, say, an LS138; if we use output '0' of the 138 to go to the chip select of the EPROM then the EPROM will occupy the memory address space 0–$3FFF. The rest of the memory space can be used for other devices, each being accessed when the microprocessor puts out the corresponding address. Such an allocation of address space is termed the microprocessor's *memory map*.

One useful timing parameter to know when designing a circuit is the *access time* of the EPROM – how long it takes from asserting /CS and /OE before valid data appears at the output pins. EPROMs are available in various speeds (the faster the more expensive), ranging from 450 ns to around 150 ns, and again as technology advances quicker EPROMs will become available. The timing diagram for an EPROM is the same as that for a static RAM read cycle, see Figure 5.3.

EEPROMs

Another type of EPROM is the EEPROM or E²PROM (pronounced E-squared PROM). These are an electrically erasable form of EPROM. They can be useful for programming in the field, or when you do not want to wait for the half hour or so a standard EPROM takes to erase. In operation they act like a static RAM chip (see below), accepting both read and write cycles. Note, however, that each byte can only be written to a finite number of times (around 10000).

Random access memory

RAM is the other type of memory which abounds in microprocessor systems. RAM stands for Random Access Memory, which means it can be both read from and written to. RAM comes in two types: *static* RAM (or SRAM) and *dynamic* RAM (or DRAM). Static means that once the memory has been written to it will keep its contents without any intervention from the user. Dynamic RAM is *volatile* – if you fill it with data and just leave it alone the data will gradually disappear! In order to maintain its contents a DRAM chip must be periodically *refreshed*. Unlike EPROMs, RAMs lose their memory contents if the power supply is switched off.

Static RAM

First let us look at the 62256 32K static RAM chip shown in Figure 5.2. The similarity of the pinout to the 27256 EPROM chip is deliberate (they are both parts of a JEDEC standard pinout). This means that, with just a couple of jumpers (or wire links) to compensate for the slight pinout differences, the same socket can be used for either type of chip. The main difference between the SRAM and the EPROM is that of the /WRITE, or /WR, line. In order to write data into an SRAM you assert /CS and /WR; this is known as a write cycle. Note that /WR and /OE should not be asserted together – you cannot write at the same time as you read. Figure 5.3 shows the timing diagram for an SRAM chip – a read followed by a write cycle.

Dynamic RAM

Since it appears fairly easy to interface to an SRAM chip, the quetion arises: why use anything else? The alternative, the DRAM, is a more compact

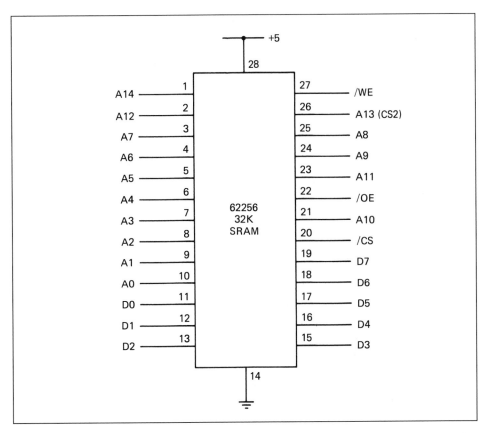

Figure 5.2 *Pinout of a 62256 32K static RAM chip. CS2 is an active-HI chip select used on the smaller 8K 6264*

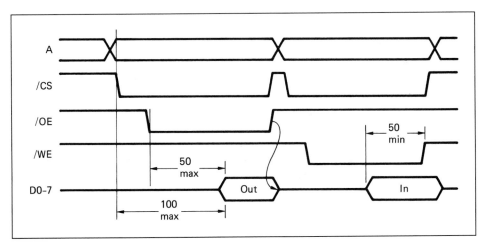

Figure 5.3   *Read and write cycles for a 100 ns access time static RAM chip (read followed by write)*

device – it packs more memory into less square inches. For example, a 20 pin 0.3 inch DRAM IC can hold 256K × 4 bits (128K bytes) of data, while the same amount of SRAM would require a 32 pin 0.6 inch package. The choice between SRAM and DRAM is basically a trade-off – DRAMs occupy less space but the circuitry required to interface to them is more complex than that of SRAMs. Thus, in general for small amounts of memory you use static RAM and for larger amounts DRAM.

Figure 5.4 shows the signals needed to interface to a 256K × 4 DRAM. The DRAM is 4 bits wide and only has four data lines, so you require two chips for a byte-wide arrangement. The 18 address lines needed to decode 256K locations are not all present on the DRAM, instead there are only nine lines, MA0–8. To obtain the 18 lines required, the DRAM latches the values presented on the MA0–8 lines on the falling edges of two signals, called /RAS and /CAS. /RAS stands for 'row address strobe', and /CAS for 'column address strobe'. Think of the memory as being arranged as cells on a large square of graph paper. The row value tells you which row to look along, the column address which column to look along; where the row meets the chosen column is the square which contains the required memory location. The 47 Ω resistors in series with the address lines prevent the MA0–8 signals from suffering from 'ringing' or overshoot; this can be a problem with the long lines often found in DRAM circuits. Figure 5.5 shows the timing diagram for a 256K × 4 DRAM read and write cycle. Notice that /RAS precedes /CAS.

As stated earlier, DRAMs are volatile and will lose their memory contents unless they are periodically refreshed. This is accomplished by performing a refresh cycle. Periodically (typically 256 times every 8 ms) external logic makes a refresh request. When such a request is made the DRAM refreshes the charge on the internal capacitors used to store the memory contents. There are several ways to refresh a DRAM. Firstly, '/RAS only' refresh. A /RAS pulse is produced together with a row address on MA0–8, no /CAS strobe is provided. This causes the DRAM to refresh that row of memory locations, and on the next refresh cycle the row address is incremented by one. This method is fine when the processor has the facility to generate the incrementing addresses, otherwise it is annoying to have to put aside a counter specially for DRAM refreshes.

An alternative way of refreshing DRAMs is the '/CAS before /RAS' mode. As stated above, for a normal read or write cycle /RAS comes before /CAS. In this refresh mode the user reverses the order of the signals so /CAS precedes /RAS; the DRAM recognizes this as a signal that it should perform a refresh cycle. In this case it uses an internal counter to generate the row address. This method is therefore preferable to /RAS only refresh – no external counter is required; however, it should be noted that only newer and therefore larger DRAMs provide this refresh mode.

A small microprocessor circuit

We shall now look at a small, indeed minimal, microprocessor circuit. It will consist of the Motorola 6809 microprocessor, 8K of EPROM and 8K

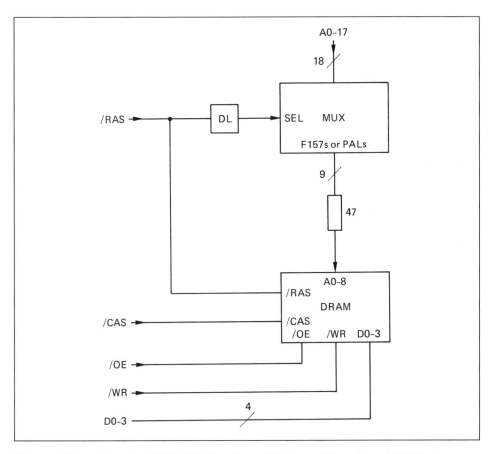

Figure 5.4 *A typical DRAM interface: DL is a delay line, MUX a two-to-one multiplexer*

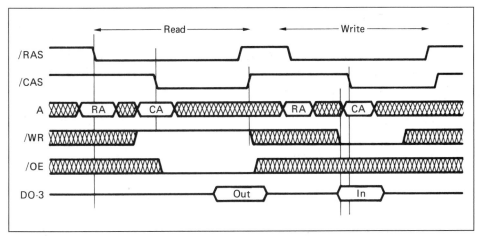

Figure 5.5 *A 256K × 4 DRAM read and write cycle. Read followed by write*

of SRAM plus two other support chips – the 6840 and 6850. The 6809 is an 8-bit CPU which handles data in byte-wide chunks. It is arguably the best 8-bit microprocessor available. Newer processors use 16 or 32-bit data buses, for instance the Z280 and 68020 respectively. The number of bits is a guide to the power of the microprocessor – the more bits it can handle at once the faster it will be. Nevertheless, before progressing to such 'number crunchers' it is essential to gain experience with smaller, not so powerful CPUs, like the 6809.

Clock cycles

All microprocessors use clocked logic, and so require clocking signals. The 6809E ('E' for external clocking) requires two clock signals, E and Q. Figure 5.6 shows how the E and Q clocks can be produced from an LS113 JK flip-flop chip. As was shown in Chapter 4, these two signals could also be derived from a PAL. For the 6809 to function the frequency of the clocks must not drop below about 100 kHz, because if it does then the 6809 can lose the contents of its internal registers. With an 8 MHz input into the circuit of Figure 5.6 the E and Q outputs are 2 MHz, which will drive the 68B09E, the faster 2 MHz version of the processor.

The clock rate sets the speed at which the CPU executes its *instructions:* the higher the frequency the faster your programs will run. Each instruction on a 6809 takes about three to four clock cycles, so in 1 second you can do about half a million operations! This sounds an awful lot, but compare it to a 32-bit 68020 running at 25 MHz, which handles four times as many bits at once, giving a substantial increase in speed.

During a clock cycle the CPU may access an external device (perhaps a memory chip or peripheral), and to do so it drives its *address bus* with the address of the device and then either outputs or inputs data from its

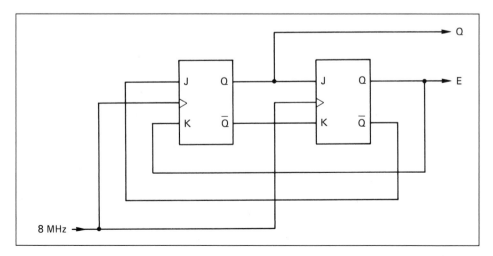

Figure 5.6 *Using JK flip-flops to generate a 6809E's E and Q clocks*

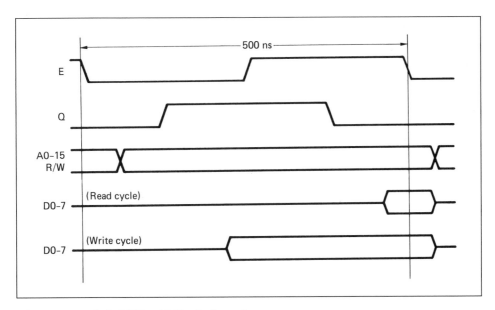

Figure 5.7 *A 2 MHz 6809 clock cycle*

data bus. The way it does this depends on the processor in use. Figure 5.7 shows the timing diagram for the 6809E. A crucial aspect of microprocessor board design is to understand the CPU's signals and to interface them to other chips, in particular to produce chip selects, read and write strobes, /RAS and /CAS signals, etc.

The microprocessor's memory map

One of the first choices which needs to be made when designing a microprocessor circuit is what the memory map should look like. The memory map indicates for each possible address that the processor puts out what device it accesses. One of the important constraints is the location in the memory map of the *reset vector*.

The reset vector

The reset vector is 2 bytes of memory space which, when the CPU is reset, indicate where the processor should 'go to'. What we mean is this: we have an EPROM which contains the code that we want our processor to read and execute; obviously when we reset the processor we want it to start executing code from the beginning of our program. The function of the reset vector is to give the processor the address of the first byte of code in our program. As an analogy, suppose the ROM was a book and the reset vector contained the number 57; then when the CPU is reset the first thing it does is read the vector, and then turn to page 57 and start reading that page.

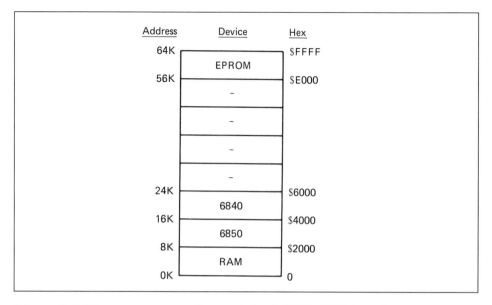

Address	Device	Hex
64K	EPROM	$FFFF
56K	–	$E000
	–	
	–	
24K	–	$6000
16K	6840	$4000
8K	6850	$2000
0K	RAM	0

Figure 5.8 *The memory map for a minimal 6809 CPU board*

The important point is that the reset vector must itself be contained in the EPROM. If it was contained in say static RAM it would disappear as soon as the power was switched off. When the circuit was switched back on the reset vector would contain random information, and the CPU would not go to the start of the program. For the 6809 the reset vector is located at address $FFFE–FFFF, right at the top of memory. Hence we must put our 8K EPROM in the address space 56K–64K. We are free to choose where to put the other devices, so we put the SRAM at the bottom and the 6840 and 6850 into the next higher 8K slots, see Figure 5.8.

Circuit implementation

To produce strobes corresponding to these eight address spaces an LS138 decoder chip is used, the inputs being A13–15, refer to Figure 5.9. As an alternative a PAL16L8 is often used as a memory map decoder chip. An advantage of using a PAL is that it can decode the address lines to produce a memory map with different-sized slots, and thus peripheral devices which have few registers need only take up a small part of the map, leaving more available for memory.

Looking at Figure 5.9 it can be seen that very little logic is needed to design a minimal microprocessor board: one inverter to invert the R/W line (which is high during a read cycle) to produce active-LO /OE signals for the memory chips, and a small bit of logic to produce a /WR signal for the SRAM – the /WR signal can only go LO if R/W is LO, indicating a processor write cycle, AND if Q is HI, the logic equation for this is /Q + RW.

The 7705 chip is a power-on reset chip – it generates an active-LO reset signal (/RST) to the processor when the board is first powered up. It also

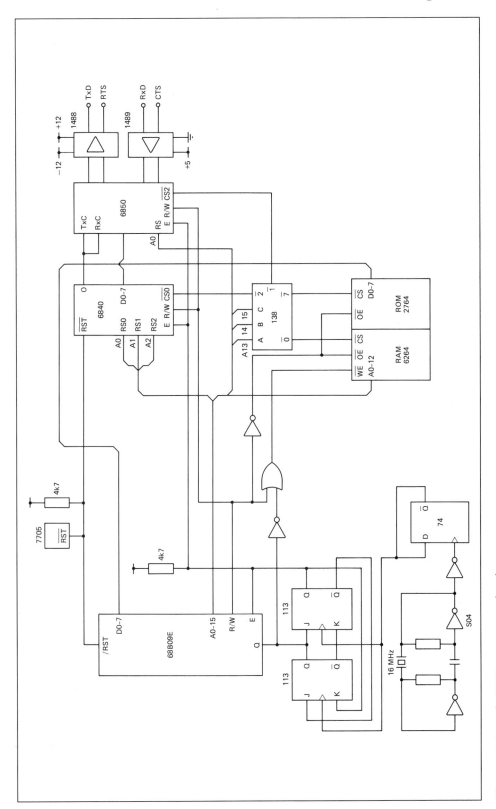

Figure 5.9 *A 6809 processor circuit*

produces this signal if the supply voltage falls below about 4.5 V. An alternative is the 7702 which can be programmed with a pair of resistors to generate a reset at a lower voltage.

Peripheral chips

The two support chips, the 6840 and 6850, belong to the same family of chips as the 6809. This is a point to look for when choosing peripheral chips: if you can use ones of the same family then, because they are designed to work together, they are generally much simpler to interface than those from another family. Here, for example, all they require is the processor E clock and the read/write, R/W, line to function. The 6840 is known as the PTM (Programmable Timer Module). When programmed correctly it produces a square wave of a given frequency.

The 6850 is called the ACIA (Asynchronous Communications Interface Adapter). Its more common name would be a UART, as discussed in Chapter 1. The 6850 is responsible for communication to the outside world, usually the user's computer terminal. When a byte is written to its 'Transmit data register' the ACIA outputs the byte 1 bit at a time via a PISO shift register, the bits then being transmitted down an RS-232 link by the 1488 transmitter chip. Similarly data can be received by the 1489 chip and read into the 'Receive data register' inside the 6850 via a SIPO shift register. This register can then be read by the microprocessor. The 6850 derives its transmission, or baud, rate from pulses that the 6840 produces. This gives a maximum baud rate of 4800.

The operation of the 6809

Hardware signals

In order to understand how our simple circuit works we need to understand roughly how the 6809 functions. The 6809 consists of clocked logic, the clocks being the E and Q signals. The aim of the microprocessor is to read, manipulate and output data to and from the memory and support chips. In each clock cycle the 6809 can do one of three things:

1 Read in a byte of data; this is called a read cycle.
2 Output a byte from an internal register, called a write cycle.
3 Perform an internal operation, perhaps an addition, on a byte or bytes.

These various operations are discussed later; for now we concentrate on the hardware side of the 6809. To understand the hardware a good place to start is with the microprocessor pins themselves, which are listed in Table 5.2.

Table 5.2 The 6809E input and output pins

D0–7	I/O	TSC	I
A0–15	O	/HALT	I
R/W	O	/NMI	I
E,Q	I	/FIRQ	I
AVMA	O	/IRQ	I
/RESET	I	BUSY	O
LIC	O	BA,BS	O

Here I means the signal is an input and O an output. D0–7 is the 8-bit data bus, which is used to transfer data to and from the 6809. It is bidirectional: on a read cycle it is configured for input and on a write cycle for output. A0–15 is the address bus, and 16 lines means the CPU can access 64K of memory space. The address bus contains the address of the data byte being accessed. R/W indicates whether the cycle is read or write – HI for read, LO for write. Note that many microprocessors, such as the Zilog Z80, have two separate lines (/RD and /WR) to indicate whether a cycle is a read or write. As we have seen, E and Q are the clocking signals for the processor. /RESET is the active-LO processor reset signal, and asserting this line causes the processor to restart at the reset vector.

The other signals are not used on our minimal CPU board. The most important ones are /NMI, /FIRQ and /IRQ, which are what are known as *interrupt* lines. They are discussed later but briefly they work like this: if a device asserts one of these lines then an interrupt is generated; this causes the CPU to stop executing its program and instead it runs a different piece of code, called the interrupt routine. When it has finished the interrupt routine it returns to what it was doing before.

Many of the other signals are only used when you have two processors and you want to allow them to share the same address and data bus – for transferring information between them. Thus /HALT when asserted causes the 6809 to stop processing and go into the HALT state putting its buses into a high-impedance state. TSC causes the buses to go tri-state if it is HI, so we keep this signal LO. AVMA indicates that the processor will use the bus in the following cycle, which again is only relevant for multi-processor systems. BUSY is HI if the processor is executing a read–modify–write cycle, a cycle where the CPU reads data from a location, does something with it and then writes it back again. LIC is a signal which indicates that the present cycle is the last cycle of this instruction. The BA and BS lines indicate what state the 6809 is in, as given below:

	BA	BS
Running	LO	LO
Interrupt acknowledge	LO	HI
SYNC acknowledge	HI	LO
HALT acknowledge	HI	HI

Thus in normal operation you would expect both these signals to be LO.

Program execution

Instructions and op-codes

Having looked at the hardware connections to the 6809, we return to the question of how a CPU works. As discussed earlier, a CPU reads in bytes of information, say from an EPROM. The CPU interprets these bytes as being either *op-codes* or data; an op-code plus its associated data byte(s) constitute a microprocessor instruction. Microprocessors have a set of instructions which can do many things: typically they might tell the CPU to perform some action on an internal register.

For example, the op-code $86, where '$' denotes a hex number, means load the internal register called 'A' with the next byte of information read in. Hence if an EPROM or RAM contained the sequence of bytes $8655, and the processor read these bytes as part of its program, then it would load register A with the hex number $55. You might be wondering how the processor can tell that '86' is an op-code byte and '55' a data byte. The answer is that the processor knows how many data bytes are associated with each op-code, and so keeps track of whether it is expecting a data or op-code byte at any given time.

Introduction to programming

Thus to write a program in principle 'all' we need to know is what each sequence of hex numbers means when interpreted as an instruction; we could then fill our EPROM with those bytes and let the CPU process them. This procedure is known as *machine-code* programming. The problem with it is that it would take a long time to learn the instruction set, and you would be very likely to make mistakes continually typing rows of numbers into a computer. To make programming a microprocessor easier manufacturers provide what are known as *assembler mnemonics*. As their name suggests, these are mnemonics which help you to remember instructions; programming with them is called assembler programming. For example, we just had the instruction $8655, which in assembler form is LDA #$55. 'LDA' stands for 'Load A', '#' means with the data which follows the op-code, known as immediate data. Obviously it is a lot easier to remember LDA than $86, especially when you have many instructions to work with.

To produce code what you do is this: firstly you write out your program using assembler mnemonics, and type it into a computer. You then assemble that code on the computer to produce the string of binary or hex numbers, called the *object code*, that the CPU will understand. Finally, you either blow this code into an EPROM, or download it via a serial link into a RAM on your microprocessor board. The code is then ready to be executed by the CPU.

The 6809's registers

Having briefly discussed programming let us return to the internal structure of the 6809. Inside the 6809 are a set of nine registers. These are used to hold information about the state of the processor and for storing data from the outside world before manipulating it. Five of the registers are 16 bits wide and are called PC, U, S, X and Y. The other four (A, B, DP and CC) are byte wide. We now discuss the PC, A, B and CC registers; the others are used for more complex functions and are discussed later.

The program counter

PC is the abbreviation for Program Counter. The program counter is the register which holds the address of the memory location of the next instruction the CPU will read. To use our analogy of a book, it indicates which word we are about to read. Normally the program counter is incremented by the number of bytes in the present instruction, so it just points to the next instruction in memory. However, there are certain instructions, called *branches* and *jumps*, which cause the processor to start executing instructions some distance away from the present instruction, and in such cases the program counter can change by quite large amounts. On a reset the first thing the CPU does is load the program counter with the data stored in the reset vector.

The accumulators

The next most important registers are A and B. These are byte wide, but can also be combined to form the 16 bit 'D' register. The A and B registers are known as *accumulators*, since it is on them that arithmetic takes place. As an example of their use the following assembler code does a simple addition sum – it adds 10 to the value contained in location $40 and stores the result in location $45:

```
LDA    #10 ;load A with 10
ADDA   $40 ;add A to what is in location $40
STA    $45 ;store the result in location $45
```

Notice the sequence: we cannot read 2 bytes from memory in one cycle, so we load A with 10 first. In the second instruction location $40 will be read and its contents added to A leaving the result in A, the original contents of A (10) being overwritten. The result is then written out in the last instruction 'STore A in location $45'. We could equally well have used the B register for this calculation.

The condition code register

The CC register is the Condition Code register. It contains flags, 1-bit stores, which are set or cleared depending on the results of operations. Table 5.3 shows the bits in the condition code register.

107

Table 5.3 Allocation of bits in the 6809's CC register

Bit 0	C	Carry flag
Bit 1	V	Overflow flag
Bit 2	Z	Zero flag
Bit 3	N	Negative flag
Bit 4	/IRQ	/IRQ mask
Bit 5	H	Half carry
Bit 6	/FIRQ	/FIRQ mask
Bit 7	E	Entire state flag

The C, V, Z and N flags correspond to those discussed in the section on two's complement. To recap, Z indicates the result of the operation was zero, N that it was negative, that is Bit 7 was set, C that the register has overflowed and V that a two's complement result is invalid. The H flag is used for BCD arithmetic, and indicates that a carry has occurred from Bit 3 to Bit 4. The /IRQ and /FIRQ flags are for use with interrupts and are discussed later.

Programming the 6809

Over the next few sections we shall introduce some of the things that the 6809 can be programmed to do. The reader should read all this section before attempting to program the 6809 – good programming requires the combination of many techniques.

Branches

The use of the condition code register described above is best discussed with reference to *branch* instructions. A branch instruction is a way of causing the microprocessor to move, or branch, to another part of its program. The simplest instruction to do this is 'BRA' – BRanch Always. On encountering this instruction the CPU always branches to the location given; it actually jumps forwards or backwards by the number of bytes indicated by the data byte after the BRA op-code.

More important than the simple 'BRA' instruction are instructions known as conditional branches. These instructions test one of the flags in the condition code register and, depending on whether it is set or cleared, cause the processor either to continue with the next instruction or to 'take the branch' and continue elsewhere. A common use of a branch instruction is to create a program loop, like a 'FOR...NEXT' loop in BASIC, or a 'DO' loop in FORTRAN. For example, the following loop is executed 20 times:

```
        LDA   $20         ;load A with starting value
        LDB   $10         ;load B with starting value
LOOP1:  INCB              ;increment B by one, start of loop
        DECA              ;decrement A by one
        BNE   LOOP1       ;branch to LOOP1 if non-zero
        NOP               ;no operation
```

Each time we go round the loop A is decremented by one. The BNE instruction checks to see if the Z flag is set, and if it is not the CPU branches to the INCB instruction. When A does become zero then the branch is not taken and the program continues at the NOP instruction. Thus at the end of the loop B will have the value 30. Table 5.4 lists the conditional branch instructions available on the 6809.

Table 5.4 Summary of 6809 branch instructions

BMI	Branch if Minus	– N set
BNE	Branch if Not Equal	– Z clear
BPL	Branch if Plus	– N clear
BCS	Branch if Carry set	– C set
BCC	Branch if Carry clear	– C clear
BVS	Branch if Overflow set	– V set
BVC	Branch if Overflow clear	– V clear
BEQ	Branch if Equal	– Z set
BGT	Branch if Greater than	
BGE	Branch if Greater than or equal to	
BLE	Branch if Less than or equal to	
BLT	Branch if Less than	

The last four branches in Table 5.4 work on two's complement numbers after a compare (CMP) instruction, while for unsigned numbers the equivalents are BHI, BHS, BLS and BLO.

For an example of the use of CC flags consider adding 127 to 10:

```
LDA   #$7F   ;load A with $7F = 127
ADDA  #10    ;add 10 to A
```

A now contains $89 so will be negative, N flag set, and will also be invalid for two's complement notation so that the V flag will be set. Thus you could use the BVC instruction to test the V flag: if it was clear then there would be no problem and you would branch to the next section of code; if it was set, and you were using two's complement representation, you would need to run a correction routine – clear the top bit and add one into a more significant byte of the representation.

Position-independent code

As pointed out above, branches change the flow of control by branching a given number of bytes, and not by going to a specific address. This facet of the branch instruction is useful since it means that it is possible to write *position-independent* code (PIC for short). What this means is this: if you have a piece of position-independent code and it is running at some address, then if you move that code to another location in memory then it will still run.

To see when code may not be position independent contrast the branch instructions with the JMP, or jump, instruction. A JMP instruction causes execution to move to a specified memory location, whose address is

109

defined when the program is assembled and is fixed thereafter. Thus the program cannot run at any address except that which it has been assembled for, and hence it is not position independent. As an analogy consider a book which contains instructions: if you come to a branch instruction it might say 'skip the next 10 lines', whereas a JMP instruction might say 'go to page 5 line 4'. Now imagine that you fill the first 10 pages of the book with blank pages. The branch will still work – skipping the next 10 lines still makes sense – but the JMP instruction will just jump into a region where there is no program and will cause the processor to 'crash'.

For this reason the use of JMP and JSR (Jump to Subroutine) instructions is 'bad' programming, and these two instructions should be replaced by BRA and BSR, or LBRA and LBSR – long branch, if the branch exceeds 127 bytes.

The stacks

Two of the registers which we have not yet looked at are U and S, which are both 16-bits wide. They are known as *stack pointers*. A stack is an area of memory where data is stored, in particular where CPU register information is saved. A stack is a LIFO (Last In First Out) structure. In other words if a stack contains a certain amount of data and you remove a byte, then the byte you retrieve is the last one you put into the stack. It is similar to a pack of cards – the last card you put on top of the pack is the first one removed from it.

In a microprocessor system a stack is arranged as follows. An area of memory is set aside to contain the bytes which will be stored in the stack. A register (U or S) is then loaded with the address of the start of the stack – where in memory the next byte to be stored in the stack will be written to. The 6809 can handle two stacks called the user and system stacks; U and S, the corresponding stack pointers, are initialized by the LDS and LDU instructions. Data can be written into the stacks, called a 'push' operation, by the PSHU and PSHS commands, and read from the stack, called a 'pull', by the PULU and PULS instructions. For example, to push the contents of register A onto the U-stack, and then pull it off the stack, the following two instructions would be used:

```
PSHU    A
PULU    A
```

After the push the memory location pointed to by U contains A (which still contains its original data), and U is decremented by one; it now points to an empty location for the next push. The pull instruction, called POP on some microprocessors, loads A with the byte on the 'top' of the stack, after which U is incremented by one. A simple application of a stack is to swap the A and B registers around:

```
PSHU    A
PSHU    B
PULU    A
PULU    B
```

After the two pushes the top of the stack will contain B, the next lower byte A. Hence when we pull data off the stack it comes off with what B contained first and this is written into A; thus A and B interchange their data (a simpler way of doing this is by the 'exchange' instruction EXG A,B).

Note that when writing a program you must have the same number of pulls as pushes, otherwise the stack will overflow if you keep pushing (the stack will expand until it overwrites an important part of your memory), or you will read off 'garbage' if you perform pull operations when you have not pushed anything onto the stack.

The 6809 has a clever technique for speeding up the coding of multiple stack pushes and pulls. The byte immediately after the PSHU (or PSHS) op-code indicates which registers are to be saved; thus the PSHU/S instruction can be followed by a list of registers to be pushed. For example:

    PSHU   A,B,X,Y,PC

would in one instruction push A, B, X, Y and PC onto the user stack. So that data does not get confused the PULU instruction pulls bytes off in the same order as the PSHU. Thus PULU A,B,X,Y,PC would restore the registers to their values before the push.

Subroutines

Apart from allowing you to store data temporarily, what does a microprocessor use a stack for? The system stack is used for saving information when the processor executes either a *subroutine* or interrupt routine. A subroutine is a way of changing the flow of control of the processor. It enables you to leave the section of code you are running and execute another piece, or subroutine, before returning to the main program. Subroutines are used for two main reasons. Firstly, for pieces of code which are often executed, for example writing a character to a screen via a UART. You do not want to have to write out the instructions for this operation each time you want to write a character to the screen, so you use a subroutine instead and *pass* the character to it for output to your VDU. The other main use of subroutines is to make programs more easily understood; instead of having one mass of code you break it down into small chunks, the subroutines, and call these up one at a time. The advantage of this is that the subroutines can be tested individually, thus leading to faster debugging of your program.

The 6809 uses two instructions to commence execution of a subroutine – JSR and BSR. The CPU then executes the subroutine, at the end of which is an RTS (Return from Subroutine) instruction. This indicates that the processor has come to the end of the subroutine and should now return to the program at the instruction after the JSR or BSR. To make the return the program counter must be loaded with the address of that instruction, but how does the CPU know what that address is? The answer is that, before jumping to the subroutine, the processor saved the value of the program counter on the system stack, just as if it had executed the instruction PSHS PC. When the processor encounters the

RTS instruction it pulls the return address off the S-stack and tranfers it to the program counter. Thus, an equally valid way of returning from a subroutine is to issue the instruction PULS PC.

As an example of a subroutine consider the following piece of code: the S-stack pointer has been set to $100, by a LDS #$100 instruction:

```
            LDA    #30
            JSR    NOACT
$F000       ADDA   20        Memory
                            $100    F0
                            $0FF    00
                            S = $FE

   NOACT: NOP
          NOP
          RTS
```

The main program starts at the LDA instruction. The CPU then encounters a JSR instruction. Firstly it saves PC ($F000) on the S-stack, S is then decremented by two to $FE, and then it executes the subroutine, which because it consists of NOPs does nothing. At the RTS instruction PC is loaded with what is on the top of the stack ($F000) and execution continues at that address (at the ADDA instruction).

Using the user stack

Because the microprocessor uses the system stack it is best for the user to leave this stack alone and use the user stack instead for data storage. A common usage of the user stack is the passing of data to a subroutine. For example, you might have a string of characters which you want the subroutine to manipulate. One way of passing this data to the subroutine would be by pushing the characters onto the user stack. The following, rather simple, example shows this method in use. We want to multiply A by B and then add two to register A. We push A and B onto the stack and call the subroutine, which pulls the data off the stack, manipulates it and then pushes the answer back onto the stack:

```
            PSHU   A,B       ;save A and B
            JSR    MANIP     ;jump to subroutine
            PULU   A,B       ;pull answer off stack

   MANIP: PULU   A,B       ;get data
          MUL              ;perform multiply
          ADDA   #2        ;add 2 to A
          PSHU   A,B       ;push answer
          RTS
```

Notice the pairing off of the pushes and pulls to ensure the stack does not overflow or underflow. Also note that if we had used the system stack, instead of the user stack, things would have been complicated by the presence of the return address being on top of the stack; it is an interesting exercise to see how to get round this problem.

Some 6809 mnemonics

This section gives a brief overview of some of the mnemonics, or instructions, available on the 6809. Although the mnemonics are specific to the 6809, most of the operations described will be found in one guise or another on other processors. In Table 5.5 we use the '=' sign to mean 'becomes', as is usual in software programming (refer back to Table 5.4 for the branch instructions).

Table 5.5 Some 6809 mnemonics

Mnemonic	Meaning
ADCA	A = A + M + C; add the memory and carry into A
ADDA	A = A + M; add memory to A
ANDA	A = A AND M; AND A with memory
ASLA	Shift left register A
ASRA	Shift right register A
BITA	Bit test A; AND A with M and set CC flags
CLRA	A = 0; clear A
CMPA	Compare M from A and set CC bits
COMA	A = /A; complement A
CWAI	AND CC with operand and wait for interrupt
DECA	A = A − 1; decrement A
EORA	A = A EOR M; exclusive-or A with memory
EXG	Exchange two registers
INCA	A = A + 1; increment A
JMP	Jump to effective address
JSR	Jump to subroutine
LDA	Load A with data
LSLA	Logical shift left A; C = Bit 7, Bit 0 = 0
LSRA	Logical shift right A; Bit 7 = 0, C = Bit 0
MUL	D = A * B; unsigned multiply of A and B
NOP	No operation
ORA	A = A OR M; A is ORed with a memory location
PSHS	Push register(s) onto system stack
PSHU	Push register(s) onto user stack
PULS	Pull register(s) from system stack
PULU	Pull register(s) from user stack
ROLA	Rotate left A through carry bit
RORA	Rotate right A through carry bit
RTI	Return from interrupt
RTS	Return from subroutine
SBCA	A = A − M − C; subtract M and borrow from A
STA	Store A in memory; M = A
SUBA	A = A − M; subtract memory from A
SWI	Generate software interrupt
TFR	Transfer register 1 to register 2
TSTA	Test A and set CC bits

The 6809 contains many more instructions, and the reader is referred to the Motorola data book or other books on programming the 6809.

Microprocessor System Design

Simple addressing modes

Table 5.5 contains a list of mnemonics but does not include the possible addressing modes, both of which are needed to form a proper instruction. For now we shall use only two addressing modes – immediate and extended. Occasionally no addresing mode is needed; this is known as inherent addressing, for example CLRA clears accumulator A and requires no other data. Immediate addressing is where the data which goes with the instruction is known at assembly time and does not need to be worked out later. Immediate addressing is indicated by the '#' sign, for instance LDA #25 loads A with 25 making no reference to memory locations. Extended addressing is used where the data is located at a fixed memory address, like an I/O port or designated piece of memory. The mnemonic is simply followed by the address. For example:

```
SUBA        $100
SUBB        #100
ADDA        #$FE
```

The SUBA is extended and subtracts the contents of location $100 from A. The other two are both immediate, SUBB subtracting 100 from B, and ADDA adding $FE to A.

To show the instructions in 'real' operation, let us do some examples.

Examples of programming

Example 1

Add the contents of locations $100–101 to those of $102–103 storing the answer in locations $104–105, assume that the most significant byte is the first and that we are using unsigned or 'straight' binary as our representation:

```
LDA         $101    ;get first least significant byte
ADDA        $103    ;add to second
STA         $105    ;store result
LDA         $100    ;get most significant byte
ADCA        $102    ;add with carry to second
STA         $104    ;store result
```

Notice that we use the two types of ADD instruction. The first, ADDA, ignores the carry flag, whereas the second adds in a one if the carry flag was set, thus allowing for any possible overflow of the least significant byte. An alternative way of carrying out this addition is to use the D register:

```
LDD         $100
ADDD        $102
STD         $104
```

This is quicker since it requires fewer instructions, but since the D register is made up of the A and B registers then it means the contents of both the A and B registers will be lost whereas in the first example we only overwrote the contents of the A register.

Example 2
This example shows the use of the shift instructions. We want to swap the upper and lower nibbles of a byte, so, for example, $5A becomes $A5:

```
LDA    $100    ;get the date byte from location $100
ASLA           ;shift the byte leftwards
ASLA
ASLA
ASLA
LSR    $100    ;shift location $100 rightwards
LSR    $100
LSR    $100
LSR    $100
ORA    $100    ;OR A with location $100
STA    $100    ;store the interchanged nibbles
```

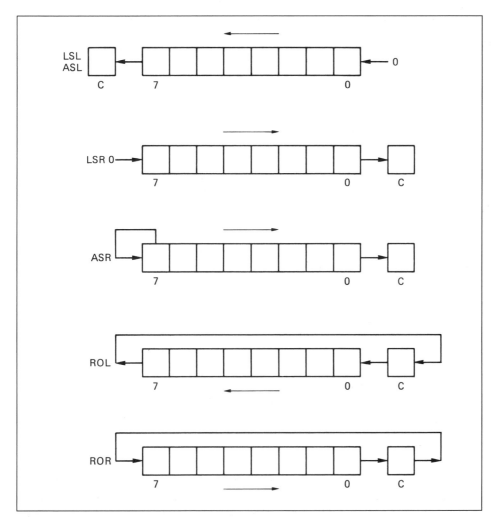

Figure 5.10 *The operation of the shift and rotate instructions*

Figure 5.10 shows how the shift and rotate instructions work. They each shift or rotate the bits in a byte, the carry bit holding bits shifted out of the byte. In the above example the four ASLAs shift the bits in the accumulator to the left, so A, which originally contained $5A, is now $A0. The LSRs shift the contents of location $100 rightwards, so $5A becomes $05. Finally we OR together $A0 and $05 to give the required answer of $A5.

Thus if we want to check to see if Bit 1 of a byte is set, one way is to use the LSR (or ASR) operation to shift bits out till Bit 1 falls into the carry flag, whence it can be tested with a BCS (or BCC) branch instruction. Alternatively we could use the ANDA instruction to test Bit 1 directly.

```
LDA   $100                  or   LDA    #2          ;set Bit 1
LSRA           ;Bit 1 → Bit 0    ANDA   $100
LSRA           ;Bit 0 → C        BEQ    NOTSET
BCC   NOTSET
```

Apart from manipulating bits (especially status bits from an I/O port) the other main use of these instructions is for multiplication or division – to double an unsigned number simply do an ASLA operation, taking care that if the number exceeds 255 you have to move the carry into a more significant byte of the number. For example, multiply the 16-bit number contained in $100–101 ($100 being the more significant byte) by four:

```
          LDA   #2      ;set up loop counter
LOOP:     ASL   $101    ;multiply lower byte by two
          ROL   $100    ;multiply upper byte by two
          DECA          ;decrement loop counter
          BNE   LOOP
```

Notice that we use the ROL instruction to ensure that any carry from the first shift is carried into Bit 0 of the most significant byte. Since we want to multiply by four we go round the loop twice. The provision of the MUL instruction means that 'longhand' multiplication like this is unnecessary on the 6809 (the other way of doing it is to keep adding a number to itself).

Similarly shift right instructions cause the byte to be divided by two. For example, the following piece of code halves a 16-bit two's complement number:

```
HALVE: ASR $100    ;divide higher byte by two
       ROR $101    ;divide lower byte by two
```

The ASR keeps Bit 15 the same, so if it was set indicating a negative number then it stays set; for an unsigned number you would use LSR. For doubling a two's complement number you use the same code as for unsigned, but you must check that the number has not overflowed, either by checking that it has the same sign before and after the left shift, or by testing the overflow flag.

Addressing modes

So far we have seen two of the many addressing modes available on the 6809. The number of addressing modes is a guide to the power of a micro-processor. To complete our discussion we now look at all the remaining modes.

Immediate addressing

The data following the op-code is the data for the instruction. As we have seen, the symbol for this is '#' as in LDA #67 – load A with 67.

Direct addressing

In direct addressing only 1 byte is used to specify a 16-bit address, the higher-order byte being taken from the direct page (DP) register inside the 6809. For example, if you set the DP register to be $55, by LDA #$55 and TFR A,DP, then the instruction LDA $20 would access location $5520. Usually you set DP to be zero. Direct addressing gives an increase in speed over extended addressing since only 1 byte needs to be read from memory to specify an address.

Extended addressing

The contents of the 2 bytes following the instruction specify the address of the operand, for example LDA $1234 loads A with the contents of location $1234.

Extended indirect addressing

It is often useful to be able to use memory pointers – bytes in memory which give the address of the data you are really looking for, as in a telephone directory, where a person's name 'points' to their number. In this mode the 2 bytes after the instruction contain the address of the data. Thus if address $2000 contains $1234 then the instruction LDA [$2000] will load A with what location $1234 contains.

Indexed addressing

In indexed addressing one of the four pointer registers (U, S, X or Y) is used to point to an address. The simplest mode is called zero offset indexed. For example, LDA 0,X loads A with whatever X was pointing to, in other words X contains the address of the required data. One of the advantages of this mode over the ones we have seen so far is that the address can be worked out whilst the program is running and then transferred into one of the pointer registers.

Constant offset indexed is the same as zero offset indexed except that a two's complement number (5, 8 or 16-bits) is added to or subtracted from the index register. For example, if X contains $4501 then the instruction LDA $36,X will load A with what is contained in location $4537.

Accumulator offset indexed is the same as constant offset indexed except that the offset is contained in one of the accumulators; thus again it can be calculated while the program is running. For example, LDU B,Y means register U is loaded with what is at address B + Y.

Auto-increment/decrement addressing

In this mode the index pointer is automatically incremented or decremented whilst performing the instruction. This mode is ideal for scanning through tables of data – a byte is read in and the pointer automatically increments so that it is pointing at the next byte in readiness for the next read operation. Examples are LDA ,X+ and LDD ,X++, where in the first case the X pointer is incremented by one after reading the data, and in the second, since D is 2 bytes wide, it is incremented by two. In auto-decrement mode the pointer is decremented before it reads the data. Thus, LDX , − −Y decrements Y by two then loads X with the data Y is pointing to.

Indexed indirect addressing

In indexed indirect addressing the effective address of the operand is found at the location pointed to by the pointer register plus any offset. For example, if X contains $2000, address $2020 contains $1234 and location $1234 contains $5555, then the instruction LDD [$20,X] results in D being filled with $5555.

Program counter relative addressing

In this mode the address is referenced with respect to the program counter, which means it is useful for writing position-independent code. Imagine you have a table of data contained in your program, and the program can reside anywhere in memory: if you want your code to run you cannot simply say LDA TABLE where TABLE is the address of the data; if you move the code around then the address of the TABLE will change but your instruction will not, so it will not get correct data. To overcome this difficulty we use program counter relative addressing. Here the address is calculated as an offset from the present value of the program counter and is thus position independent – if your data table is 300 bytes away from the instruction that wants to access it, then program counter relative addressing records this offset when the program is assembled. Thus wherever you run the program correct data will be obtained. The mnemonic for program counter relative is LDA TABLE,PCR.

Examples of addressing modes

Suppose we have a table of data located at $4000 which is 20 bytes long and we wish to copy it to memory starting at $6000. We can do this by using the auto-increment addressing mode:

```
        LDX     #$4000
        LDY     #$6000      ;set up pointers
        LDA     #20         ;set up loop counter
LOOP:   LDB     ,X+         ;get data byte and increment pointer
        STB     ,Y+         ;store data byte
        DECA                ;decrement loop counter
        BNE     LOOP        ;branch if non-zero
```

Another application might be to output a string of data to a serial device. The string can be of any length but is terminated by the ASCII code for an '@' sign and starts at $5000:

```
        LDX     #$5000      ;set up pointer
LOOP:   LDA     ,X+         ;get data
        CMPA    #'@'        ;is it last byte?
        BEQ     END         ;if so finish
        STA     SERIAL      ;store data byte in serial device
        BRA     LOOP        ;get next byte
END:    NOP                 ;continue with rest of program
```

As we shall see in the next section, before outputting data to a serial device it must be polled, or tested, to see whether it can accept new data; we would usually write a short subroutine to handle the actual polling and data output, so the STA SERIAL instruction would be replaced by BSR OUTPUT.

As an example of the use of position-independent code consider the following problem. We have a program somewhere in memory which contains a table of data which we wish to access. However, the program can be running anywhere in RAM or ROM, so how are we to determine the address of the data table? The answer is to use program counter relative addressing. The following piece of code accesses a table of data (terminated in $0000) and copies it to memory at locations $8000 onwards:

```
        LEAX    TABLE,PCR
        LDY     #$8000
LOOP:   LDD     ,X++        ;get data bytes
        CMPD    #0          ;is it zero?
        BEQ     END         ;if so finish
        STD     ,Y++        ;store it
        BRA     LOOP
END:    NOP
```

```
TABLE: DW $5678    ;list of data bytes in table
       DW $3344
       DW $1122
       DW $0000
```

The first instruction LEAX TABLE,PCR needs some explanation. LEAX means load X with the effective address of the operand rather than the data it points to. Here X is loaded with the address of the program counter plus the number of bytes the offset TABLE is away from it, and thus X is loaded with the address of the start of the table.

Programming the 6840 and 6850 chips

The 6840

Now that we have looked at how to program the 6809 it is time to return to our minimal computer. In order to get it to function we need to program the 6840 and 6850 support chips – we can then get the computer to talk to a terminal and communicate with us. The 6840 is the programmable timer chip and can generate clocking waveforms or measure frequencies. Here we use it to produce a square wave input for the 6850 UART device. The frequency we require is the baud rate (4800) multiplied by 16; the UART internally divides the incoming clock by 16, so 16 $\times$ 4800 = 76.8 kHz. The 6840 works by dividing down the incoming E clock (2 MHz) by a programmable factor. Since 2 MHz divided by 76.8 kHz is very nearly 26, we program the 6840 to divide by that factor. To program any I/O chip it is most important to read its data sheet. Doing this for the 6840 we find that it has three control registers, one for each frequency channel. We are going to use the first channel, numbered #1. Table 5.6 shows the meaning of the bits in the first control register.

Table 5.6 The 6840's first control register

Bit 7	1	Output enabled
	0	Output disabled
Bit 6	1	Interrupt enabled
	0	Interrupt disabled
Bits 5–3		Timer counter mode
Bit 2	1	Dual 8-bit counting mode
	0	Normal 16-bit counting
Bit 1	1	Use E clock to generate waveforms
	0	Use external clock
Bit 0	1	Timers deactivated
	0	Timers allowed to operate

Bits 5–3 select whether the counter operates as a square wave generator (all bits zero) or whether it produces just one pulse or compares frequencies; we can see that the 6840 is quite a versatile device. Hence, we need to program the 6840 as follows.

The control register should contain 10000010 or $82. The 6840 also contains timer latches which hold the value we want to divide by; actually it takes the number we give it, adds one to it and doubles it! Thus we have to write 12 to the latches. The code to perform all these operations is as follows:

```
LDA    #1
STA    PTM+1
LDA    #$82
STA    PTM
LDA    #0
STA    PTM+2
LDA    #12          ;divide by 2 × (12 + 1) = 26
STA    PTM+3
```

where PTM is the base address of our 6840. Referring back to the memory map, Figure 5.8, this is 16K or $4000. The first STA is necessary so that the write to location PTM writes to control register #1 and not #3. The timer latches are at addresses PTM+2 and PTM+3 so we load them with 00 and 12. The 6840 will now be producing a 76.8 kHz square wave. Incidentally notice that the fact that it doubles the timer input value means it is not possible to obtain 9600 baud, so our terminal will be slower than usual.

The 6850

The other chip we have to program is the 6850 (ACIA or UART). The 6850 has only one control register to worry about whilst some peripheral chips have lots, for example the Z8530 UART. The bits of the control register are given in Table 5.7.

Table 5.7 The Motorola 6850 ACIA's control register

Bit 0	Counter divide select 1
Bit 1	Counter divide select 2
Bit 2	Word select 1
Bit 3	Word select 2
Bit 4	Word select 3
Bit 5	Transmit control 1
Bit 6	Transmit control 2
Bit 7	Receive interrupt enable

Bits 0–1 set how the chip divides the clock from the 6840. It uses the incoming clock to time the incoming edges of the RS-232 signals, and we want ÷16 mode for which the bits have to be set to 01. A master reset of the device is obtained by setting both of these bits. The word select bits indicate the format of the words being transmitted – whether 7 or 8 bits, even/odd parity and number of stop bits. You have to ensure that your terminal agrees on the format, otherwise you will obtain either rubbish or possibly nothing at all. We choose eight data bits and two stop bits – the

code for this is 100. Transmit control 1 and 2 select the state of the 6850's /RTS line and whether transmitting interrupts are enabled; we do not want any interrupts and we want /RTS LO – the code for this is 00. We also want to disable interrupts when data is received, so we put a zero into Bit 7 of the control register. Hence, overall, we fill the control register with $11.

Apart from the control register the 6850 has three other registers as shown below, where ACIA is its base address:

ACIA	Control register (Write only)
ACIA	Status register (Read only)
ACIA+1	Transmit data register (Write only)
ACIA+1	Receive data register (Read only)

Notice that the registers are not both readable and writeable. This is quite common on peripheral chips, and means that if you want to know what you have written to the control register then you must save a copy of its value in memory somewhere – you can't read the device.

The status register, as its name suggests, gives the status of the ACIA. Table 5.8 lists its data bits.

Table 5.8 The ACIA's status register

Bit 0	Receive data register full
Bit 1	Transmit data register empty
Bit 2	Data carrier detect
Bit 3	Clear to send
Bit 4	Framing error
Bit 5	Receiver overrun error
Bit 6	Parity error
Bit 7	Interrupt request

The two that are of most interest to us are Bits 0 and 1. If Bit 0 is set then it means that the ACIA has received a byte of data from the RS-232 link, which is stored in the receive data register at address ACIA+1. Bit 1, when set, indicates that the ACIA can accept more data to transmit down the RS-232 link. The following fragment of code shows how to set up the ACIA and then how to transmit and receive a byte:

```
          LDA    #3
          STA    ACIA        ;reset ACIA
          LDA    #$11
          STA    ACIA        ;initialize the ACIA
SEND:     LDA    #'A'        ;get character 'A'
WAIT:     LDB    ACIA        ;get status
          LSRB
          LSRB               ;get Bit 1 into carry
          BCC    WAIT        ;if clear then have to wait
          STA    ACIA+1      ;store the character
RECEIVE:  LDB    ACIA        ;get status
          LSRB               ;shift Bit 0 into carry flag
          BCC    RECEIVE     ;if clear no character
          LDA    ACIA+1      ;get character
```

The instructions which examine the status register are said to be *polling* the device. They check to see if the UART is free to accept more data for transmission, or whether it has received a byte. A disadvantage of polling is that if you want to see if a character has been received then you have to keep checking or polling the status register. This wastes time that the processor could put to better use; it is as though, to check if anyone was ringing you up, you had to keep lifting the telephone receiver to see if there was anyone there. The solution to this problem is to use a system known as interrupts, which are the subject of the next section.

Interrupts

As stated in the last section, continually polling a device is wasteful of a CPU's time. Instead of polling we employ a system known as interrupts. An interrupt is a hardware signal into the processor which causes the processor to stop whatever it is doing and run a different section of code (known as the interrupt routine). When it has finished the interrupt routine it returns to what it was doing before.

The 6809 interrupts

The 6809 has three interrupt lines: /IRQ, FIRQ and /NMI. /IRQ stands for interrupt request, /FIRQ for fast interrupt request and /NMI for non-maskable interrupt. The /IRQ and /FIRQ interrupts are known as maskable, that is interrupts along these lines can be prevented by setting the appropriate bits in the CC register; the instructions to manipulate the CC bits are ORCC and ANDCC. If the /IRQ interrupt is enabled in the CC register and the /IRQ line goes LO then an interrupt will be generated. The CPU completes its present instruction and then saves its registers on the system stack. It then reads the *IRQVECTOR* from locations $FFF8–9 and jumps to the address contained in that vector. The code at that address is known as the interrupt handling routine.

The interrupt handler must do three things. Firstly, it must establish which device caused the interrupt – more than one device can use the same /IRQ line (by using open-collector drivers). It finds out which device caused the interrupt by polling the devices' status registers. Having found the interrupting device the 6809 must service the interrupt by performing whatever action is necessary to clear the interrupt – for the 6850 it might mean reading a character. Finally, at the end of the interrupt routine will be an RTI (Return from Interrupt) instruction, which causes the processor to pull the saved registers off the stack and resume processing at the point where the program was interrupted.

The /FIRQ line behaves in the same way as the /IRQ line except as follows. Firstly it is a higher-priority interrupt than /IRQ, so if the processor is executing an /IRQ handling routine and a /FIRQ occurs then the /IRQ handler will be interrupted and execution will continue at the /FIRQ handler. The converse is not true; if the processor is executing a /FIRQ handler and an /IRQ occurs then the /IRQ is ignored until the processor has finished the /FIRQ handler. Secondly the /FIRQ does not cause the processor to save all its registers like an /IRQ does, instead it only saves CC and PC. Hence the interrupt routine is entered more quickly, but it also means the user must push any registers used in the interrupt handler, execute the handler and then pull them off again before issuing the RTI instruction.

The third type of interrupt is called /NMI and cannot be masked off by software. This means it is used for situations that the processor must take note of, for instance the power supply has just failed and so the CPU has a few milliseconds to perform an orderly shut-down. The /NMI line is not level sensitive, like /FIRQ and /IRQ, but is edge triggered. This means that only one device can use the line.

Using interrupts

To return to our minimal computer, to speed up I/O processing we could program the 6850 to generate interrupts. Two events (if we ignore error conditions) can cause an interrupt on the 6850: firstly a character has been received and secondly the device has just finished sending a character and can now accept a new data byte for transmission. Thus by using these interrupts the need for polling is reduced and so the processor does not need to waste time reading the 6850's status register but can get on with its main program. When the 6850 needs attention it will signal this by interrupting the 6809.

One of the problems with interrupts is that they are unpredictable – they can happen at any time, regardless of what the processor is doing, and more than one may occur at once. These facts often mean that debugging interrupt-driven systems can be quite difficult. Nevertheless the fact that they speed up I/O processing so much means that the trouble has to be taken.

Vectored interrupts

Vectored interrupts do not concern the 6809 but are applicable to some microprocessors, for example the Z80, so we discuss them here. Remember that the first thing we had to do when we entered the interrupt routine was to poll external devices to determine which one was the source of the interrupt. If there are a lot of devices then this can obviously take some time.

To avoid this time lag some processors and peripheral chips provide what are known as vectored interrupts. On receiving an interrupt request the processor performs what is known as an interrupt acknowledge cycle. This is a read cycle directed at the peripheral chips. The chip that is producing the interrupt responds to the interrupt acknowledge cycle by outputting a byte of data, known as a vector, onto the data bus. The

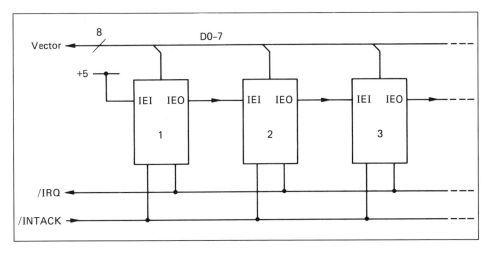

Figure 5.11 *A vectored interrupt daisy chain*

processor uses this byte to tell it which interrupt routine to run. If two or more devices are interrupting simultaneously you might think that they would all drive the data bus at once so the processor would just receive nonsense. However, to avoid this the devices are arranged in a *daisy chain* in order of priority, and each has two signals, IEO (Interrupt Enable Output) and IEI (Interrupt Enable Input). A device may only provide a vector if IEI is asserted; if it does not want to provide the vector it passes the state of its IEI input onto the next-lower priority device via its IEO line. So if the highest-priority device is requesting an interrupt it disables its IEO signal, which prevents lower-priority devices from driving their vectors onto the bus. Hence the processor only receives a vector from the highest-priority interrupting device, see Figure 5.11.

Many people have argued about the merits of vectored interrupts. Their advantage is that they give a quicker response, though often the interrupt handler is quite large, so as a percentage the saving is minimal. A disadvantage is that if, for any reason, the peripheral device develops a fault and outputs a wrong vector then at best the processor will execute the wrong interrupt handler and at worse it will 'crash'.

Parallel I/O

The minimal computer discussed so far would, with the right software, enable one to communicate with a terminal, write and run programs. Often, however, we are interested in controlling other pieces of electronics, for example equipment in a laboratory or factory. To do this we require a means of getting electrical data into and out of the computer. The electronics which enables digital signals to be transmitted is called *parallel I/O*.

The simplest form of output for a microprocessor board would be an LS374 octal latch chip. You simply produce a write signal corresponding to

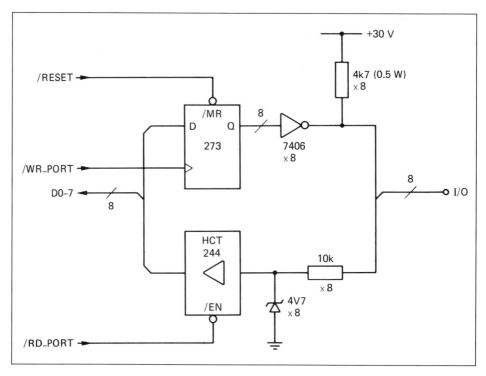

Figure 5.12 *A parallel I/O interface, bit bidirectional and capable of handling signals up to 30 V*

a given address; for our circuit ORing one of the unused LS138 outputs with the RAM write line would generate a write strobe. Then when you write to that address the outputs of the LS374 will reflect what you wrote to it. Input is even simpler: connect an LS244 or LS245 to the data bus and enable it by one of the unused outputs of the LS138; when you read the address selected by the LS138 you will read what is coming into the chip.

These simple gates are fine for most purposes, but sometimes you need something more sophisticated. For these situations parallel I/O chips are available. These chips are designed for a particular microprocessor family which enable you to configure I/O ports as input or outputs, generate handshaking signals and produce interrupts on certain conditions. Most of them come in a 40 pin package and contain two or three 8-bit ports. The output drive on these ports is often quite low (3.2 mA LO level for the 6821) so they are usually buffered with a 245. The 6821 is the Motorola part for use with the 6809, and also compatible is the 6522 which has more features. Also available are the 8255 from Intel and the Z8536 from Zilog. Again it often makes interfacing simpler if you choose a chip from the same family as the microprocessor you are using.

Figure 5.12 shows a useful parallel I/O circuit. The outputs are open-collector 7406 gates which can be pulled to +30 V and the inputs use zener diodes to limit the voltage to the TTL input range. The resistor limits the current into the zener and an HCT buffer is used because of its high input impedance. The circuit has the advantage of being bit bidirectional – by programming the 7406 to be high impedance each I/O pin can be individually used as an input rather than in groups of eight as in a 374 or 245. Note the use of a resettable latch – this ensures the I/O lines are configured for input on a reset and are in a known state so that they do not inadvertently activate external devices.

Battery back-up

It is often useful to maintain the contents of RAM even when there is no power applied to the board. For example, a monitoring system may take readings every minute or so and you do not want to lose the readings if there is a power cut. Alternatively you might want to disconnect the processor board from its position in the 'field', take it back to your main computer and read out its data. In both cases you need to protect or *battery-back* the memory.

Powering the RAM

The first requirement of the RAM we are going to back-up is that its power consumption must be very low; if it draws too much current then the battery would soon be drained. This means that it is not feasible to back-up DRAMs, for they take too much power (in any case you would also need to power the circuitry that generates their refreshes). Thus we are restricted to using CMOS static RAM. The first thing our battery back-up circuit must do is to let the RAM be powered from +5 V normally and from a battery if the power fails.

Figure 5.13 shows one way this can be achieved. When the 5 V line is present the RAM is supplied with 5 V minus a diode drop, and when the 5 V supply fails it is powered by the battery. The diode prevents the battery from powering the rest of the circuit, which would rapidly drain it. The resistor permits a small amount of current to flow into the battery when the main 5 V is present; this 'trickle-charges' the battery which is a rechargeable 'Nicad' (nickel cadmium) type. If you do not use a rechargeable battery then connect it through another diode to the RAM's power pin. How long the RAM will hold its data depends on the total current taken by the RAMs you are backing up and on the capacity of the battery. The capacity of a battery is measured in mAh (milliamp hours); if its capacity is 10 mAh and you draw 100 µA then it would last for about 100 hours. The quiescent current consumption can be measured by putting a voltmeter across the 47 Ω 'charging' resistor and applying Ohm's law.

Write protection

To complete the circuit we need to ensure that the RAM's control pins (/CS, /OE and /WR) are inactive when the RAM is powered by the battery.

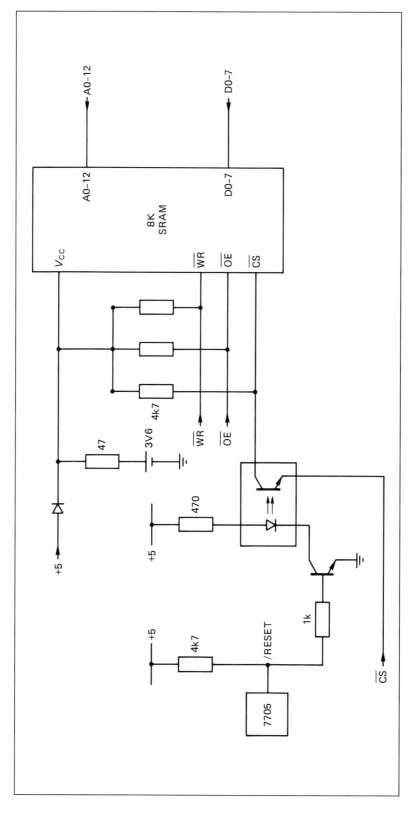

Figure 5.13 *Battery back-up of a static RAM chip*

This prevents spurious reads and writes which would increase power consumption, and in the latter case would cause memory corruption. Three 4k7 pull-up resistors achieve this. If the RAM was not connected to the rest of the circuit we would now have a satisfactory system.

However, we have to consider how the rest of the circuit will behave as the board is powered up or down. Once the power drops to below around 4.5 V the behaviour of the TTL chips in the rest of the circuit becomes unpredictable, and there is a good chance that random write and chip select signals will be generated thus corrupting the RAM. We must prevent such spurious write signals from affecting the RAM.

Firstly, we need to detect when the supply voltage is too low for reliable operation. The TL7705 reset chip drives its /RESET output LO if the voltage drops below about 4.5 V. We use /RESET to disable the RAM; note that you cannot use a logic gate to do the disabling – it will not work at low voltages. Instead you must use an analog circuit to prevent accesses. Figure 5.13 shows one method: when the TL7705 asserts /RESET the transistor is switched off, so no current flows in the LED of the opto-isolator and therefore the opto's transistor is also switched off. Hence, there is effectively no connection between the TTL circuit that generates the chip select (or alternatively the /WR line) and the RAM itself. Thus on power up or down memory corruption is prevented. Of course when the 5 V line is within specification current flows through the opto's LED, its transistor is switched on, and the RAM can be accessed normally. Memory back-up/protection ICs are in fact available as discrete devices (for example, the Dallas-1210).

Real-time clocks

Another facility that is useful on a control or monitoring board is that of knowing the time. For example, you may want to take measurements every minute, or to switch on a piece of equipment at 4 o'clock in the afternoon and then turn it off again 2 hours later. There are two ways of implementing a *real-time clock*; one uses mostly software the other additional hardware.

Software implementation

In the software method a counter timer chip is programmed to interrupt the microprocessor at a given rate (say a hundredth of a second). The CPU on receiving the interrupt updates the time which is stored in RAM locations. Referring to our minimal CPU board, we can use the 6840 programmable timer module to count the incoming 2 MHz E clock pulses and produce interrupts every 0.01 s. The interrupt handler would then look like this:

```
IRQ:      LDA    PTM+1      ;read PTM status register
          BMI    PTMIRQ     ;branch to PTMIRQ if Bit 7 set
            .               ;
            .               ;poll other devices here
            .               ;
PTMIRQ:   LDA    PTM+4      ;read register to clear IRQ
          LDA    HUNDS      ;get hundredths of second byte
          ADDA   #1         ;increment it
          CMPA   #100       ;has it overflowed?
          BNE    EXIT1
          CLR    HUNDS      ;if so reset to zero
          LDA    SECONDS    ;and get seconds byte
          ADDA   #1         ;and increment it
          CMPA   #60        ;has seconds overflowed?
          BNE    EXIT2
          CLR    SECONDS    ;if so reset seconds byte
          LDA    MINUTES    ;and get minutes count
          ADDA   #1         ;increment minutes
          CMPA   #60        ;has minutes overflowed?
          BNE    EXIT3
          CLR    MINUTES    ;if so zero minutes
          LDA    HOURS      ;get hours count
          ADDA   #1         ;increment hours
          CMPA   #24        ;has hours count overflowed?
          BNE    EXIT4
          CLR    HOURS      ;if so zero hours counter
          BRA    EXIT5
EXIT1:    STA    HUNDS      ;update hundredths byte
          RTI               ;exit
EXIT2:    STA    SECONDS
          RTI
EXIT3:    STA    MINUTES
          RTI
EXIT4:    STA    HOURS
EXIT5:    RTI
```

The interrupt handler starts at the label IRQ, which is the address loaded into the IRQVECTOR at the top of the EPROM. It first polls the possible sources of the interrupt by reading device status bytes – often Bit 7 will be set if a device is requesting an interrupt. The handler first clears the interrupt, in this case by reading the timer counter register. It then advances the time by one-hundredth of a second. If the byte which contains the hundredths has reached 100 then it is reset to zero and the second's byte incremented. Similarly if the second's byte has reached 60 then it is reset and the minute's count advanced. The code looks long but most of the time only the hundredth's byte is incremented and the first branch is taken.

Using the clock

We now have a functioning real-time clock, and we need two small additional routines: one to set the clock – a piece of code to prompt the user for the time and then transfer it into the time bytes – and a second routine to read the clock. Some care is required here. Imagine you simply write a routine which reads the bytes in the order hours, minutes and seconds. Consider what happens if the time is 4:59:59.99. Your program might read the hour's byte at which point a clock interrupt occurs causing the time to be updated to 5:00:00.00. Control then returns to your program which reads the minute's and second's bytes, and gets the value 00:00. The program thinks the time is 4:00:00 instead of 5:00:00 – it is an hour out! To overcome this problem we must prevent the clock from changing whilst it is being read. Since it is an interrupt that causes the clock to be updated we must disable the IRQs before reading the clock bytes. We do this by setting the I bit in the CC register:

```
CLOCKREAD:   ORCC     #$10         ;disable IRQs
             LDA      HOURS
             STA      ,X+
             LDA      MINUTES
             STA      ,X+
             LDA      SECONDS
             STA      ,X+
             ANDCC    #$EF         ;re-enable IRQs
             RTS
```

X contains the address where the calling program wants the time to be stored. The ORCC instruction disables interrupts, and the ANDCC re-enables them. This technique is quite common in critical sections of code, especially where two or more programs are being executed concurrently and they each share data which must only be modified by one program at a time.

Hardware implementation

The above method of generating a real-time clock is adequate for most purposes, but it has a few drawbacks. Firstly, each time the processor board is switched on the clock will need to be reset. Secondly, the CPU has to spend time updating the clock which it could use for other processing, and thirdly if the CPU wants to know if it is 5 o'clock then it has to keep reading the time to find out.

For these reasons dedicated real-time clock chips (RTCs) exist. These use an external crystal oscillator circuit to generate clock pulses which cause internal registers to be updated with the time. An example of an RTC is the Motorola MC146818, see Figure 5.14. It has a cycle time of just less than 1000 ns and so is used with a 1 MHz 6809. Notice that it has an 8-bit bus labelled AD0–7, which is a multiplexed address and data bus: A0–7 and D0–7 time-share the bus and are valid at different times; the advantage is that fewer pins are needed on the chip, but the disad-

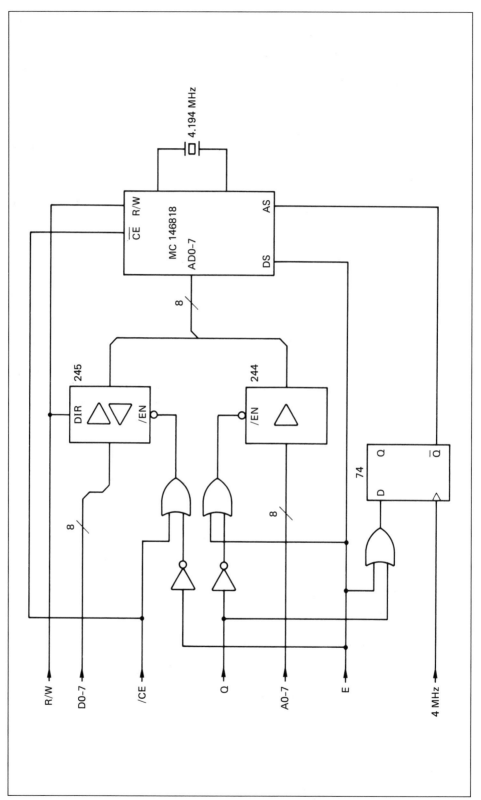

Figure 5.14 *Interfacing the MC146818 real-time clock chip to a 1 MHz 6809*

vantage is that if the processor is not also multiplexed then additional interfacing logic is required.

Figure 5.14 illustrates the disadvantage of not using peripherals of the same family as the microprocessor; look at all the additional logic required to interface the 146818's multiplexed address and data bus to the non-multiplexed 6809E's. The 245 and 244 are enabled at different times so as to multiplex the 6809's address and data bus. The address on AD0–7 must be valid for at least 50 ns either side of the falling edge of AS. Since the 74 D flip-flop clocks on the rising edge of the 4 MHz clock, whereas the 113 JK flip-flop used to produce E and Q clocks on the falling edge, the transitions of AS are midway between the edges of E and Q. Figure 5.15 is the timing diagram of this interface. The most critical parameter is the AD0–7 setup time before the falling edge of AS – AD0–7 is valid 250 + 65 = 315 ns after the falling edge of E, and AS occurs 125 + 250 = 375 ns after E, giving a worst case setup time of 60 ns which is greater than 50 ns and so the circuit will work. In practice you would probably replace all the discrete logic with one PAL16R4.

The 146818 chip contains 14 registers and 50 bytes of static RAM for miscellaneous storage. This RTC can keep track of the date as well as the time, and also has two useful interrupt modes: it can be programmed to produce interrupts periodically from about once every 30 µs to 500 ms, which can be useful if you wish to take measurements at frequent intervals. An 'alarm' interrupt produces an interrupt at a programmed time, ideal for switching equipment on and off at set times. To enable the RTC to keep time whilst the board is powered down it should be battery backed.

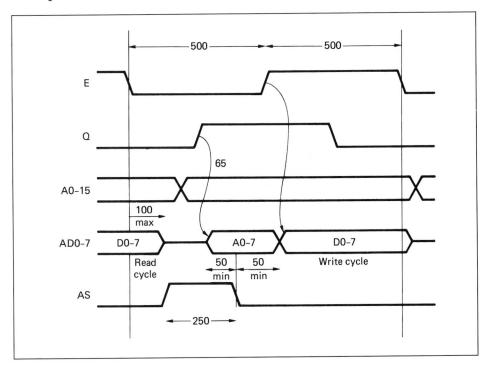

Figure 5.15 *The timing diagram for the circuit of* Figure 5.14

6 Bus-based systems

Expanding a microprocessor system

Having studied the previous chapter the reader should be able to design a microprocessor board for control or monitoring purposes. Suppose we build such a board, perhaps with some digital or analog I/O, to control something. The system works well for a few months but then we realize that it needs to control more I/O lines or perhaps be interfaced to a completely different piece of electronics. The problem is that our original design has no room for expansion or flexibility, and unfortunately a new board will need to be designed from scratch. How can we avoid this problem? The answer is to build expandability into the original board. This can be achieved by using the idea of an *expansion bus*.

The idea of a bus

An expansion bus is a set of signals (address, data and control lines) which are generated by the CPU board (called a *master*) and are routed to a connector on the board. The connector can be joined to other connectors using a *backplane* (a PCB with parallel tracks to connect the pins on the connectors together) or, for low-speed systems, a short length of ribbon cable. Two types of connectors are in common use. Firstly the gold-edge type where the connector consists of rectangles of gold plated onto the edge of the printed circuit board. Secondly, DIN41612 connectors which contain 64 or 96 pins and are especially designed for industrial use.

To use our bus we design other boards (called *slaves*) which, in response to the signals on the bus lines, either supply or accept data to and from the CPU board, see Figure 6.1. Thus, if we have a CPU with an expansion bus and we need a larger system, we only have to design a new I/O board and not a whole new CPU card. We simply plug the I/O board into a vacant slot in the backplane and the CPU can talk to it. Another advantage of a bus-based system is that the individual boards can be tested and designed separately – it is a lot easier to produce four boards with 20 chips on each than one with 80.

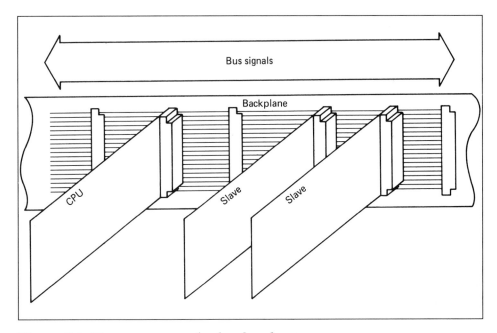

Figure 6.1 *The appearance of a bus-based system*

Bus-based systems are sufficiently important that precise 'standards' have been formulated which define the signals used on the bus and their timing relationships. If you design a board to such a standard then it will work with any other board (from any manufacturer) built for that bus. This means that you can buy off-the-shelf boards to work with your system. For example, you may be happy to design a specialized I/O board but not a complex CPU board, so you could just purchase the latter. Later in this chapter we shall look at the STE and VME standard buses, but for now we investigate how to expand a system without resorting to such standards.

An 'I/O'-orientated bus

We shall develop our discussion of bus-based systems in stages, providing the reader with various techniques that can be used depending on requirements. The simplest way of producing a bus-based system is to employ a couple of parallel I/O ports. Figure 6.2 shows the idea. A 374 octal latch can be loaded by the CPU and its eight output bits are used as the bus address lines (BA0–7). Data can be transmitted through the 245 when /IO2 is asserted. Two strobes (/READ and /WRITE) are generated to inform the slaves when to latch or return data. Each slave decodes the bus address and only responds if it corresponds to its own address (generally configured by links on the slave). Notice that the slaves receive the signals via gates with Schmitt trigger characteristics. This improves noise immunity which can become a problem on long backplanes. The backplane terminating resistors also improve performance, reducing undershoot and reflections on the signals. To conclude the design we draw up

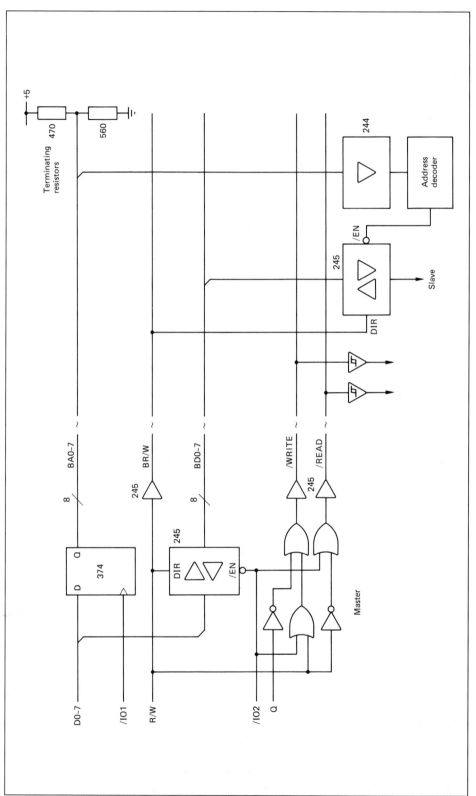

Figure 6.2 *An I/O-orientated bus*

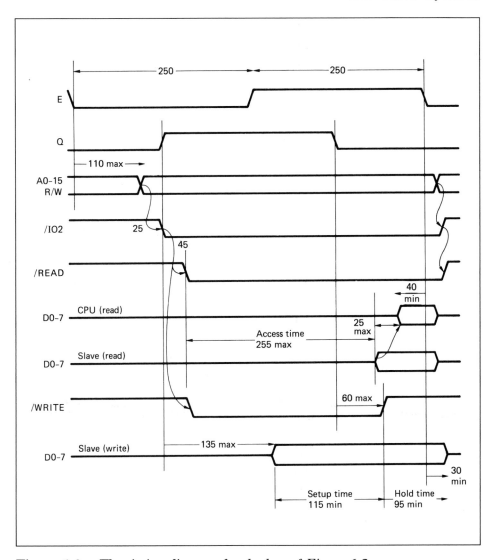

Figure 6.3 *The timing diagram for the bus of Figure 6.2*

the timing diagram (Figure 6.3) of the signals as seen by the slaves. This indicates the constraints that the slaves must obey to work on the bus.

This bus is fine for simple digital I/O slaves. It also has the advantage that 256 bus locations can be accessed, yet only 2 bytes of CPU memory space are needed (this technique whereby 1 byte is used as a 'pointer' is also used on some peripheral chips). However, referring to Figure 6.3, we can see that from receiving the /READ strobe the slave has about 250 ns to supply its data. This is adequate for TTL logic but insufficient for microprocessor peripheral chips. We need a means of extending the bus cycle to give the slave more time to respond. The way to do this depends on the processor being used: some (like the 68000) do not terminate a cycle until they receive a '/DTACK' signal, while others (such as the Z80) can be made to wait by asserting a WAIT signal.

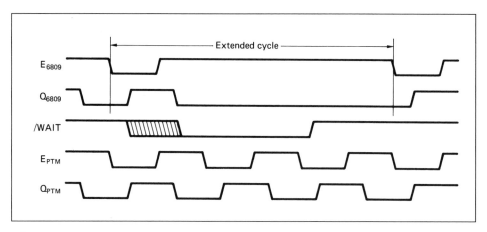

Figure 6.4 *Stopping the E and Q clocks to extend a bus access*

The 6809E, which we used in Chapter 5, does not have these options. Instead we generate its E and Q clocks in a PAL, and if the PAL receives a wait signal from a slave it freezes the clocks until the slave is ready, thus stopping the 6809E. To avoid reducing the UART's baud rate the PAL produces a free-running E clock for the 6840. Figure 6.4 shows the timing diagram for this action. The processor clocks are stopped (for up to 10 μs) by the /WAIT signal, and restarted when both /WAIT has gone HI and the 6840 (PTM) clocks are back in phase. Since any slave might need to delay the CPU /WAIT must be driven by open-collector devices.

An alternative to using a wait line is always to stop the processor until the addressed slave returns a /DTACK (data acknowledge) signal, indicating it has accepted or provided data. This method is used on the STE and VME buses. One disadvantage of it is that all slaves must generate /DTACKs, whereas only slow ones need produce /WAITs.

A memory-orientated bus

The above approach to a bus-based design is especially good where the requirements are heavily I/O orientated. Little logic is needed and the circuitry is relatively straightforward to implement. It is, however, less suitable for memory expansion. This is because the bus address is stored in one or more latches so it is not possible to run programs in off-board memory (the latches do not increment with the program counter). To achieve this facility we need a bus that more closely resembles the operation of the processor itself. One possibility is simply to buffer the CPU's data, address and control lines down the backplane so that the bus is identical to the CPU's.

There are several drawbacks to this approach. Firstly, the signals will be driven and received on each board by buffer chips (say 245s) for drive, noise immunity and to protect more costly on-board devices. Each buffer will add in a propagation delay (up to 12 ns for an LS245) so skew can develop between the control and data/address signals. Thus care must be taken with timings, which will not be as conservative as those on the processor board itself. For example, on a 6850 ACIA incoming data must be valid for a minimum of 10 ns after the falling edge of E; data coming out of a 6809 is valid for 30 ns after E, so on the CPU board there is a 20 ns margin and no problem. However, if the 6850 resides on a slave then, with skew of up to 24 ns for the two 245s, the system goes out of spec. – it is not guaranteed to work. How important this effect is depends on your choice of processor; the faster it is the harder it is simply to buffer its bus. The second drawback is that if you provide all the processor's address bus on the backplane then each slave has to decode all these signals. For example, if a slave uses 16 bytes of memory from \$0400–040F then it has to decode all the lines from A4–15 to see if it is being addressed. Yet the CPU will decode many of the higher address lines, so each slave is duplicating work the CPU has already carried out.

Figure 6.5 shows an example of this type of bus – many are possible. An advantage of designing your own bus is that it can be tailored to specific requirements, and you do not have to make it conform to the timings of a 'standard'. The top half of memory is allocated to the processor board and the bottom half to the bus. The PAL16L8 decodes A6–15 producing eight strobes each corresponding to 64 bytes in the region 0–1K. These strobes can be used by I/O slaves which therefore do not have to decode any of the bus address lines. /READ and /WRITE strobes are produced to indicate that a bus cycle is in progress, and the rising edge of /WRITE occurs roughly in the middle of the time when data is valid, giving around 100 ns of setup and hold time thus avoiding skew problems. In addition we have given the bus a /RESET and a 16 MHz clock signal; both these utilities save slaves having to generate their own.

Multi-processor systems

Often a control system can be implemented with a single microprocessor. Sometimes, however, it is necessary, desirable or simpler to use more than one CPU. Firstly, a system could be monitoring a waveform and performing some high-speed signal processing on it. The CPU performing the calculations might not have much time left to carry out basic I/O, yet the system calls for some sort of interactive graphics facility. It is therefore necessary to add a second CPU responsible for the I/O. Secondly, a system might need to be ultrareliable. Since you can never be totally certain that a microprocessor board will never 'crash' (there might be some obscure software or hardware fault), it is desirable to have a second CPU which can shut down the system if the first fails. Thirdly, suppose you are controlling (say) three identical pieces of equipment. It may make sense to use three 'slave' processors receiving orders from one controller, rather than one more powerful one which does everything. This has several advantages: if you later need more units, then you can just add more processor boards with the same software, the system is already tested and you do not have to reconfigure the software. Also if a CPU board breaks

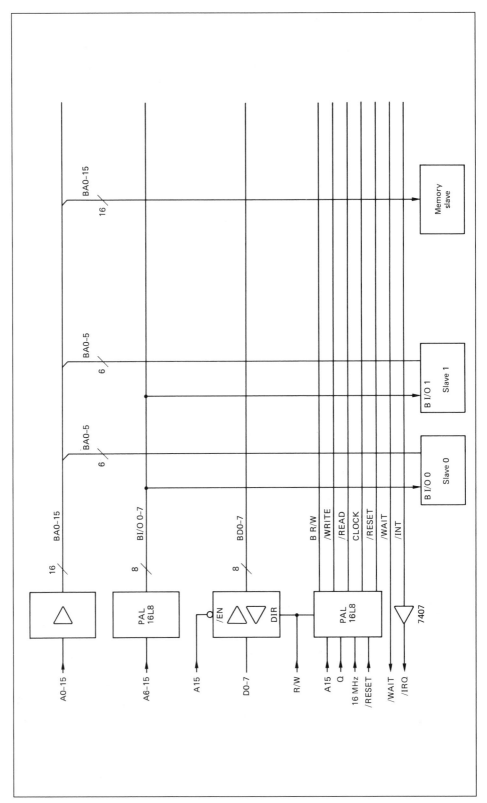

Figure 6.5 *A bus suitable for I/O and memory*

down only one unit is put out of action; the rest of the system can continue unaffected.

Such systems could be implemented on a bus-based system, and we shall see how this can be achieved later in this chapter. However, a bus-based approach is not essential unless we wish the processors to share devices. Here we only have to pass information between the CPUs.

Serial links

Various methods for passing messages are available. Firstly, data could be passed via a serial link (for example, RS-232), and for widely separated CPUs this is the best solution. A drawback is that it is rather slow – at 9600 baud a 1 byte transfer takes around a millisecond, and software is needed to program the UART and handle its interrupts. For linking many CPUs serial network protocols have been developed which define hardware and software such that many CPUs can communicate using a shared serial line. Examples are ETHERNET, ARCNET and BITBUS, and these allow transmission speeds of up to 10 Mbits/s, 2.5 Mbits/s and 375 kbits/s respectively.

Parallel I/O

A second method is to interface the two CPUs via some parallel I/O, see Figure 6.6. Two 'back-to-back' latches are used, where processor A can read the first and write to the second, and processor B vice versa. The latches let data pass from one bus to the other (note that the buses could be totally different in operation). The D flip-flop is reset when processor B writes to its latch, thus generating an interrupt to processor A informing it that there is data available. When A reads the latch the interrupt is cleared and the status line can be read by B to discover if A has accepted its data. Similarly we could have circuitry to interrupt B after A has written data.

FIFOs

An improvement on the previous circuit is to use a FIFO to connect the two buses. This has the advantage that the processor writing the information does not have to wait for the receiver to read each byte before sending the next. Instead, the transmitter has to poll the FIFO full flag to check the FIFO can accept more data before loading each byte – some large FIFOs have a half-full flag, so if the CPU knows it isn't half-full it can write a string of bytes (up to half the depth of the FIFO in number) without having to check the FIFO full flag before each transfer. A FIFO is most useful when you have a very fast CPU that sends bytes to a slower one which handles the basic I/O. You could generate an interrupt to the receiving processor by driving the interrupt line with the FIFO empty signal – the processor clears the interrupt by emptying the FIFO.

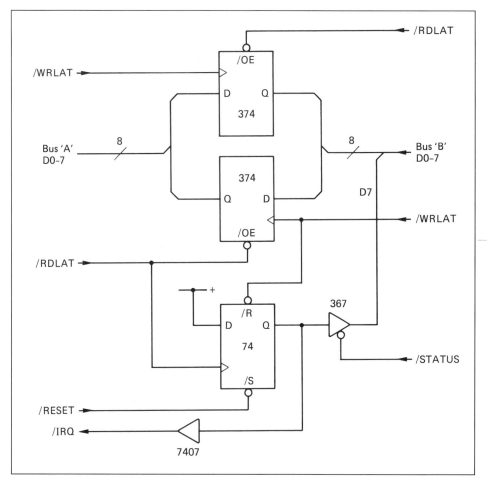

Figure 6.6 *Transferring data between CPUs via 'back-to-back' latches*

Dual-port RAM

Another way of transferring data between two CPUs is to provide some RAM which can be accessed by either processor. Such RAM is called *dual-port* RAM. Real dual-port RAM chips are available, though they are somewhat expensive and it is much more usual to design your own using discrete components. Figure 6.7 shows the basic idea. The RAM chip sits between the buses of the two CPUs so either can access it.

An application would be as follows: CPU A is the system controller and once a second it loads the RAM with data and instructions for the slave CPU B. It then generates an interrupt to CPU B which reads in the data. This specific system would work fine, but what we have overlooked is that if both CPUs accessed the RAM at random intervals there is nothing to stop them doing so simultaneously, which would cause erroneous data to be read from and written to the RAM. How we can overcome this *bus contention* is the subject of the next section.

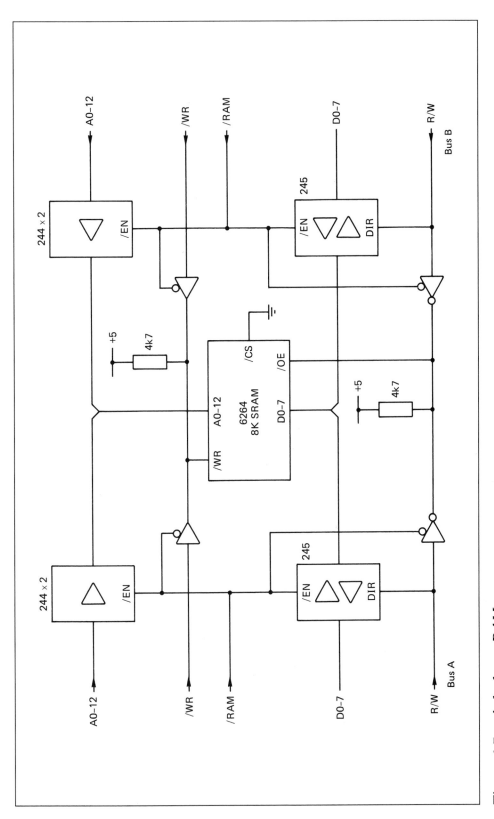

Figure 6.7 *A dual-port RAM*

Sharing of devices

In the previous sections we have seen how to design a single-processor bus, and how to pass information between CPUs in a multi-processor system. The final stage in our development is to allow more than one processor to access the same peripheral device or memory. A very common example of this is a system with two or three computers but only one printer; each processor must be able to output data to the printer interface which they thus need to share.

To share a bus between processors the following conditions must be satisfied. Firstly, all lines emanating from a master must be tri-stateable and only be driven when the master is making a bus access, for if it drove them at other times it could interfere with another master's access. Secondly, if the master is not making a bus access it must ignore incoming lines (like /WAIT or /DTACK). Thirdly, for the bus to function properly we must ensure that only one master accesses it at a time. The concept that lets us achieve this is called *bus arbitration*.

Bus arbitration

Since the bus may only be driven by one master at once, we need a way of determining which master is allowed to (this master is said to have control of the bus). Which master has control is decided by bus arbitration and it works like this: when a master wishes to perform a bus access it asserts a *bus request* signal, which goes into a piece of logic (often a PAL) called the *arbiter*. The arbiter waits for the bus to become free and then asserts a signal called bus acknowledge or bus grant to inform the master that the bus is available for its use. Let us now look at some practical implementations of bus arbitration.

A two-level arbitration scheme

Figure 6.8 shows a simple way of arbitrating between two masters. /BR0 and /BR1 are the two request lines from the masters and /BG0 and /BG1 the corresponding acknowledge signals from the arbiter. The arbiter asserts only one of /BG0 or /BG1 at any given time, thus ensuring that only one master has control of the bus. Each master asserts /BRn when it wants the bus and keeps on asserting it till it has finished with it. Since bus requests can arrive at any time the arbiter must be designed to avoid metastable states by clocking the /BRn signals twice, as in the following PAL (clocked at, say, 16 MHz):

```
SBR0.D  = BR0;
SBR1.D  = BR1;
/BG0.D  = /SBR0 & BG1;
/BG1.D  = /SBR1 & SBR0 & BG0
        + /BG1 & /SBR1;
```

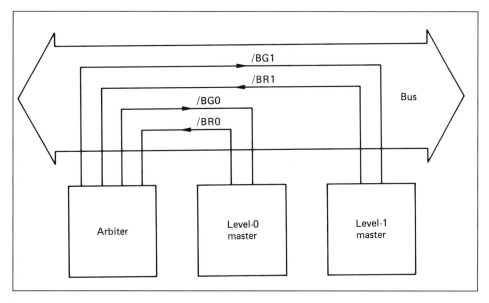

Figure 6.8 *A two-level arbitration scheme*

If /BR0 and /BR1 both go LO simultaneously then only /BG0 is asserted (the 'SBR0' term in the /BG1 equation ensures this); /BR0 is said to be of higher priority than /BR1. The '/BG1 & /SBR1' term ensures that once the Level-1 master has control of the bus it keeps it regardless of the state of /BR0. Figure 6.9 shows the timing diagram for this particular arbitration scheme. This arbitration method is used on the STEbus and we discuss a couple of its other facets later in this chapter.

In principle you could extend the above arbitration method to as many CPU boards as you want, but each would need a /BR and a /BG line. In practice it is not feasible – each additional master would take up two tracks on the backplane and you would soon run out of pins and registers on the arbiter PAL. Nevertheless, there are occasions when it is necessary to have a system with a large number of processors (for example, you might have

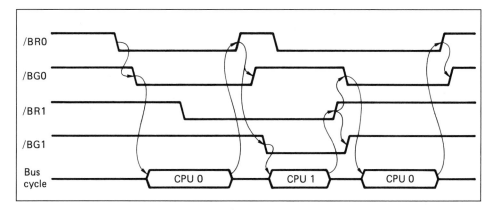

Figure 6.9 *The timing diagram for a two-level arbiter*

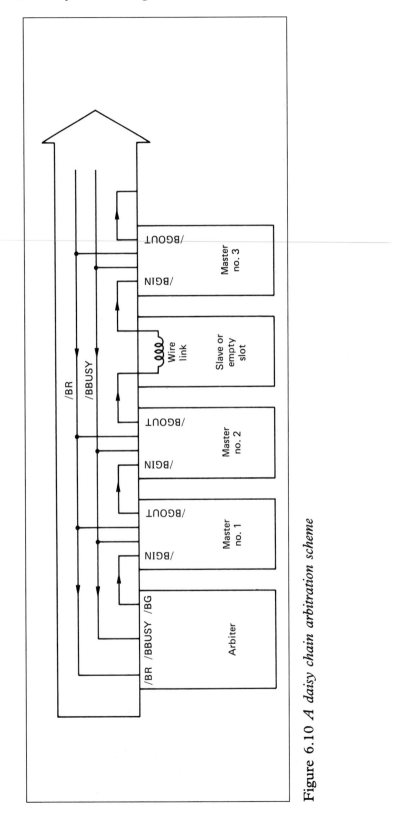

Figure 6.10 *A daisy chain arbitration scheme*

10 pieces of equipment each controlled by its own CPU). To get round this limitation we use a bus grant daisy chain.

Daisy chain arbitration

Figure 6.10 shows this type of arbitration. It uses the same principle as the vectored interrupts we discussed in Chapter 5. There is only one bus request line (/BR) along the backplane and it is driven by any master that wants the bus (using an open-collector driver). The arbiter on seeing /BR asserted examines the state of /BBUSY (bus busy) to see if the bus is in use; if it is not the arbiter asserts /BGOUT. This signal does not travel the whole length of the backplane, instead it only goes as far as the /BGIN pin of the first connector; if there is no master inserted in that connector a wire link must be made to join /BGIN to /BGOUT. However, if there is a master present it interprets the falling edge (not the level) of /BGIN as permission that it may use the bus. It then asserts /BBUSY (open-collector) and releases /BR, but it does not allow /BGIN to pass to its /BGOUT pin. Often a master on seeing /BGIN go LO will not desire to use the bus (it was requested by a master further down the daisy chain), and it therefore allows its /BGOUT pin to follow its /BGIN pin. /BGOUT then travels to the next master in the daisy chain, and so on. Hence many masters may share the bus with no additional hardware requirements. Figure 6.11 illustrates the operation of this method of arbitration.

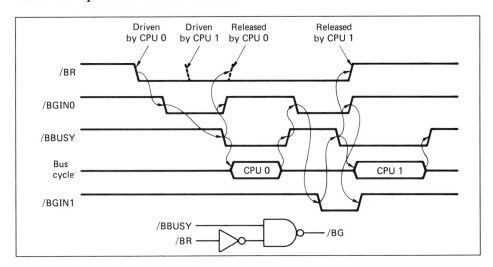

Figure 6.11 *A timing diagram for daisy chain arbitration*

Priority schemes

As we have seen, a daisy chain system lets you use many masters on a bus. However, a problem arises if some masters are making very intensive use of the bus. For example, if the first two masters in the daisy chain are using the bus nearly all the time, then bus grant will hardly ever travel further down the daisy chain and other masters will have to wait for long periods before they can make a bus access. The same problem can arise in the non-daisy chain scheme if there are more than two masters on the bus. A solution is to have more than one daisy chain (with signals /BR0–3 and /BG0–3 say) and for the arbiter to allocate the bus in a 'fair' manner between the daisy chains.

There is scope for flexibility here depending on the system requirements. One commonly used method is called *round-robin* – the arbiter grants the bus in order of the daisy chain priorities (say 0, 1, 2 and lastly 3) but the priorities change with time, so a bit later /BR2 might have highest priority followed by /BR3, etc. Or you might have a system with one CPU which must have quick access to the bus (perhaps it is the overall controller). You could then make /BR0 always have highest priority, but let /BR1–3 operate in a round-robin scheme so that less important masters had equal priority amongst themselves but less than the overall master. These priority ideas can be applied equally well to the non-daisy chain system discussed earlier. As a simple example consider the following arbiter:

```
PRI.D    = /PRI;
SBR0.D   = BR0;
SBR1.D   = BR1;
/BG0.D   = /SBR0 & PRI & BG1
         + /SBR0 & /PRI & SBR1 & BG1
         + /SBR0 & /BG0;
/BG1.D   = /SBR1 &  /PRI & BG0
         + /SBR1 &  PRI & SBR0 & BG0
         + /SBR1 &  /BGl;
```

The priority bit, PRI, changes state on each clock edge and determines whether /BR0 or /BR1 has highest priority. If PRI is HI then /BG0 is asserted if SBR0 is LO and BG1 HI, regardless of the state of SBR1, so /BR0 has highest priority. However, if PRI is LO then /BG0.D examines the second term and SBR1 must also be HI, so /BR0 now has lower priority. The arbiter should be clocked at a frequency which is not a multiple of the processor's clock rate, otherwise the two could become synchronized so that each time the Level-0 master requested the bus PRI was HI which would defeat the aim of alternating priorities.

Indivisible bus cycles

We now have a bus-based system whereby multiple processors can share the same peripherals. This arrangement is all that is needed for a large number of applications. However, there is one final trick that the reader should be aware of. What if we have a bus slave that more than one processor needs to use, but only one master is to have control of it at any given time? For example, suppose the slave was a printer interface; then if one CPU is printing a document it does not want another butting in and sending characters too – the printout would just be a mess.

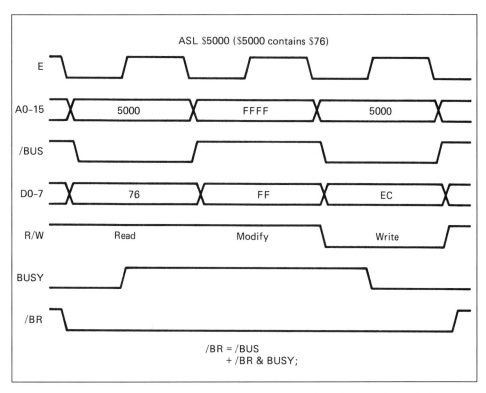

Figure 6.12 *An indivisible read–modify–write (ASL) instruction; if there was no BUSY signal the bus request would be released during the modify cycle*

We need a way of indicating which master has control of the slave. The obvious method is to load a bus memory location with a value, say $FF if the device is busy, and $00 if it is not. Then when a CPU wants to use the device it reads this status byte; if it is $FF it has to wait, but if it is $00 the CPU writes $FF into the byte, uses the device and finally clears the byte to indicate the device is free again. Code that accomplishes this is shown below:

```
BUSY:   LDA   STATUS    ;get device status
        BNE   BUSY      ;re-read status if busy
        LDA   #$FF
        STA   STATUS    ;set device busy status
        BSR   USEDEV    ;use the device
        CLR   STATUS    ;set device free status
```

There is a crucial flaw in the above program. What if two processors decide to use the device at nearly the same time? There is a chance that the second may read the status byte before the first has time to set it to $FF. They will both have read it as $00 and so each will assume it has sole control of the device – if the slave was a printer you would just get garbled printout, but if it was a disk drive the consequences could be serious loss of data.

To overcome this problem we must ensure that the first CPU has control of the bus for the whole period between the read and subsequent write to the status byte. To achieve this we use an indivisible read–modify–write cycle. A read–modify–write cycle is an operation that reads a memory location, does something to the data and then writes it back to the same location. An example is the INC (increment) instruction – read memory, add one to it, write it back. During the modify cycle the CPU does not use the bus so we must prevent another master getting control of it during that period; the whole cycle is then said to be indivisible. The 6809E has a signal (BUSY) that lets us produce an indivisible cycle: BUSY goes HI during a read–modify–write cycle. We can use BUSY to keep /BRn asserted (or /BBUSY with a daisy chain) thus preventing another processor gaining control of the bus, see Figure 6.12. Finally we need a read–modify–write instruction that tests and sets a status byte in memory. One possibility is ASL:

```
BUSY: ASL   STATUS   ;indivisible RMW cycle
      BCC   BUSY     ;if carry clear have to wait
      BSR   USEDEV   ;use device
      LDA   #$80
      STA   STATUS   ;set device free status
```

Here the status byte contains $80 if the device is free, and $00 if it is busy. Thus, ASL in one indivisible operation reads the status byte, examines it (shifts Bit 7 into the carry flag) and clears it to indicate the device is busy.

If your processor does not have a BUSY line or something similar, you have to provide a flip-flop that the CPU can set under software control and use its output as a 'BUSY' signal.

Acquisition of a processor's bus

The bus-based techniques discussed above let many CPU boards share slaves by allowing them all to access a common bus. There is one other facility that is sometimes useful, that is to permit a processor to access a device which is connected to another processor's own bus and not on an independent shared bus. The commonest example of this is the provision of dual-port RAM on processor A's board that can be accessed by processor B.

To allow for such a circuit most processors have a /HALT line (or equivalent), which when asserted causes the processor to complete its present instruction and then tri-state its buses. With the 6809E you know it has halted because its BA and BS status lines will both go HI. The other processor can now drive the address, data and control buses and perform its transactions, see Figure 6.13.

The details of Figure 6.13 are not important – they will vary for each CPU and bus – but the ideas are worth noting. BA13–15 are decoded by a 138 and when they are 100 respectively the 6809's /HALT line is driven and /WAIT asserted to extend the bus cycle. When the 6809 halts BA and BS go HI and the PAL commences a memory cycle on the falling edge

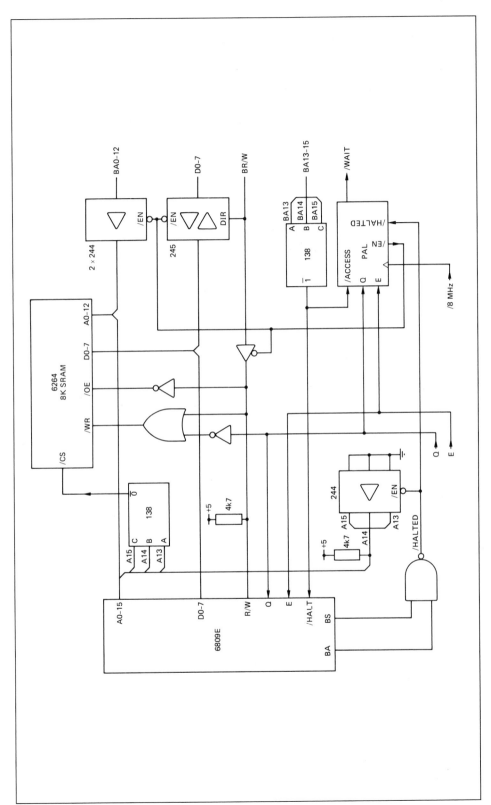

Figure 6.13 *Accessing dual-port RAM on another processor's board*

of E (just like a CPU cycle) and enables the address and data bus drivers. Once the cycle is complete it releases /WAIT to terminate the access. Note the pull-up resistors on R/W and A13–15, which ensure that when the buses are tri-stated a read cycle to 56–64K occurs, which is where EPROM resides. Thus spurious writes or reads of peripheral status registers (which might clear unserviced interrupts) are avoided.

There is one trap to be aware of here. It occurs if both processor boards are capable of accessing the common bus. Consider the following scenario. Processor B wants to access a location in processor A's dual-port RAM, so B gets control of the common bus and puts out the bus address for A's dual-port RAM. A's board decodes the bus address and so asserts /HALT to processor A. Processor A must therefore finish its present instruction and relinquish control of its bus, but unfortunately its instruction requires it to make a bus access. It therefore asserts its bus request signal, but as B has control of the bus the arbiter will not grant A control. We have a *deadlock* situation – processor A will only halt after it has finished its instruction for which it needs control of the common bus, but processor B will only relinquish the bus after it has completed its own access, which it can only do after A has halted.

This is a difficult problem and one which cannot be readily solved with an 8-bit processor like the 6809. Clearly, one of the processors must be made to give way, by terminating its access prematurely. The one that is forced to give way will not have read correct data on a read cycle or have written any at all if it was a write cycle. With a 6809 the best you can do is generate an interrupt to inform it that a deadlock has occurred, so its last instruction will not have been properly executed. You then need some clever software to backtrack an instruction (making sure all the registers are correct) and then rerun it; this is not a trivial task! Fortunately, more powerful processors (like the 68000 series) let you terminate a cycle so that the processor halts and reruns the cycle when it regains control of its bus.

Direct memory access

Apart from another CPU there is one other device which often acquires a processor's bus. This device is called a DMAC (Direct Memory Access Controller). A DMAC is used when it is necessary to transfer data between memory and a peripheral at a rate which exceeds the processor's capabilities. Consider the following code which reads 100 bytes from an I/O port and transfers them to memory starting at location $5000:

```
           LDB     #100
           LDX     #$5000    Cycles
    LOOP:  LDA     PORT      5
           STA     ,X+       6
           DECB              2
           BNE     LOOP      3
```

Adding up the CPU cycles taken by each instruction gives 16 cycles (8 µs for a 2 MHz 68B09), per transfer. The data rate would be even less if we

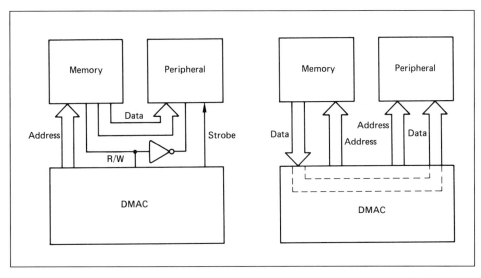

Figure 6.14 *DMA controllers in action: left, flyby type; right, read/write type*

had to poll the device to see if it had data available, or if data could arrive at any time because we were using interrupts. For data rates higher than this you have to resort to direct memory access.

Direct memory access is a hardware method that allows fast data transfer between peripherals and memory. DMACs come in two varieties and operate in two modes, see Figure 6.14. Both types have the following in common. In response to a signal from a peripheral the DMAC requests control of the CPU's buses – either by asserting /HALT or, with some processors, a special-purpose /DMAREQ line. Having got control of the buses, the DMAC drives the address lines and transfers data between the peripheral and memory. The DMAC has an internal address register which it increments or decrements at the end of each transfer. It also has a counter which the CPU initializes. When the counter decrements to zero the DMAC has transferred a complete block of data and produces an interrupt to inform the CPU. Thus the DMAC performs the operations of the above loop in hardware and so is very much quicker than the CPU itself.

The two varieties of DMAC are as follows. In the first (called *flyby*) the DMAC generates the memory address and a strobe for the peripheral; the data then flows directly from peripheral to memory or vice versa. In the second the DMAC acts more like a CPU and carries out two cycles: first it reads the peripheral, then it writes out the data to memory, or vice versa. The second is more easily interfaced to a bus-based system, where the peripherals may be located down the backplane. The two modes of operation are known as cycle steal and burst. In the former the DMAC does one transfer and then returns the bus to the processor; in the latter it performs multiple transfers whilst keeping the processor in the halted state. Burst mode is used for maximum data rate transfer but leaves the processor halted for long periods, so you must check that your system can tolerate this.

Expanding a processor's memory map

So far we have used the 6809 as an example of a microprocessor, and as we have seen this has an 8-bit data bus and a 16-bit address bus. Such a processor is adequate for many control purposes. However, what if we either need more processing power or want to access more memory? In the former case there is no real option – you have to use a more powerful CPU, say one with a 16 or 32-bit data bus. In the latter case you could also use a larger processor, though this could entail rewriting software, and a 16 or 32-bit CPU to perform tasks that an 8-bit one could cope with if it had enough address lines.

In a bus-based system, especially with the increasing size of memory chips, it is desirable to be able to access large amounts of memory. How then can we take a processor, such as the 6809, which can only access 64K of memory, and expand its address space? There are in fact two distinct ways. The first is somewhat 'crude' but quite effective, and the second sufficiently flexible that it is also used with processors that already have a large addressing range.

Expanding address space with a latch

The first way to expand the memory map is simply to enlarge the address bus. Figure 6.15 shows how. A 273 octal latch is used to store eight more

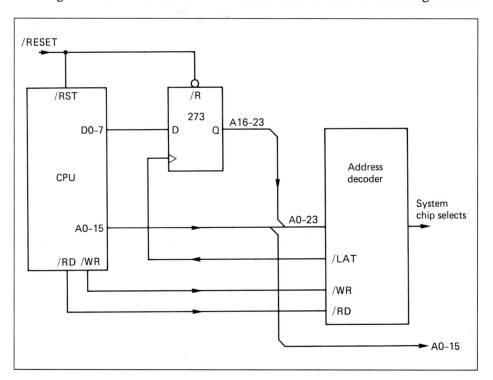

Figure 6.15 *Using a 273 latch to expand accessible memory space*

address lines, thus extending the address bus from A0–15 to A0–23. The board's logic can decode these 24 lines giving a total memory space of 16Mb. We should immediately point out that this simple trick has not turned our 64K processor into a *bona fide* 24-bit address bus machine. The reason is simply that the internal registers and instruction set of the CPU are still 16-bit – you cannot write LDA $501234 because the processor will not understand it. The processor is restricted to accessing 64K of locations at once, but by changing the address latch it can access different blocks, or *pages*, of 64K at any given time.

Another restriction is this: a program running in one page can access any location in that page, but in order to access other pages it must modify the address latch. However, as soon as it changes the latch another page will be mapped in, and the CPU can no longer read instructions from the page that the program resided in – the CPU will promptly 'crash'. To avoid this we have to set aside an area of memory (say 8K) which is decoded to appear in every page. This 8K block would contain the address latch itself, some EPROM and I/O devices that code running in any page might wish to access. We can place some code in the EPROM which lets a program running in any page write a byte to any location, for example:

```
WRITE:  ORCC   #$50          ;disable FIRQs and IRQs
        STB    ADDR_LATCH    ;swap map
        STA    ,X            ;store data
        LDB    OLD_LATCH     ;get old value of latch
        STB    ADDR_LATCH    ;swap map back
        ANDCC  #$AF          ;re-enable interrupts
        RTS
```

On entry to this routine the byte to be written is contained in A and the 24-bit address of where to write it in B + X. The code disables interrupts, since once it changes the address latch the interrupt handlers will be mapped out (NMI which cannot be disabled should not be used in this type of system). It then stores the data byte and reloads the address latch with its old value.

This method of memory expansion has the merit of being easy to implement, and is most effective if you have a problem that requires only a small program (less than 64K) but large amounts of data storage. The technique gives the program fast access to a large amount of store without the need for saving and retrieving data from floppy disks and other such media.

Memory management units

The other way of expanding a processor's memory map is by using a so-called *memory management unit* (MMU). Figure 6.16 shows how a typical MMU (the 6829) works. The MMU accepts address lines A11–15 from the CPU and uses their value to decide what states to make the lines PA11–20, which are used as address lines for the rest of the system and are known as the *physical address*. Thus each 2K block of *logical* memory (as defined by the CPU lines A11–15) is mapped into 2K of physical

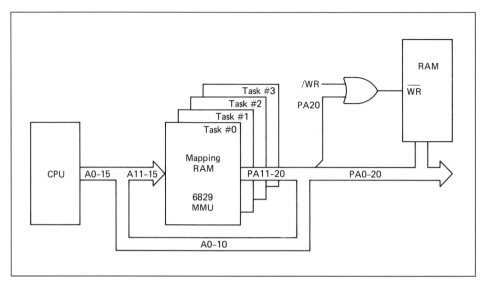

Figure 6.16 *The 6829 memory management unit, also showing write protection of memory – when PA20 is HI writes to the RAM are disabled*

memory in the range 0–2Mb. The 6829 contains four maps, and at any given time one of these performs the address translation. Usually, each map is allocated to a separate task, or program, and the operating system arranges for the tasks to take turns to run, which is known as multi-tasking.

Multi-tasking

In a multi-tasking system a processor is configured to run more than one program at once (possibly for more than one user). To achieve such a system the minimum that is required is a periodic interrupt from a counter timer chip, say every 10 ms. Each time the timer produces an interrupt the operating system returns from the interrupt handler to a different task, which then executes until the next timer interrupt, and thus the various tasks appear to run simultaneously. Such a software implementation of a multi-tasking system can be successfully used (for example, the OS-9 operating system), but has some problems which can only be solved by hardware (MMU) means.

For example, firstly there is no memory protection – there is nothing to stop one task from overwriting another's data, its program or even the operating system itself, any of which will probably cause a 'crash'. With an MMU we can allocate areas to specific tasks and since only the operating system (task #0) can alter the MMU's mapping RAM unauthorized accesses are prevented. An enhancement is to designate areas of memory that can be accessed normally by some tasks but can only be read (not modified) by others. Figure 6.16 shows how. When PA20 is HI write cycles to the RAM are disabled. Thus if task #0 can access memory at 2–4K in physical space and task #1 at 514–516K (PA20 HI plus 2–4K) then they can both access the same data but task #1 cannot modify it.

Secondly, for efficient use of memory it is necessary to be able to piece together small unused fragments into a larger contiguous block. An MMU lets us do this by mapping a block of logical memory into smaller (2K in the case of the 6829) pages of physical memory. The CPU has no idea that the MMU is present, so to it the memory looks like just one contiguous piece located at the logical address. This point also means that code which is not position independent must be mapped at the correct logical address, though it could be located anywhere in physical memory.

How do we combine these ideas to produce a functioning multi-tasking system? Firstly, task #0 (mapped in after a reset) must initialize the MMU so that each task's memory space corresponds to where its program lies. Secondly, we need a periodic interrupt to tell the operating system when to switch tasks. Note that an interrupt causes the MMU to switch task #0 in (it monitors the BA and BS status lines to detect interrupts). When task #0 receives an interrupt it must first ensure that it can at a later date return to the interrupted task (say task #2). The CPU's registers have been saved on the S-stack in the memory space of task #2 prior to the MMU switching to task #0. The only register the operating system must preserve is S (the location of the S-stack used by task #2), which it saves in RAM. Task #0 then loads S with the address of the S-stack of task #0, and then selects which task to run next – possibly the tasks take it in turns or perhaps a priority scheme is used. Finally it switches the new task (say task #3) into the logical memory map and executes it. Code to do this is as follows.

```
IRQ: LDA   TASK_NO    ;task number times two (4 for task #2)
     LDX   #SP_BASE   ;address of table containing SPs
     STS   A,X        ;save task #2's SP at SP_BASE + 4
     LDS   ,X         ;load task #0's SP, decide on next task
     LDA   NEW_TASK   ;load A with new task number (3)
     STA   OPER       ;store in MMU – select next map
     STS   ,X         ;save SP
     ASLA             ;double task number
     STA   TASK_NO    ;update task number location (with 6)
     LDS   A,X        ;get task #3's SP from SP_BASE + 6
     LDA   #1
     STA   FUSE       ;load MMU 'fuse' register with one
     RTI              ;return from interrupt to new task
```

To swap the memory map the MMU is loaded with the new task number, S is loaded with the address of the S-stack in the new task's map and one is written to the 'fuse' register inside the MMU. This causes the MMU to swap the map after a one-cycle delay, giving the CPU time to read the RTI op-code from the memory of task #0 before it is mapped out. The MMU then switches the map and the RTI is executed using the data stored on the stack of task #3. Task #3 then continues where it left off.

The interrupt line used for the periodic interrupt should be the highest priority in use. This is to prevent an interrupt arriving when S is loaded with the address of the stack in a task that is not presently mapped in. If you use FIRQ for this then task #0 must save all the 6809's registers in RAM since they are not automatically pushed when FIRQ occurs.

MMUs and DMA

As a final point, can an MMU be used with a DMA controller? The answer is yes. The DMA controller should drive the logical address lines (those emanating from the processor) and these will be translated normally by the MMU using one of its task maps (the 6829 switches to task #1 if it detects a DMA cycle).

The STEbus

Having looked at bus-based systems in general, we now turn our attention to one of the 'standard' buses – the STEbus. The STEbus has been developed to cater for industrial users who require a low-cost bus-based control system. Its specification has been ratified by the IEEE and it is also known as IEEE-1000. The fact that it is approved by the IEEE means that many manufacturers are likely to develop boards for the standard, so users do not have to rely on just one source of products.

STEbus signals

The STEbus is an 8-bit bus designed for 8-bit microprocessors, although larger processors can use it if they are capable of handling data in byte-wide chunks. The STEbus uses DIN41612 connectors, and its pinout is shown in Table 6.1.

The signals are not based on those of any particular processor, and they operate in an asynchronous fashion – transfers are not synchronized to some clock like the E clock on the 6809. The advantages of this will be discussed later.

Signal description

D0–7: The 8 bit data bus, driven by a master on a write cycle, driven by a slave on a read cycle.
A0–19: The address bus. The number of bits used depends on the type of bus access. For a memory access all the bits are used giving 1 Mb of address space. For an I/O access A0–11 are valid, giving 4K of I/O locations. For a 'vector fetch' cycle only A0–2 are used, giving eight 'locations'.
CM0–2: Command modifiers. These indicate the type of cycle being performed, according to Table 6.2.

The unused codes are reserved for future expansion and must not be used by STEbus boards. Thus we can see that CM0 behaves in the same way as the 6809's R/W line discussed in Chapter 5: HI for read and LO for write.

Table 6.1 The STEbus pinout; '*'signifies signal is active-LO

Pin	Row 'a'	Row 'c'
1	0V	0V
2	5V	5V
3	D0	Dl
4	D2	D3
5	D4	D5
6	D6	D7
7	A0	0V
8	A2	Al
9	A4	A3
10	A6	A5
11	A8	A7
12	A10	A9
13	A12	A11
14	A14	A13
15	A16	A15
16	A18	A17
17	CM0	A19
18	CM2	CM1
19	ADRSTB*	0V
20	DATACK*	DATSTB*
21	TRFERR*	0V
22	ATNRQ0*	SYSRST*
23	ATNRQ2*	ATNRQ1*
24	ATNRQ4*	ATNRQ3*
25	ATNRQ6*	ATNRQ5*
26	0V	ATNRQ7*
27	BUSRQ0*	BUSRQ1*
28	BUSAK0*	BUSAK1*
29	SYSCLK	+VSTBY
30	−12V	+12V
31	5V	5V
32	0V	0V

ADRSTB*: Address strobe – this indicates that the address lines and CM1–2 are valid. ADRSTB* is driven by the master after it has set up the address lines and CM1–2 at the start of an STE cycle. It indicates to a slave that it can decode the address to see if it is being selected.

DATSTB*: Data strobe – this is driven by the master to indicate that D0–7 and CM0 are valid. Thus on a write cycle the selected slave on seeing DATSTB* LO can latch D0–7.

Table 6.2 Coding of the command modifier lines

CM2	CM1	CM0	
LO	HI	HI	Vector fetch cycle
HI	LO	LO	I/O write
HI	LO	HI	I/O read
HI	HI	LO	Memory write
HI	HI	HI	Memory read

DATACK*: Data acknowledge – this is driven by the selected slave to indicate that it has accepted data on a write cycle or else is supplying data on a read cycle. DATACK* indicates to the master that it can terminate the present cycle.

TRFERR*: Transfer error – this indicates that there is something wrong with the present STEbus cycle and is driven by a slave or other error detection device. On receiving this signal the master should attempt some sort of error recovery procedure.

ATNRQ0-7*: Attention request lines – these are intended for interrupts and DMA requests, though there is nothing in the STE specification prohibiting their use for other purposes.

SYSRST*: System reset – this causes all STEbus boards to enter their reset state. SYSRST* should be asserted for at least 100 ms after the power supply reaches its nominal value.

BUSRQ0-1*: Bus requests – these are asserted by a master wishing to use the STEbus, received by the arbiter.

BUSAK0-1*: Bus acknowledges – these are driven by the arbiter to grant control of the bus to a requesting master.

+VSTBY: Voltage stand-by – this is an optional line for use in systems requiring a battery back-up facility; it supplies 5 V.

SYSCLK: System clock – this is a 16 MHz clock and is normally supplied by a master.

Electrically the following lines are tri-state: D0-7, A0-19, CM0-2, ADRSTB* and DATSTB*.

The following are open-collector: DATACK*, TRFERR*, ATNRQ0-7*, SYSRST* and BUSRQ0-1*.

The following are totem-pole (standard TTL): BUSAK0-1*, SYSCLK.

STEbus operation

A write cycle

Having looked at a description of the signals we can now examine how they work. Figure 6.17 is the timing diagram for an STEbus memory write cycle. The master first sets up the address, data and command modifiers. It then waits a minimum of 35 ns before asserting ADRSTB* followed by DATSTB*. The 35 ns of setup time allows any reflections on the backplane to die away. The slaves decode the address and command modifier information and each determines whether it is being accessed. The selected slave then latches the data being written into its appropriate memory location and having done so it asserts DATACK*. If the slave found a fault, for example an attempt to write to read–only–memory, then instead of DATACK* it could assert TRFERR*.

Notice that the whole cycle is asynchronous – the slave can take as long as it wants to accept the data (actually systems often contain a timeout module which asserts TRFERR* after a certain amount of time has elapsed, thus ensuring the master does not wait for ever for a malfunc-

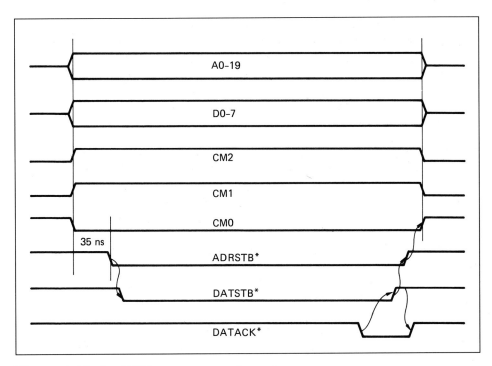

Figure 6.17 *An STEbus memory write cycle*

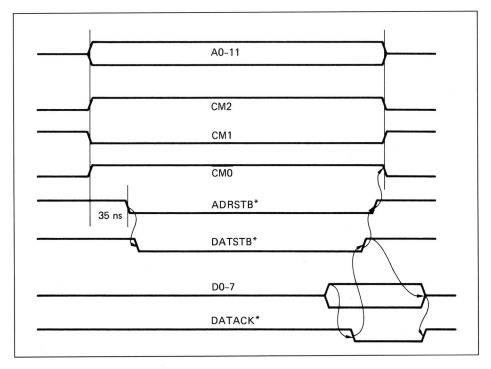

Figure 6.18 *An STEbus I/O read cycle*

tioning slave). Giving the slave as long as it needs has several advantages. Firstly, as processor speeds increase slower slaves do not suddenly become obsolete, but can still communicate with the faster masters. Hence the STEbus will not become outdated as technology improves. Secondly, because the bus is not tied to a set of synchronous signals, any slave device can be simply interfaced to the bus.

At the end of the cycle, when DATACK* is asserted, DATSTB*, ADRSTB*, A0–19, D0–7 and CM0–2 are tri-stated. The next cycle is not allowed to start till after DATACK* has gone HI again – the slave will release DATACK* on seeing DATSTB* go HI.

A read cycle

Figure 6.18 illustrates an I/O read cycle. Again the address is output together with the command modifiers. After 35 ns ADRSTB* and DATSTB* are asserted. Each slave decodes the address and command modifiers, and the one selected drives D0–7 with its data and then asserts DATACK*. The master on seeing DATACK* LO reads in the data, and then releases DATSTB*, ADRSTB*, A0–11 and CM0–2. The slave on seeing DATSTB* go HI releases D0–7 and DATACK*.

Cycle types

The above two examples looked at two of the five cycle types, namely a memory write and an I/O read. The question arises: what is the difference between the types of cycles? Firstly, a memory cycle is used to access, as its name suggests, memory locations such as RAM, ROM or perhaps a memory-mapped video display. I/O cycles are used to access peripherals (I/O devices) such as parallel I/O, serial I/O, floppy disk controllers, etc. Many processors have actual in-built I/O instructions, for example the Z80. Others, such as the 6809, 6502, 68008 and 68020 treat all locations as memory. With the latter type of CPU it is necessary to allocate part of the processor's memory map as I/O space. When the processor accesses that section of memory the on-board hardware causes the STEbus interface to perform an I/O cycle (CM1 LO).

Why does the STEbus define these two types of memory? The reason is that usually peripherals do not take up many locations, so if they are designed to be in I/O space they only need decode A0–11, not all of A0–19, and thus fewer chips are required. Also, having two types of memory space means that the system is given added flexibility – if you decide to change the addresses of some I/O boards then you do not affect the memory map of the memory boards.

The third cycle type is called the vector fetch cycle. This can be used to determine the source of an ATNRQ* (recall the discussion in Chapter 5 on vectored interrupts). When a master receives an ATNRQ0–7* it can perform a vector fetch cycle – it puts the number of the ATNRQ* on A0–2 and does a read cycle with CM2 LO. The slave that generated the

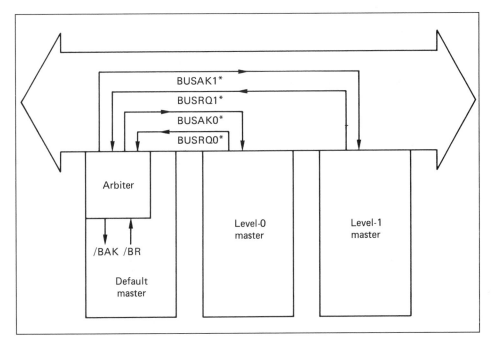

Figure 6.19 *The STEbus arbitration scheme*

ATNRQ* puts out its vector onto D0–7. The master reads this byte and uses it to vector to the required interrupt handler.

Arbitration

The STEbus can support up to three masters. It uses the two-level arbitration scheme that we have already discussed. The STEbus has two request and acknowledge lines (BUSRQ0,1* and BUSAK0,1*). To let three masters use the bus the arbiter can be located on a master (called the default master), which requests the bus with an on-board /BR signal receiving back /BAK. See Chapter 4 for a PAL version of this arbiter.

Figure 6.19 shows the configuration of the arbiter and the other bus masters. The highest-priority device is the Level-0 master, then the Level-1 master and finally the default master.

Requesting the bus

When a master wants to use the bus it asserts its request line. The only proviso is that before it asserts BUSRQn* (or /BR) it must check that BUSAKn* (or /BAK) is HI. If this rule did not exist then a very fast master could interpret the bus acknowledge from the arbiter incorrectly. Figure 6.20 explains why. The Level-0 master wants to perform a cycle and so asserts BUSRQ0*; it receives back BUSAK0* and so takes control of the bus and performs its transfer. At point A it has finished with the bus and

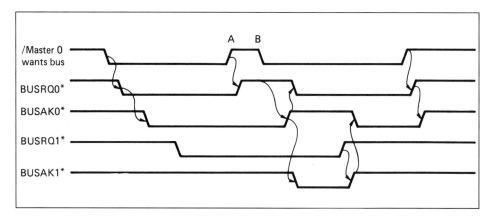

Figure 6.20 *The timing diagram of STEbus arbitration and requesting the bus*

releases BUSRQ0*. The arbiter then decides to grant the bus to the Level-1 master, so it releases BUSAK0* and asserts BUSAK1*. Unfortunately, however, the Level-0 master is very fast and at point B decides it needs the bus for a second cycle. If it did not examine the level of BUSAK0* before asserting BUSRQ0* it would assert BUSRQ0* and so at B it would assume it had control of the bus, BUSRQ0* and BUSAK0* both being asserted. Thus it would attempt an STEbus cycle, but unfortunately as the arbiter has given the bus to the Level-1 master it too would access the bus.

The resultant bus clash would cause both processors to receive erroneous data possibly leading to their crashing. The proviso prevents a fast master incorrectly assuming it has got control of the bus; it only has control if both BUSRQn* and BUSAKn* are asserted.

Summary of bus protocol

To clarify how the STEbus works we can draw up a flow diagram, as in Figure 6.21, to illustrate a bus cycle. In the figure we will do a read cycle, either memory, I/O or vector fetch.

STEbus interfacing

Slave interfacing

Having looked at the operation of the STEbus we shall now investigate how to interface a peripheral to it, that is how to make it function as a slave. The first thing we have to do is deduce when the slave is being accessed. To achieve this we decode A0–11 (assuming our slave is an I/O device) and the command modifiers. Figure 6.22 shows one way of decoding addresses. An LS688 comparator chip compares two incoming bytes (P0–7 and Q0–7); if they are equal then the /P=Q output is driven LO,

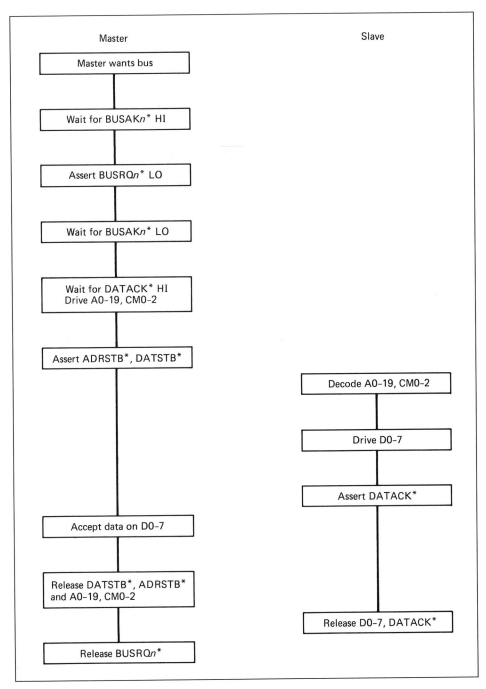

Figure 6.21 *A flow diagram of STEbus operation*

provided that the /G enable input is also LO. Address lines A4–11 go into the P side of the 688 and are compared to the input data on the Q side; the Q data is set by a link, or jumper, area. If a link is inserted then the chosen Q input is LO, but if a link is omitted then the 4k7 resistor pack

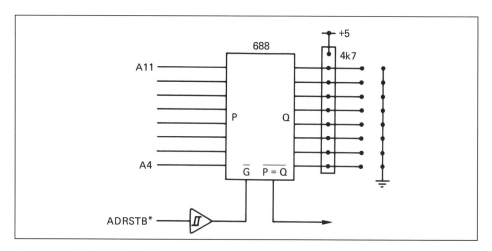

Figure 6.22 *STEbus I/O-slave address decoding*

pulls that input HI. Since links are fiddly to insert and remove, an improvement on this circuit is to use binary-coded hexadecimal switches. Such a switch has four outputs which are shorted to ground to reflect in binary the number dialled up on the switch. The links or switches designate the I/O base address of the slave, and since we have not decoded A0–3 the slave will occupy 16 I/O locations. The 688 enable input is driven by ADRSTB★, which ensures that /P=Q is only LO during a valid STEbus cycle, and incidentally makes the slave obey that part of the STEbus spec. which states that a slave must do nothing unless ADRSTB★ and DATSTB★, are asserted.

Notice that ADRSTB★ is buffered before driving /G. This is because the strobe signals ADRSTB★, DATSTB★ and DATACK★ should all be received by Schmitt trigger input gates, such as LS245s.

Slave control circuit

The /P=Q output is routed to a PAL which controls the operation of the slave, see Figure 6.23. The slave PAL, a 16L8, examines CM1–2 to check that an I/O cycle is in progress (CM2 HI and CM1 LO). It also confirms that DATSTB★ is LO. If all these conditions are satisfied then the slave knows the present STEbus cycle is for it, and it therefore begins to respond to the access.

The /ACT line stands for 'action'; by driving this line LO the 164 shift register is taken out of its reset state. On each subsequent clock edge the shift-register will clock a HI down its outputs. When Q1 goes HI, the PAL16L8 asserts the /CS line (chip select to the peripheral IC), and if the cycle is a read cycle (CM0 HI) it also asserts /RD, the read strobe to the peripheral. Two clock cycles later Q3 will go HI and if the STE cycle is a write, the PAL will drive /WR LO. When Q5 goes HI /WR is negated, and at this point the cycle is terminated by the PAL asserting DATACK★. The master then reads D0–7 (if it was a read cycle) and releases

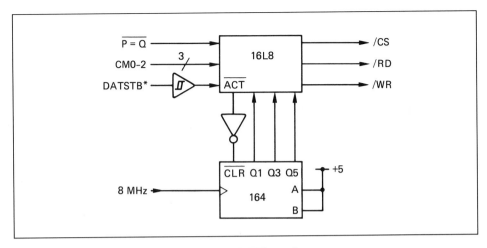

Figure 6.23 *A control circuit for an STEbus slave*

DATSTB*, ADRSTB*, CM0–2, A0–11 and, if it was a write cycle, D0–7. When the PAL sees DATSTB* go HI it negates /CS and /RD (for a read cycle), disables the data bus drivers and releases DATACK*.

The PAL equations for this operation on the 16L8 are fairly straightforward and so are given below:

```
Inputs
Pin 1 = PQ;          /* Address comparison line */
Pin 2 = CM2;         /* Command modifier 2, HI for an I/O cycle */
Pin 3 = CMl;         /* Command modifier 1, LO for an I/O cycle */
Pin 4 = CM0;         /* Command modifier 0, LO for write cycle */
Pin 5 = DATSTB;
Pin 6 = Ql;          /* Output of timer chain */
Pin 7 = Q3;
Pin 8 = Q5;

Outputs
Pin 12 = CS;         /* Chip select to I/O device */
Pin 13 = RD;         /* Read line to I/O device */
Pin 14 = WR;         /* Write line to I/O device */
Pin 15 = DATACK;     /* Data acknowledge to STEbus */
Pin 16 = ACT;        /* Activate timer cycle in progress */
```

Equations
/CS = /PQ & CM2 & /CM1 & /DATSTB & Q1;
   /* /PQ & CM2 & /CMl & /DATSTB indicates a valid cycle */

/ACT = /PQ & CM2 & /CM1 & /DATSTB;

/RD = /PQ & CM2 & /CM1 & /DATSTB & Q1 & CM0;

/WR = /PQ & CM2 & /CM1 & /DATSTB & Q3 & /Q5 & /CM0;

/DATACK = /PQ & CM2 & /CM1 & /DATSTB & Q5;
DATACK.OE = /PQ & CM2 & /CM1 & /DATSTB & Q5;
   /* DATACK* is an open-collector line so put in a tri-state term */

Barring a few minor changes most I/O slaves can be interfaced this way and so are relatively quick to design. To show these ideas in action we shall now look at some real STEbus slaves. The boards we have chosen to examine are some of the range from Arcom Control Systems Ltd.

Example STEbus slave boards

A parallel I/O board

As an example of an STEbus slave we first consider the SPINC board, see Figure 6.24. This board is a parallel I/O interface, the heart of which is two Zilog Z8536 CIO chips, ICs 12 and 14. These chips are quite intelligent and can not only perform parallel I/O, but also count and generate pulses. The inputs and outputs of the CIOs are buffered by ICs 15–19 (LS245s), giving each output 24 mA of LO level drive capability and a Schmitt trigger on each input.

The STEbus interface works as follows. IC1 (LS688) decodes the address as shown earlier. IC2 (245) buffers A0–2 and CM0–2. The heart of the interface is the control PAL (IC4, a 16L8), which generates the chip select, /RD and /WR strobes. IC8 generates two chip selects, one for each CIO, depending on the state of A2. IC4 also produces write strobes for two latches, ICs 7 and 10, the signal being labelled WRL. The data written into these latches goes to the output enable and direction pins of the output buffers, thus determining which ports are for input and which for output under software control. IC13 (LS138) decodes A0–2, and one of the 138 outputs can be jumpered to the INT line going into the control PAL, which enables the board to respond to vector fetch cycles. Notice how IC6 (LS245) is enabled by the same signal (EN) which after being inverted by IC3 allows IC5, the shift register, to count. This signal, EN, corresponds to the one we called ACT; it is LO if a valid cycle is in progress. The direction pin of IC6 is the inverse of CM0; if we turned IC6 around we wouldn't need the inverter, but this would make the PCB layout more difficult! IC8 pin 11 encodes /P=Q and DATSTB*, so in this case DATSTB* does not go directly into the control PAL. Finally, TR2 can generate ATNRQ*s if the CIOs are producing interrupts.

SCSI board

For our second look at a slave we consider an SCSI interface (*Small Computer Systems Interface*) board (Figure 6.25). This is an interface used for communicating to mass storage devices like hard disks and tape streamers. The SCSI interface consists of nine control lines, an 8-bit data bus and a parity signal. The SCSI interface need concern us no longer, but suffice it to say that IC11 (NCR5380) carries out all the necessary interfacing.

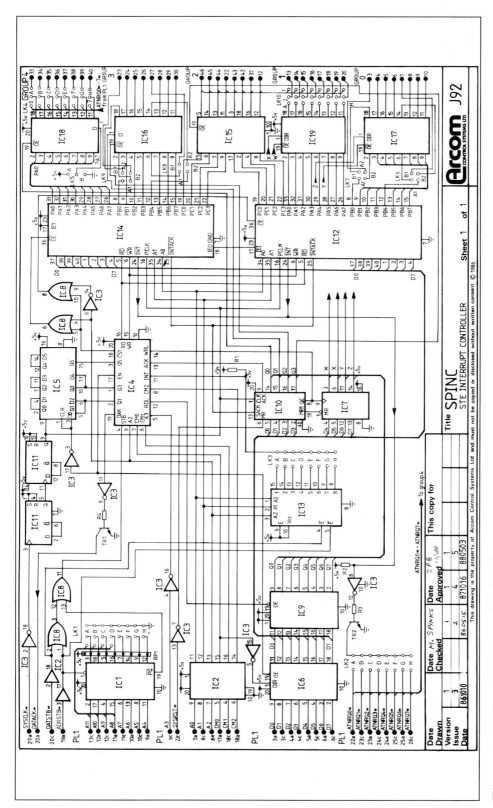

Figure 6.24 *The SPINC parallel I/O board*

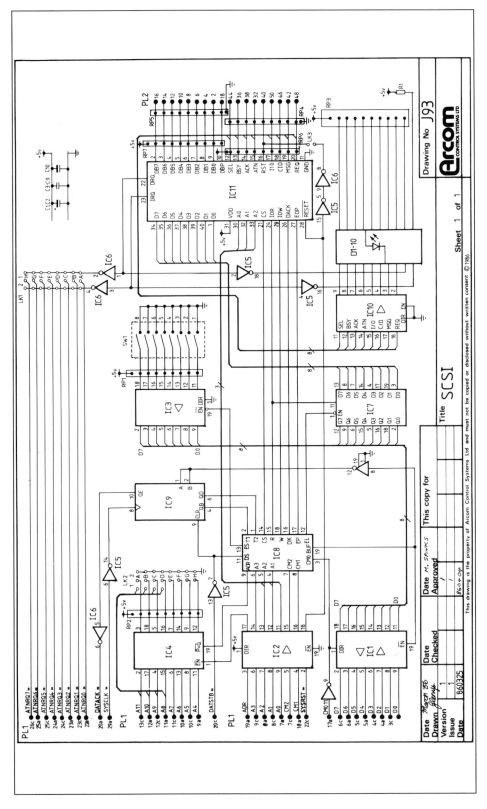

Figure 6.25 *An STEbus SCSI*

On the STEbus side of things IC8 is the control PAL and IC4 the 1688 comparator chip. The shift register IC9 is clocked by the 16 MHz SYSCLK signal, and is cleared by DATSTB* inverted. On this diagram the 'ACT' signal is called BUF. BUF is driven LO when the PAL recognizes it is being accessed. BUF going LO causes the inputs to the shift register to go HI, so HIs start to be clocked down the outputs. As before the PAL looks at the Q outputs and generates chip select, read and write signals.

A couple of other points are worth noting on this board. Firstly, for user-friendliness Dl–10 display 10 of the control signals associated with the NCR5380. These give a visual indication of what state the NCR5380 chip is in, so making software programming very much easier. Secondly, SW1 is a bank of eight switches which can be changed by the user and read by an STEbus master. These switches can be used to provide information to an operating system on start-up, for example which mode to start-up in. Note that these two facilities are only available because there is plenty of room on the board for such 'luxuries'.

Master interfacing

Designing STEbus masters is more difficult than slave interfacing. As a basis we can use the master control PAL given in Chapter 4, but as every processor has its own idiosyncrasies each design is pretty much unique. We shall therefore look straight away at some real boards.

STEbus 6809 board

We start by looking at the Arcom SC09 board, see Figure 6.26(a). IC8 is the 680B09E processor and its E and Q clocks are produced by PAL IC10. However, since the data could take some time arriving when an STEbus access is performed, the E and Q clocks are stopped during the STEbus access, thus 'halting' the 6809. IC10 waits for RESP to go LO (DATACK* or TRFERR* asserted) before releasing the processor from its stopped state. The maximum amount of time a 6809 can have its clocks stopped is 10 μs if it is left longer than this it can lose the contents of its internal registers. To prevent this happening IC16, a counter, drives Q3 HI after 8 μs, and when IC10 sees Q3 go HI it restarts the clocks. The timeout signal is also sent to IC9, another PAL, which triggers the 6809's /NMI line, thus informing the processor that a timeout has occurred. A timeout can occur for two reasons: either a slave malfunctions and doesn't assert DATACK* or the 6809 accesses an STEbus location where there is no slave.

Passing on to Figure 6.26(b) of the circuit diagram, we notice four memory chips. IC12 is a 4K EPROM located at the top of memory, IC15 a 2K (6116) static RAM chip. The sizes of these chips would now be classed as small, but they are indicative of the date of design (1985). ICs 20 and 22 are RAM or EPROM chips (size 8K to 16K). IC11 is the memory map decoder PAL (16L8). This PAL also maps STEbus I/O locations into 6809 memory space – if a certain region of memory is accessed then the SC09

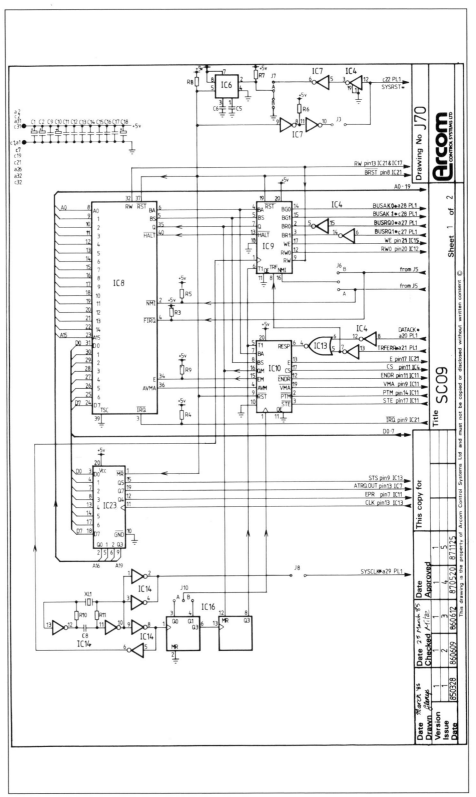

Figure 6.26(a) *The SC09 – a 6809 STEbus CPU board*

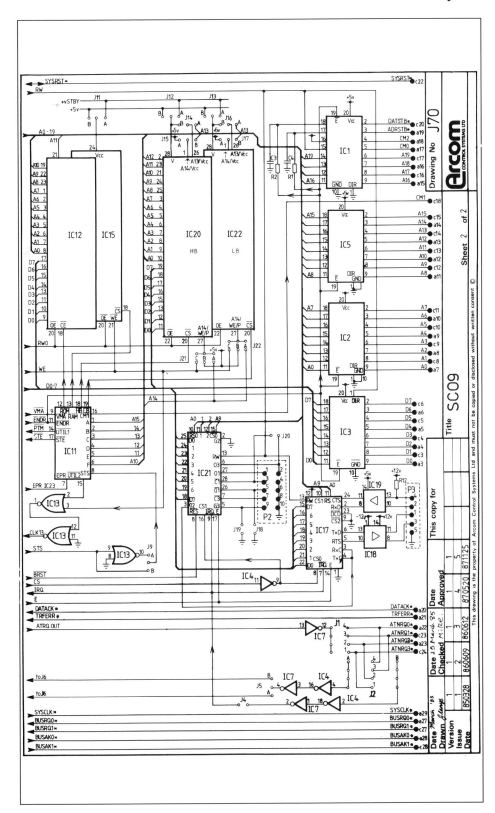

Figure 6.26(b) *SC09 sheet 2*

performs an STEbus cycle with CM1 LO (an I/O cycle). IC21 is a PTM (Programmable Timer Module, 6840), and IC17 is an ACIA (Asynchronous Communications Interface Adapter, 6850) or UART. ICs 18 and 19 drive and receive the RS-232 lines to and from the ACIA.

IC23 is a latch which stores the top four address lines, A16–19, for STEbus accesses, thereby extending the 6809's address space from 64K to 1Mb. The latch also contains two control bits (EPR and STS) which modify the SC09's memory map when set or cleared.

ICs 1, 2, 3 and 5 buffer data and address bus signals onto the STEbus. The buffers are enabled by the ENDR signal from IC10. ADRSTB* and DATSTB* are just this signal delayed by a resistor and capacitor to give the minimum 35 ns setup time required by the STEbus spec.

PAL IC9 contains the STEbus arbiter: BUSRQ0,1* come in and cause IC9 to assert the 6809's /HALT signal. When the 6809 has halted, as indicated by its BA and BS status signals, IC9 grants the STEbus to the appropriate requester. Notice that this means that the SC09 always acts in the default master mode and assumes it has control of the bus when it is running.

A good exercise for the reader is to compare the SC09 circuit with that of our minimal microprocessor board in Chapter 5, noting where the boards are alike and where they differ.

A 68008 processor board

The second master we look at is the SC008, see Figure 6.27. This board uses the Motorola 68008 processor, IC16, which is the 8-bit version of the powerful 16-bit 68000. Although its data bus is only 1 byte wide, the 68008 uses the same mnemonics as the 68000 and so is software compatible. The chip has 22 address lines and so can access 4Mb of memory space. Like the STEbus, the 68008 acts on the data acknowledge principle. When it accesses a location the processor waits for a /DTACK signal which terminates the cycle. While waiting for /DTACK the 68008 goes into a wait state; note that the processor clock continues to operate whilst in this state so that the 68008 will not lose the contents of its registers if a cycle takes a long time, in contrast to the 6809. The /DTACK line is open-collector, and three devices can drive it LO – the UART (IC18), the ROM or RAM from the PAL (IC22) and the STEbus control PAL (IC6). Alternatively a cycle can be terminated by /BERR (bus error), which is linked to the STEbus TRFERR* signal thus if an error occurs on the STEbus then the 68008 is informed of it.

The other PAL on Figure 6.27(a) (IC14) is an interrupt encoder. The STEbus ATNRQ*s come onto the board via IC11 to link area 9, where they are joined by the interrupt line from the UART (/UINT). The ATNRQ*s and /UINT can be jumpered to drive the AT0–6 inputs on the interrupt encoder PAL. The PAL looks at AT0–6 and produces three outputs (IPL0–2) which encode the highest-priority interrupt, in a similar way to the PAL example in Chapter 4. In response to an interrupt the 68008 can generate an interrupt acknowledge cycle to retrieve a vector from the bus. Actually the SC008 does not have interrupt acknowledge capability. Instead, in response to an interrupt acknowledge cycle IC14 generates an /INTA signal which is fed into the VPA input of the 68008. This causes the 68008 to fetch an 'auto-vector' from a fixed point in its memory map. The CPU then vectors off to that location to commence the interrupt handler.

IC18 is the UART (68681), which derives its baud rate from a crystal (X2) and so can work at 9600 baud and beyond (unlike the 6850 on the SC09 which could only manage 4800). ICs 20 and 21 are the RS-232 driver and receiver chips. IC19 is an RS-485 chip; RS-485 is a transmission protocol like RS-232 but the transmitting device can be tri-stated so that the line can be shared by many transmitters.

IC8 (74S04) provides the 16 MHz STEbus SYSCLK, and is divided down by IC9 to give an 8 MHz processor clock. The second half of IC9 is a bus-timeout circuit. The MR (master reset) input is connected to the output enable pins of the STEbus driver chips. When an STEbus cycle is in progress MR will be LO so the second half of IC9 can count. After about 8 µs 2QC will go HI indicating that the STEbus cycle has taken too long, so something must be wrong (a bus-timeout has occurred): 2QC goes into the STEbus control PAL (IC6) which then asserts /BERR to terminate the cycle, rather than waiting interminably for DATACK*.

IC6 is the STEbus control PAL. When the processor asserts /AS and /DS and A21 is HI the access is deemed to be for STE. IC6 then drives /ENDR (enable driver) LO, which enables the STEbus drivers (ICs 1, 5, 2 and 4). After a delay given by R1C5 /ENDEL goes LO and IC6 then asserts ADRSTB* followed by DATSTB*. When a DATACK* or TRFERR* is received IC6 releases the signals in the order DATSTB*, ADRSTB* and /ENDR. The SC008 does not have an STEbus arbiter, so cannot accept BUSRQ*s. When it wants to use the bus IC6 asserts /BRQ, which can be linked to either BUSRQ0* or BUSRQ1*. LK2 selects which BUSAK* signal the SC008 should monitor, and by making LK2C the SC008 acts in a 'permanent' master mode and always assumes it has control of the bus. This mode can only be used when the SC008 is the sole bus master. Notice that CMl is simply A20, so STEbus accesses with A20 LO will produce I/O accesses, and with A20 HI they will be memory accesses. Thus, as with the SC09, a processor without any specific I/O instructions can perform STEbus I/O accesses by defining an area of its memory map to produce I/O cycles.

The reader should now try to compare and contrast the more powerful SC008 with the SC09 discussed previously.

BBC micro to STEbus interface

The final master we shall look at is called the BEEBOP. It is an interesting master since it does not contain a CPU. Instead it interfaces one bus, in this case an Acorn Computers BBC micro's 6502 bus, to another, the STEbus. The BBC side of the interface is shown in Figure 6.28(a). The core of the interface is two parallel I/O chips ICs 11 and 20. These chips

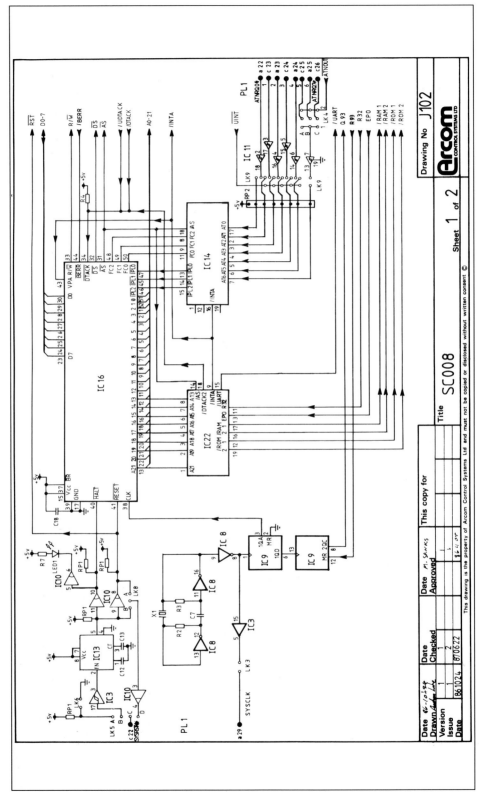

Figure 6.27(a) *The SC008 – a 68008 STEbus CPU board*

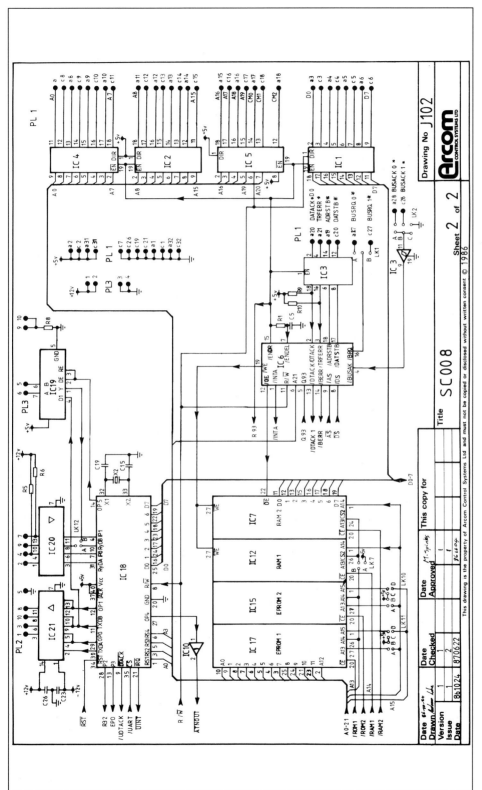

Figure 6.27(b) *SC008 sheet 2*

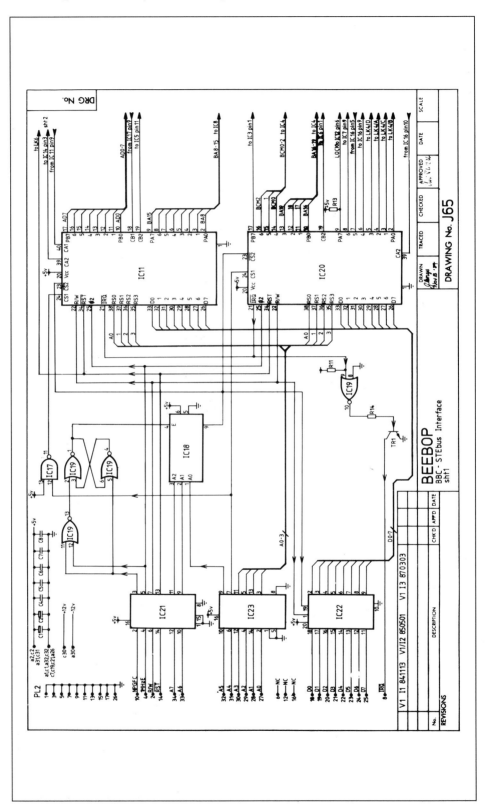

Figure 6.28(a) *The BEEBOP – an STEbus to BBC micro interface*

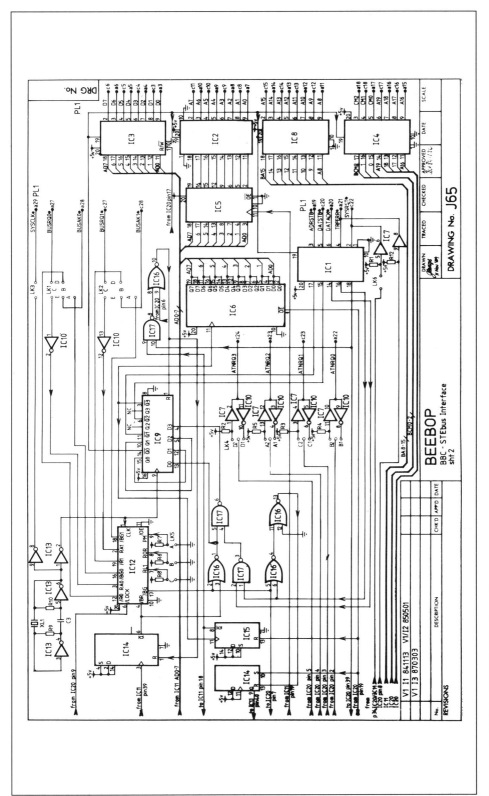

Figure 6.28(b) *BEEBOP sheet 2*

are 6522 VIAs (Versatile Interface Adapters). The BBC can write data into these chips, which is used to provide the address and data for STEbus transfers. So that the user doesn't need to use assembler to communicate at the device level with these chips, a 'filing system' ROM was written for the BBC. With such a ROM inserted into the BBC the user can communicate with the STEbus using simple BASIC commands.

Figure 6.28(b) shows the STEbus side of the interface. Remarkably, apart from IC12 (the arbiter), the whole interface is achieved with no programmable logic at all! A quad flip-flop, IC9, does most of the timings. When /Q0 goes LO it enables the bus driver chips (ICs 3, 2, 8, 1 and 4). ADRSTB*, driven by /Q1, goes LO one cycle after the address and data have been set up. One clock cycle later DATSTB* is asserted. IC5 latches the PB0–7 data bus from IC11, the latch being clocked by CB2 from the VIA (IC11). The data stored in IC5 provides the STEbus address lines A0–7. IC6 latches the data on the STEbus during a read cycle. The data is held by IC6 until it is read at a later time by IC11, which can then transfer its contents to the BBC under software control.

IC13 is the 16 MHz clock circuit, and IC 12 the STEbus arbiter, similar to the PAL in Chapter 4. Pins 7, 8 and 9 of the arbiter determine its mode of operation: if it is a potential master what level to request on; whether it is a default master; and whether it keeps requesting the bus until another master wants it (release on request mode). Thus PAL IC12 functions as both an arbiter and a bus requester – this is quite common on STEbus masters. The LOCK signal, when asserted, prevents the arbiter from granting the bus to a second requester, and thus enables the BEEBOP to perform indivisible bus cycles.

Overview of typical STE boards

STEbus boards are available from quite a few manufacturers, including Arcom, British Telecom, Control Universal, DSP design, Databeta and GMT Electronics. To give the user a feel for the versatility of STEbus boards we shall briefly survey some of those available from Arcom. Since Arcom have the largest selection of boards, this means our coverage will give a good idea of the range that is available, and also how flexible the STEbus is. We shall look firstly at CPU boards.

Overview of CPU boards

Table 6.3 shows some of Arcom's CPU boards. Note the range of operating systems and processor manufacturers, indicating the adaptability of STE for different system requirements.

Table 6.3 contains processors made by Motorola, Zilog, Intel and Hitachi, thus showing how easily an independent bus like STE can be interfaced to. Most of the boards in Table 6.3 are similar to those we have looked at, differing mainly in speed and amount of memory. As the

Table 6.3 A selection of STEbus CPU boards

Name	Processor	Operating system	Comments
SC09	6809	OS-9[1]	
SC008	68008	OS-9/68K[2]	
SC020T	68020	OS-9/68K	
SCPUA	Z80	CP/M+[3]	Floppy disk interface
SCPUB	Z80	CP/M+	
SC180	64180	CP/M+	
SC280	Z280	CP/M+	
SC88T	80188	Concurrent DOS[4]	
SC88PIO	80188	Concurrent DOS	Parallel I/O interface
SC52	8052	–	
SCPC88	8088	MS-DOS[5]	

[1,2] from Microware, [3,4] from Digital Research, [5] from Microsoft.

SC52 and SCPC88 are rather different so we will take a closer look at these two.

The SC52

The SC52 illustrates a very quick and cheap way of putting together a simple control system. The processor used is the Intel 8052, which is compatible at the assembler level with the 8051 series of microcontrollers. The difference that sets the 8052 apart from most other CPUs is that it contains a ROM which has the code for a BASIC interpreter. Thus when the 8052 is powered up, or reset, you enter BASIC. You can then type in a BASIC program, perhaps to send bytes down the STEbus to control something. When you have finished debugging the program, it can be saved by blowing it into an EPROM (the software and hardware required to do this are contained in the 8052 and the on-board circuitry). The EPROM can then be used to cause the 8052 to run your program each time it is switched on. Thus you can very quickly put together a small control system; you don't need any expensive disk drives, disk controller board or operating system, just a terminal.

An STEbus PC

The SCPC88 is a wholly compatible PC processor board which runs on STE. There are many IBM PCs and their 'clones' around, so this compatibility means that software for the SCPC88 can be developed on a PC system and then downloaded onto the SCPC88 where it will run in exactly the same manner as on the original PC. The SCPC88 runs the popular MS-DOS operating system, which uses one of the EPROM sockets. The other EPROM socket is available for user applications. The SCPC88 contains 256K of on-board DRAM, and can use up to 640K by expansion down the STEbus.

Microprocessor System Design

One of the great advantages of an STEbus PC system is that, rather than having a real PC computer in a factory, with all the mess and dust that that implies, you can have an STEbus system which is rigged and designed especially for that environment.

STEbus slaves – a brief overview

Table 6.4 gives details of some of Arcom's I/O boards. They can all be used with the masters discussed previously though some, such as the PC compatibles, are meant to be used with just one master.

Table 6.4 Typical STEbus slaves

Type	Name	Funtion
Utility	STELA	Bus analyser
Utility	SEP	EPROM programmer
Utility	SPCl	Prototyping board
Utility	SYSCON	System controller
Digital I/O	SPIBB	40 channel digital I/O
Digital I/O	SPINC	40 channel digital I/O plus timers
Analog	SADC12/16H	High-speed A/D
Analog	SDAC12–4	High-speed D/A
Analog	SADA8/16	8-bit A/D and D/A
Communications	S488	IEEE Bus interface
Communications	SERCOM4	Four-channel serial board
Communications	SISER	Intelligent serial board
Communications	SPCOM	Two-channel serial for PC
Video	SVC	80 $\times$ 25 mono video board
Video	SG84	High-resolution colour video
Video	SG84X	Genlock for SG84
Video	SPCGA	CGA graphics for PC
Video	SPEGA	EGA graphics for PC
Mass storage	SCSI	SCSI bus interface
Mass storage	SFDC	Floppy disk controller
Mass storage	SPDC	Floppy disk controller for PC
Memory	SDRAM	512K DRAM card
Memory	SCRAM	48K CMOS SRAM + clock
Memory	SEERAM	256K RAM, EPROM or EEPROM
Networking	SNETS	BITBUS – STE slave
Networking	SNETM	BITBUS – STE master
Networking	SARC01	ARCNET interface
Motor control	STMC	Stepper motor driver
Motor control	SEMC	Servo motor driver

Some of the terms in Table 6.4 may be unfamiliar, so we shall elaborate a few: A/D and D/A stand for analog-to-digital converter and vice versa; an A/D converts an analog signal to a digital representation of it for reading by a computer (A/Ds and D/As are looked at in more detail in Chapter 7). IEEE is an abbreviation for the IEEE-488 GPIB (General-purpose Interface Bus), a bus often found on laboratory equipment.

Genlock is a technique whereby two video pictures are combined into on; the SG84 and SG84X are discussed in full in Chapter 7. A network is a way of connecting together a group of computers to allow communications between them. BITBUS (from Intel), ETHERNET and ARCNET are examples of network protocols.

You can see from Table 6.4 that there are a great number of different types of STEbus slaves. Hence it should be clear that STE allows you to design almost any control system by using off-the-shelf boards, and, as stated above, if you do need an unusual board then slaves are relatively straightforward to design. We shall now look at some typical systems which might be designed using STEbus boards.

Typical systems

Having looked at STEbus masters and slaves, we can now examine some typical systems. What is in a system depends on whether it is for development or target use. A development system is used for creating code to run on a target, or perhaps it is just for word-processing. A target system is the final system used to control or monitor something. Since most target systems do not use disks, the development system must possess an EPROM programmer for ROMming the target's code; the SEP board is an ideal choice for this – it can program up to 27512 size EPROMs. To program an EPROM it is firstly inserted into a ZIF (Zero Insertion Force) socket. A software routine is then run which reads bytes from a source file and programs them into the EPROM, in preparation for use on the target board.

The use of disks is mandatory on all development systems (with the exception of the SC52). The floppy disk driver board is called the SFDC. Also useful is a hard disk drive, both for speed of access and storage capacity (20Mb and above). For a hard disk drive you use the SCSI board and the appropriate software driver.

The other boards used depend on the exact nature of what the target system will be controlling, though for a printer interface you could use a SERCOM4. For a PC system an SPDC for disks and an SPEGA or SPCGA to drive a graphics display are a must. Other processors usually talk to terminals via one of their on-board RS-232 ports, so if you want graphics then the SG84 board can be used. Figure 6.29 shows a number of possible development systems – from a stand-alone SC52 to a full-scale 80188 system. These diagrams illustrate again how flexible a bus-based system is; by adding or subtracting I/O boards countless variants can be drawn up.

As stated earlier, the requirements of a target system depend heavily on what is being measured or controlled. For example, if you are monitoring an analog signal then an A/D converter will be needed, for which the SADC12/16H could be used. If you are dealing with digital signals then an SPINC or SPIBB with their 40 I/O lines might suffice. One neat feature of the SPINC and SPIBB is that they can interface to a 16 way keypad.

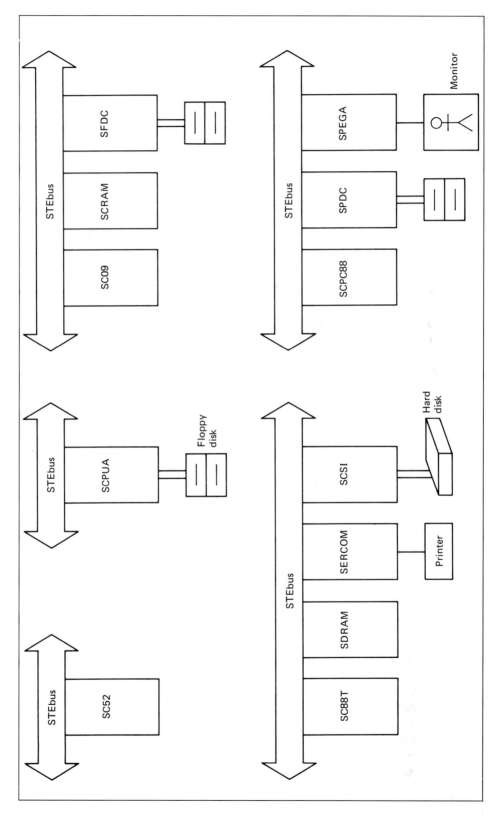

Figure 6.29 *Some typical STEbus development systems; all would attach to a terminal (not shown)*

This means that the target system can have data entered into it without the need for an expensive terminal.

A full description of the versatility of target systems must wait till after we have discussed *signal conditioning* boards. However, until then, Figure 6.30 illustrates a couple of simple systems. The first shows an SC008 controlling some digital equipment by means of an SPIBB, and also being hooked up to accept input from a keypad. The second shows an SC180, with graphical output via an SG84, connected to the BITBUS network via an SNETS.

Signal conditioning boards

With all of the STEbus slaves available you might think that you could produce a target system for any purpose. However, there are times when you need to do some initial processing on an input or output signal. For

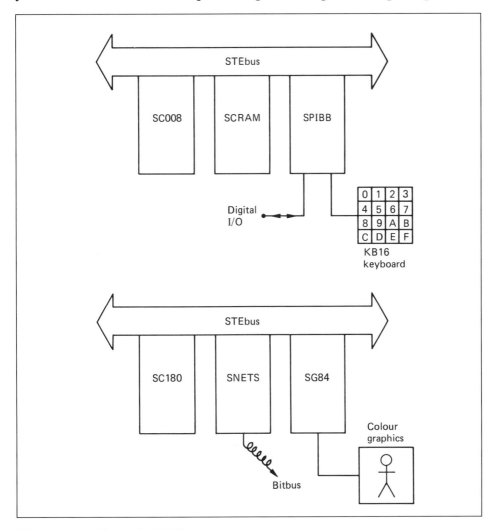

Figure 6.30 *Example STEbus target systems*

example, you might want more output drive than is available on an SPINC, or you might want to opto-isolate the computer system from the factory equipment. You might think that in such cases it would be necessary to return to the drawing board and redesign your I/O boards. Fortunately this is not the case. Instead we can make use of so-called signal conditioning boards. These are boards that sit between the plant electronics and the computer and modify the incoming or outgoing signals in some way. The signal conditioning concept was developed at Arcom and has become the *de facto* standard for STEbus users.

An SCB (Signal Conditioning Board) has a 50 way connector at one end which has either the same pinout as the digital I/O cards (such as an SPINC and SPIBB) or the analog I/O boards (such as an SDAC and SADC). Thus a ribbon cable can connect together an SCB to an STEbus I/O board. At the other end of the SCB is a heavy-duty 48 way 'DIN' connector, which can take up to 6 A per contact. The DIN connector plugs into a signal conditioning terminator (SCT1), a small board that joins the DIN connector to 40 screw terminals. Thus the plant connections are made with screws and the computer side with ribbon cable; hence all the connections can be made quickly and neatly. In addition to the SCT1 there are four other SCTs: the SCT2 connects to the SCB7 thermocouple board, the SCT3 joins a 50 way edge connector to the DIN connector, the SCT5 is similar to the SCT1 except that it joins a 32 way heavy-duty screw connector to the DIN connector, and the SCT7 joins a 50 way edge connector to 48 screw terminals.

Let us now look at some of the available signal conditioning boards in Table 6.5, thus seeing the additional flexibility they give the STEbus user.

Table 6.5 Some signal conditioning boards

Name	Analog/digital	Use
SCB2	A	4–20 mA Current input/temperture sensor
SCB3	D	Opto-isolated inputs
SCB4	D	Darlington driver output
SCB5	D	Solid state relays
SCB6	A	Input filters
SCB7	A	Thermocouple input board
SCB8	A	Op-amp prototyping board
SCB9	D	Opto-isolated inputs
SCB10	D	Opto-isolated outputs
SCB11	D	Relay outputs
SCB12	A	Analog isolated inputs
SCB16	D	High-power solenoid driver outputs
SCB18	D	Opto-isolated inputs
SCB19	A	Analog outputs
SCB20	D	Serial current loop interface
SCB22	A	Relay multiplexer board
SCB25	A	Analog isolated outputs

It should be obvious that by combining these boards with STEbus slaves many possible system configurations can be designed. Hence if you have a problem for which no ready-made solution is available, it may be possible to avoid designing a full STEbus slave by building a signal conditioning board instead. Consequently, you may not even need to know how the STEbus works – you design an SCB to fit onto an existing I/O board and you nearly have a working system. Also, since the I/O boards have the same (*de facto* standard) pinout, you can use different I/O boards with your SCB.

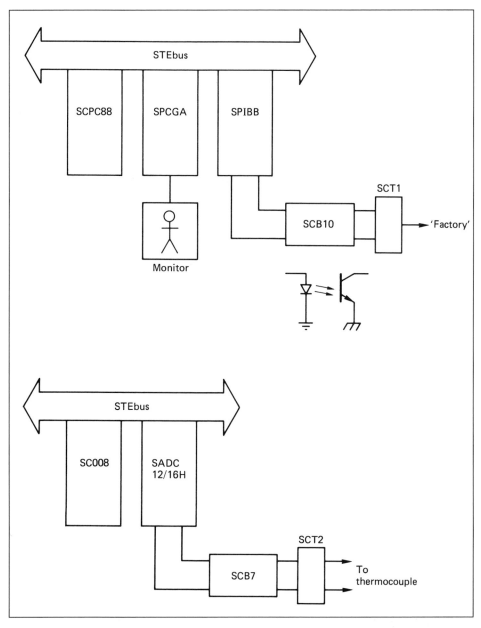

Figure 6.31 *Example STEbus target systems using signal conditioning boards*

Example systems employing SCBs

Figure 6.31 illustrates a typical target system using an SCB. A minimal PC system (SCPC88 and SPCGA) is driving a set of 'factory' lines via an SPIBB (an SPINC would do just as well). To protect the computer the lines are opto-isolated by an SCB10 which is connected to an SCT1.

The second example shows an analog interface. We want to measure temperature, and to do this we use an SCB7 and an SCT2. The input is connected to an SADC12/16H A/D board, the controller being an SC008.

An introduction to the VMEbus

There are many other 'standard' buses besides STE, for example STD, G64, G96, Multibus, Futurebus and VMEbus. Here we shall look briefly at the VMEbus, which like STE has been ratified by the IEEE as IEEE-1014. VME is a 16 and 32-bit bus and is much more complex than STE. For a full understanding you should read the bus specification; here we shall just describe a few of its features without going into details. A good place to start is with the connector pinouts in Table 6.6.

Both connectors are 96 way DIN41612 types. The P1 connector allows 16-bit transfers (on D00–15) over a 24-bit addressing range. Many VME systems and boards use only P1 connectors and backplane. The P2 connector expands the VMEbus to 32-bit transfers over a 32-bit addressing space. The 'a' and 'c' rows on the P2 connector are free for user-defined signals.

Like STE, VME has an address strobe (AS*) to indicate when addresses are valid, but two data strobe lines (DS0–1*). When both are asserted the transfer is 16 bits (word) wide; if only one is LO then it is a byte transfer (DS0* for D00–07, DS1* for D08–15). LWORD* is asserted if the master is making a long-word (32-bit) access, in which case data also appears on the P2 connector. Note that the slave must accept all 32 data bits – it cannot indicate to the master that it has only taken 16. Such a facility would require two DTACK* signals which the VMEbus does not possess (the 68020 CPU does have two, precisely so that peripherals can accept byte, word or long-word data widths). This means that the type of slave (D8, D16, D32 or combination thereof) must reside in a region of the master's memory map corresponding to these data widths; so if for example a master can make long-word accesses in the region $00000–FFFFF then slaves placed there must be able to respond to D32 accesses.

AM0–5 are known as address modifiers and are similar to the STEbus command modifiers. They define the type of address space being accessed, which can be 16, 24 or 32 bits wide (A16, A24 or A32). Small slaves would reside in A16 space and so only need to decode A01–15, whereas large memory boards would reside in A32 space, decode all the address lines and use the P2 connector. In addition AM0–5 encode three types of address space – reserved (boards may not use these AM codes), user defined (users and board manufacturers may use these codes for their own

Table 6.6 The VMEbus pinout

	Connector Pl			Connector P2
Pin	Row 'a'	Row 'b'	Row 'c'	Row 'b'
1	D00	BBSY★	D08	+5V
2	D01	BCLR★	D09	0V
3	D02	ACFAIL★	D10	RESERVED
4	D03	BG0IN★	D11	A24
5	D04	BG0OUT★	D12	A25
6	D05	BG1IN★	D13	A26
7	D06	BG1OUT★	D14	A27
8	D07	BG2IN★	D15	A28
9	0V	BG2OUT★	0V	A29
10	SYSCLK	BG3IN★	SYSFAIL★	A30
11	0V	BG3OUT★	BERR★	A31
12	DS1★	BR0★	SYSRESET★	0V
13	DS0★	BRl★	LWORD★	+5V
14	WRITE★	BR2★	AM5	D16
15	0V	BR3★	A23	D17
16	DTACK★	AM0	A22	D18
17	0V	AM1	A21	D19
18	AS★	AM2	A20	D20
19	0V	AM3	A19	D21
20	IACK★	0V	A18	D22
21	IACKIN★	SERCLK	A17	D23
22	IACKOUT★	SERDAT★	A16	0V
23	AM4	0V	A15	D24
24	A07	IRQ7★	A14	D25
25	A06	IRQ6★	A13	D26
26	A05	IRQ5★	A12	D27
27	A04	IRQ4★	A11	D28
28	A03	IRQ3★	A10	D29
29	A02	IRQ2★	A09	D30
30	A01	IRQ1★	A08	D31
31	−12V	5V STBY	+12V	0V
32	+5V	+5V	+5V	+5V

purposes), and defined codes which define areas as data or program and privileged and non-privileged. These options allow areas to be reserved for the operating system that user programs cannot access.

The VMEbus arbitration uses a daisy chain scheme with four request lines BR0–3★ and four daisy chains BG0–3IN★ and BG0–3OUT★. The arbiter must reside in slot 1, so as to be at the start of the daisy chain. With a daisy chain system, which uses the falling edge (rather than the level) of BG*x*IN★ to indicate the bus is available, there is always a small probability (due to metastabilities) that a master may miss the edge and so no-one will take control of the bus, which will therefore 'hang' up. To prevent this it must be ensured that the arbiter has a timeout monitor which will negate BG*x*OUT★ after, say, 64 μs before re-arbitrating. Unlike STE where interrupt acknowledges are a (rarely used) option, on VME all interrupts are vectored using the IACKIN★ and IACKOUT★ daisy chain.

The presence of these daisy chains means that more care is required to set up a VME system than with STE. Thus in STE any board can go in any slot, whereas with VME slot 1 must contain the arbiter and IACK daisy chain driver (the device that takes the IACK* signal and drives the start of the daisy chain). Also, all empty slots require links to be inserted to propagate the daisy chains, whereas slots with boards that use a daisy chain do not. This means you can't simply remove and replace boards at will – you have to put them back in the slot where you got them from.

VME has two other useful signals not included on STE. These are ACFAIL* and SYSFAIL*. The former is asserted by a device that has determined that the 50 Hz a.c. mains supply has failed, so processors have a few milliseconds to perform an orderly shut-down before the 5 V line drops. SYSFAIL* is asserted by any board that has noticed a fault. Whether a board is driving SYSFAIL* is often indicated by an LED on its front panel. On reset the LEDs are lit and as each slave is initialized they go out, and thus you can see at a glance if a slave fails to program because of a faulty bus interface. For readers designing their own buses both these signals could be usefully incorporated. Similarly, such readers should note the way critical strobes like AS* and DTACK* are next to 0 V lines to improve noise immunity from adjacent signals.

We can see that VME is similar to STE, but in view of its more numerous options (A16, A24, A32, D8, D16, D32, AM0–5) and its daisy chains more care is required when setting up a VME system to ensure that boards can communicate with one another.

Dual-bus architectures

As we have seen above, the VMEbus uses two DIN41612 connectors, labelled P1 and P2. The 'a' and 'c' rows on the P2 connector are unused by VME and are therefore available for STE signals which only use these two rows. This means it is possible to build a system which contains both the VME and STE buses.

This has many advantages. A powerful VME processor can be designed which can also access low-cost STE I/O boards, so dramatically reducing the cost of a target system, compared to one built from just VME boards. Alternatively STEbus masters could make use of VME I/O boards which have an STEbus interface, with a consequent increase in I/O power. The flexibility is most useful with systems where you do not know initially how much computing power is required. Thus you might commence work with an STEbus processor and later realize that the power of one based on VME is required; you can then swap the processor board but still use the same STEbus slaves, which do not then become redundant.

To take advantage of this concept Arcom have developed a number of dual-architecture boards, as follows.

VSC020   – 68020 CPU board for development or target work
VSC020T   – 68020 target board
VSER8   – eight-channel serial board
VSIXER6   – intelligent serial I/O board
VSAD12/32 – 32 channel 12-bit A/D board
VSP80   – 80 channel digital I/O board

All these boards have both STE and VME interfaces, so ensuring optimal flexibility. The slaves can be controlled by either VME or STE processors, and the masters can access VME or STEbus slaves and also have on-board dual-port RAM so that other masters can pass messages without the need for an external memory board. Thus with these boards the user can configure systems with both the power of VME and the low-cost of STE, so getting the best of both worlds.

7 | Some miscellaneous circuits

In this chapter we shall be concerned with describing some common circuits and the building blocks that make them up. In particular we shall look at A/Ds, D/As, graphics and phase-locked loops.

Analog-to-digital conversion

An analog-to-digital converter, or A/D or ADC, is a circuit that takes an analog voltage and converts it to a digital representation of that voltage. Thus it enables a microprocessor to analyse an analog waveform and perform calculations on it. An A/D chip has associated with it a figure called the *resolution*, the number of bits it converts to. For example, a 12-bit A/D operating over 5 V will have a resolution of 5 V/4096, or 1 bit will represent approximately 1 mV. Generally speaking, the more bits an A/D resolves to the slower it is. Thus the AD574A is a 12-bit converter which takes 25 μs to do a conversion, but it can also act in a faster 8-bit mode with a conversion time of 17 μs. Another example is the MAX172 chip which is also a 12-bit A/D but with a faster conversion time of 12 μs.

An A/D circuit in practice

The simplest A/D circuit would just consist of the A/D chip and a sample signal, which indicates to the A/D to take a conversion. For the following reasons this is unsatisfactory.

Firstly, the signal you are looking at is almost certainly varying with time; if it was not you probably wouldn't be looking at it! The problem is that if the signal varies while the A/D is converting then you can get confusing results. To prevent the signal altering a sample and hold amplifier is used to keep the A/D's input signal constant whilst conversion is taking place.

Secondly, you may be looking at small signals and not ones in the A/D's range of 0–5 V; thus you need an amplifier before the A/D. In practice a

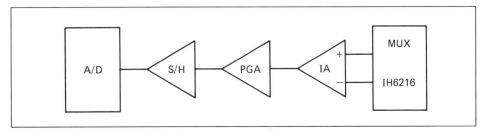

Figure 7.1 *Block diagram of an analog to digital converter system: MUX, analog multiplexer; IA, instrumentation amplifier; PGA, programmable gain amplifier; S/H, sample and hold amp; A/D, analog-to-digital converter*

programmable gain amplifier is used, which lets you select the gain under software control; gains of $\times 1$, $\times 10$, $\times 100$ and $\times 1000$ are common.

Thirdly, you often want to measure the difference between two signals not their absolute value. For example one signal is 4.01 V and the other 4.03 V, what you want is an answer of 0.02 V not 4.02 V; to achieve this you place an instrumentation amplifier before the programmable gain amplifier.

A final point is that it is rather a waste for the A/D to measure only one signal, especially as A/Ds are moderately expensive. Hence at the front end of the circuit you place an analog multiplexer, which lets you select under software control which of a number of different channels to look at. Figure 7.1 shows how these various components are put together. The IH6216 multiplexer gives 16 channels.

A real A/D board

As a practical example Figure 7.2 shows the SADC12/16H board. ICs 1 and 11 are two IH6216 multiplexers giving a total of 16 bipolar input channels. IC12 is the instrumentation amplifier and IC7 the programmable gain amplifier, its gain being selected by the logic inputs on pins 1 and 2. Notice also the way IC2 (an analog switch) removes offsets on the programmable gain amp. The offset is cancelled separately on each gain range by VR1–3 and then the analog switch selects which pot to use depending on the gain range selected by Q6 and Q7 of IC5. IC8 is the sample and hold amplifier, being controlled by the STS (status) pin of the A/D AD574A (IC13), the status pin indicating to the S/H that a conversion is in progress. VR4 and VR5 are two pots which adjust the gain and offset of the A/D. The offset changes the position of the A/D curve, the gain its slope.

An alternative way of arranging things is used on the VSAD12/32 board. Here an instrumentation amp with in-built programmable gain is used. On such a chip the gain is programmed by shorting two pins together. To obtain a change of gain under software control this shorting must be done by a relay. This has the disadvantage that since relays are mechanical

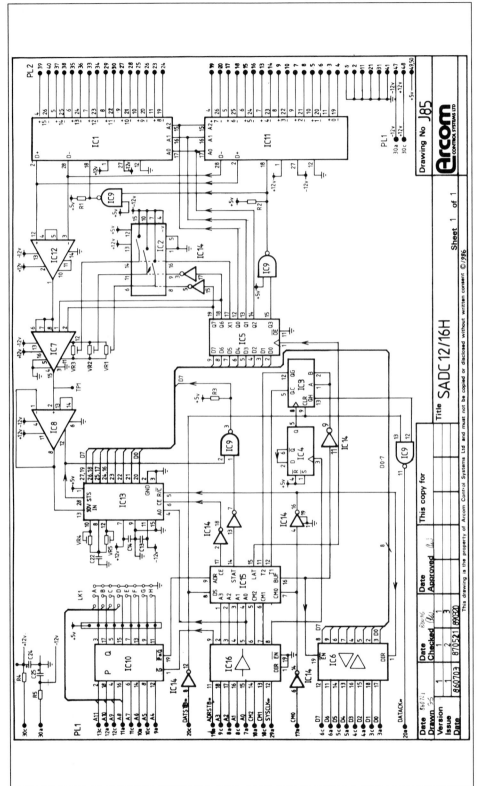

Figure 7.2 *The SADC12/16H analog-to-digital converter board*

devices time (around a millisecond) must be allowed for them to settle after switching gains.

Finally, any A/D board requires careful PCB layout to function at its best, see Chapter 8.

Digital-to-analog conversion

We saw in Chapter 3 how an op-amp adder circuit using weighted resistors could be used as a digital-to-analog converter (D/A or DAC). In practice you would use a ready-made D/A chip.

A digital-to-analog converter circuit is much simpler to design than an A/D circuit. All that really needs to be done is to choose a D/A chip, that is its speed and number of bits, and then interface it to the digital circuitry. Typically the digital side of a D/A looks like a latch (such as a 74LS374) which must be written to in order to produce an analog output of the required size. The D/A output is usually buffered with an op-amp – ensure that the chosen op-amp is fast enough for the D/A! Since almost all the analog circuitry is inside the D/A chip itself ground noise is much less of a problem than with an A/D, so the PCB layout does not need to be as good. Finally the lack of multiplexers means that you only get one channel per D/A chip (though dual D/As are available), so the cost per channel moves up relative to an A/D.

Apart from the simple D/A that takes a binary number and generates an analog output, there is another useful feature that some D/As possess. This is to take an analog and a digital input signal and to multiply the two together to give an analog output; such a D/A is said to be a multiplying D/A. It lets you chsnge the amplitude of the analog voltage under software control, for example a computer-controlled volume control for a sound system. It is also useful when you are controlling a piece of equipment and need to send it signals not of a given magnitude but rather of a fraction of some reference signal. For example, suppose you have a device which is powered off around 5 V and it needs an input of 60% of its supply voltage to function properly. If you use a 'normal' D/A and set it to give an output of 3 V this may be above or below the 60% threshold depending on the accuracy of the supply. With a multiplying D/A you feed back the supply voltage and use that as the D/A reference, so that when the supply varies the D/A output follows it.

Graphics

A graphics board lets you display information in an easily digestible form, for example as graphs, block diagrams and pie charts. Thus one can be useful at the output of a computer system. To understand how a graphics board works it is first necessary to explain how a display screen functions.

Microprocessor System Design

Video terminology

We first consider a simple black and white monitor. In such a display the screen is covered in a material called phosphor. At the back of the monitor tube is a gun which fires electrons at the screen. Where these electrons impinge on the phosphor it emits light and the point, or *pixel*, is lit up. The gun sweeps across the screen horizontally one *line* at a time, and at the end of each line it moves down and sweeps across the next. When it reaches the bottom of the screen it moves back to the top.

Video signals

The movement of the gun is controlled electronically by what are known as *synchronization* or *sync* pulses. There are two types – horizontal *syncs* which occur at the end of each line and vertical syncs which occur at the end of each screenful or *field*, see Figure 7.3. The syncs can be either negative or positive going, though they are normally negative going – the sync is logic LO. To reduce the number of connections that need to be made the two syncs can be combined into one *composite* sync. This is done by EX-NORing the two signals together.

A television signal has an additional type of signal known as equalization pulses. These are transitions that occur midway between adjacent horizontal syncs, but only for a few line periods either side of the edges of the vertical sync pulse. Equalization pulses are not generated by computer graphics boards, but you need to be aware of them if you are trying to process a TV signal (see the SG84X circuit later in this chapter).

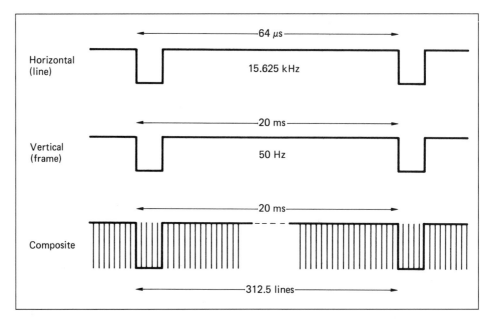

Figure 7.3 *The format of video sync signals*

Interlace modes

The number of lines in a field defines the vertical resolution of the screen. The number can be an integer or an integer plus a half, such as 312.5. If the number is an integer then the picture is said to be *non-interlaced*: on successive passes of the screen the lines are drawn on top of one another. With an integer plus a half the screen is said to working in *interlaced* mode, as used on a television set. Here, as the electron gun moves down the screen it leaves gaps between the lines, and on the next pass down the screen the gaps are filled in. The advantage of the interlaced mode is that it reduces screen flicker. For a television screen there are a total of 625 lines (525 in the US) in two consecutive fields (called odd and even fields); a pair of fields is called a *frame*. For a television set there are 312.5 lines every fiftieth of a second, and thus line syncs occur every 64 μs or at a frequency of 15.625 kHz.

Colour displays

For producing colour additional signals are required (red, green and blue – RGB). There are two types of colour monitors available: TTL (or digital) and analog. In a digital monitor the RGB signals are standard TTL levels, so a total of eight colours are available. To increase the number of colours to 16 an intensity, I, bit is often added.

An analog monitor in contrast uses a continually varying voltage from 0.3 to 1.0 V to represent the intensity of each colour. Thus a much greater range (theoretically infinite) of shades and colours can be produced. The syncs in an analog monitor are generally combined with the green gun and range from 0 to 0.3 V.

Operation of a computer graphics board

We shall now describe how a typical graphics board (the Arcom SG84) works and define certain terms as we go along.

Most graphics boards are known as *memory mapped*. What we mean by this is that RAM is used to contain the data that is to be written to the screen. For example, if we have a black and white display and the first nibble of memory contains in binary the number 1001, then the first four dots or pixels on the top left-hand corner of the screen will be white, black, black and white. Hence by filling the memory with appropriate data the screen can be made to produce pictures or characters (imagine pencilling in squares on a sheet of graph paper to sketch a picture). The first point to note here is that video data is output to the monitor serially, but as it leaves the RAM in parallel form a PISO shift register is required. This is commonly called a video shift register.

Now let us look at the SG84, see Figure 7.4. Like all clocked logic a graphics board depends on a master clock. For the SG84 this clock is supplied by a 25 MHz crystal oscillator circuit – XL1 and IC10 74S04.

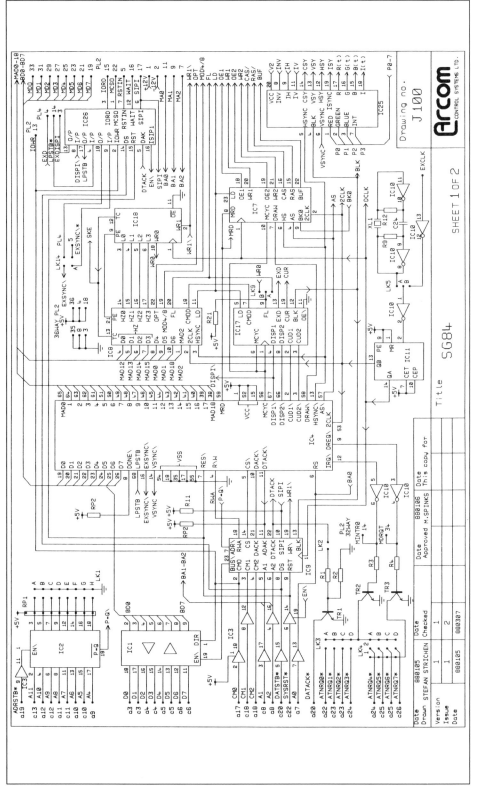

Figure 7.4(a) *The SG84 graphics board*

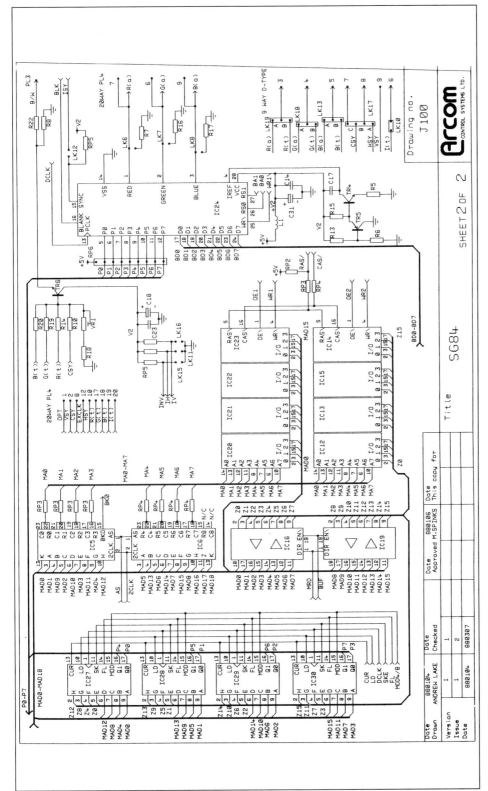

Figure 7.4(b) *SG84 sheet 2*

The clock is immediately divided down by two by IC11. Output QA runs at 12.5 MHz and is labelled DCLK, which stands for dotclock, also known as the pixel clock. It is called this since it represents the rate at which the video shift registers (ICs 27–30) clock out data into the monitor. This speed of 12.5 MHz determines the horizontal resolution of the screen – the number of pixels in one line. At this rate one pixel takes up 80 ns of space, so if the line were 64 μs long (in practice some of this time is taken up by the horizontal sync) then the resolution would be 64 μs/80 ns = 800 pixels. The vertical resolution is given simply by the number of lines per screen.

The video shift registers are 22V10 PALs (for their equations see Chapter 4). Each shift register takes in eight bits of information at a time, when loaded by the LD signal. They produce two pixel outputs (P0 and P4 for IC27). They also have the following inputs: CUR causes the P outputs to go tri-state, and is used to produce a *cursor* on the screen; SK enables the shift clock and when this pin is disabled the shift registers ignore clocking signals and maintain the same pixel outputs, a feature used in the horizontal zoom mode, see later; FL inverts the bits, so black becomes white and vice versa, and by using a *palette* chip (IC24) on the output the FL signal can cause chosen colours to flash, see later; finally MOD selects whether the shift registers are in 4 or 8 bits per pixel mode.

The number of bits per pixel

The quantity 'the number of bits per pixel' is important. It indicates how many bits are incorporated into each pixel. If it is four then the 4 bits correspond to RGB and I, and so only 16 possible colours are available. In 8 bits per pixel mode each pixel is represented by 8 bits and so 256 colours are available. One advantage of 4 bits per pixel mode is the following, see Figure 7.5. At the output of the SG84 we have four video shift registers which each take in on a load cycle 8 bits of information. Thus we have a total of 32/4 = 8 pixels stored in the shift registers. Contrast this with the case of 8 bits per pixel mode. Here we only have 32/8 = 4 pixels stored in the shift registers. Thus, since each pixel takes up 80 ns of time, in 8-bit mode the shift registers need to be updated every 320 ns, whereas in 4-bit mode they only need to be reloaded every 640 ns. In fact for this circuit each DRAM cycle takes 320 ns, so this means that if you have an 8-bit screen then you have to read data out of memory continually to keep up with the shift registers, whereas in 4-bit mode every alternate cycle is free for something else.

What might this something else be? Well at some point you will want to change what is appearing on the screen. To do this you have to write to memory (actually the graphics controller chip does, so you only have to send commands to it). Thus in 4-bit mode you can interleave memory–write and display–read cycles, and hence you do not lose any speed or picture quality. In 8-bit mode the following happens. If you do not want to lose any speed then the controller chip has to 'pinch' one of the display–read cycles, and hence the shift registers are not reloaded with

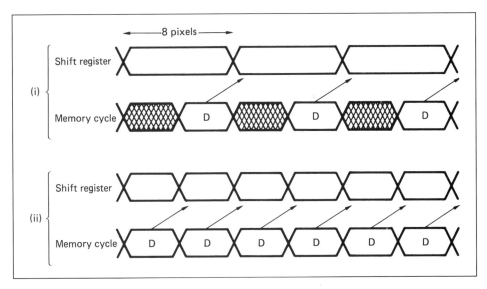

Figure 7.5 *A comparison of 4 and 8 bits per pixel modes: D is a display read cycle; (i) is 4 bits per pixel and (ii) 8 bits per pixel*

the correct data and four pixels are lit with random data, which means some noise appears on the screen. If you are writing a lot of data this noise can become annoying, so if you want to use 8 bits per pixel mode but avoid noise what should you do?

The answer is to program the controller chip (the SG84 uses one called an advanced cathode ray tube controller or ACRTC, part number Hitachi 63484) only to write to memory whilst the screen is in a horizontal or vertical sync, during which time the electron gun is disabled. This means you have noise-free screens but have to wait for syncs before you can update the screen, thus changing a screen becomes slower. Hence you can see that 4 and 8 bits per pixel modes imply a trade-off between number of colours and either slower or noisier updates of the screen. On the SG84 the number of bits per pixel mode can be set under software control.

ACRTC operation

The ACRTC provides the vertical and horizontal syncs, their frequency being set up under software control by writing to the ACRTC. It also produces two cursor and two 'display' signals. The cursor signals are decoded by ICl7 to produce one signal, CUR, which goes to the video shift registers; when it is active it tri-states the pixel outputs. Resistor pack RP6 ensures that the voltage level of the tri-stated outputs is HI, so that the TTL output PAL (IC25) drives RGB and I all HI, thus producing a white cursor. The two display signals are used to generate the blanking of the screen; when neither of them is active the screen is blanked, which the BLK signal achieves.

The ACRTC can accept data from an STEbus master CPU and write this information into the video memory. It can also read data from the memory. The SG84's memory consists of eight 64K $\times$ 4 DRAM chips (ICs 12–14 and 20–23). For write cycles they are arranged 16 bits wide, the data lines being MAD0–15, whereas for display–read cycles they are arranged 32 bits wide (MAD0–15 and Z0–15). ICs 5 and 6 (PAL22Vl0s) perform the DRAM address multiplexing for the three types of DRAM accesses – display–read, ACRTC–write and ACRTC–read. The ACRTC is IC4 and is operated at a speed of 6.25 MHz.

Attributes and picture zooming

IC8 acts on the *attribute* bits produced by the ACRTC. At the end of each line the ACRTC outputs data called attribute bits, and these are latched by IC8. For example, MAD12–15 contain the horizontal zoom factor which indicates by how much to stretch or zoom the display in the horizontal direction. The way horizontal zooming works is as follows. If the zoom factor is two then each pixel is repeated twice, if the zoom factor is three then each pixel is repeated three times and so on. The effect of this repetition is that the picture appears larger in the horizontal direction – we have 'zoomed' in on it.

The way the electronics works is as follows. IC18 acts as a down counter which cycles down to zero from the horizontal zoom factor, HZ. Every HZ clock pulses it will reach zero at which point the terminal count (TC) output goes HI, and is connected to the SK input of the video shift registers. SK prevents the shift register from shifting pixels when it is LO, and hence the same pixel is displayed whilst SK is LO, thus performing the required repetition. Figure 7.6 illustrates this operation for HZ equal to three.

We can also make the picture zoom in the vertical direction. No additional hardware is required for this. An instruction is sent to the

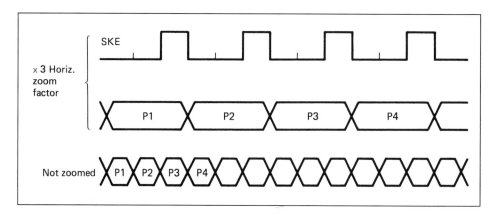

Figure 7.6 *Horizontal zooming of a video picture; SKE is the video shift register shift clock enable signal*

ACRTC which causes it to repeat the information displayed in consecutive horizontal lines (by reading pixel information out of the same addresses).

In addition to the horizontal zoom factor, MOD4/8 (the number of bits per pixel attribute) is latched by IC8. As is the flashing bit (FL), the ACRTC can be programmed to make this bit change polarity at a given rate. The effect on the SG84 hardware is to cause the shift registers to invert their data.

Output circuitry

On the output side of the SG84 board are three options. Firstly, IC25 buffers out the TTL RGB and I signals and creates a composite sync signal. These signals are suitable for a basic digital colour monitor.

If you do not have a colour monitor, and many target systems will not, a monochrome option is available. TR6 takes in RGB and a composite sync signal and acts as a transistor mixer producing a grey scale suitable for a monochrome monitor.

The third option is most useful with the 8-bit per pixel mode, that is the *palette* chip IC24 (Inmos G170). A palette chip is a way of producing more than the apparent 256 colours available from the 8 bits per pixel. It works as follows: 8 bits of information (P0–7) come into the palette and this selects one memory location out of 256 inside the palette. Each location has stored in it an 18-bit number. This number is split into three 6-bit numbers, one for each colour red, green and blue. For each colour the 6-bit number drives a D/A, which produces a voltage in the range 0.3–1.0 V for driving an analog monitor. Thus each *logical* pixel colour (out of 256) can select one *physical* colour out of 256K (18 bits) possible colours. The actual colours produced depend on how the palette is programmed; only 256 colours are available at any one time, but by re-programming alternative colour sets can be made available.

More complicated effects can be obtained by using the following facilities. Firstly, under software control the palette can be made to ignore certain incoming pixel bits by an internal AND gate. This means that if colours are chosen with, say, the top bit set, then by switching on and off the top bit inside the palette the whole or selected parts of the colour spectrum can be made to change.

The use of the flashing bit can now be understood. Remember that the flashing bit causes the video shift registers to invert their data, so if the 8-bit pixel data is $4F then when the flashing bit is set this becomes $B0. In order to get a colour to flash you first program the palette up to $7F with your required colours and then duplicate the colour set into the inverted logical colours. Thus if you make $4F correspond to orange then you write the same 18-bit value for orange into $B0. This means that when you set the flashing bit going orange will stay as orange, and the screen won't change. The trick is this: if you now change the value in just $B0 to be green then the flashing bit will cause green to flash into orange and all the other colours will simply 'flash' into themselves. This is all under the control of the ACRTC once you've set it flashing it will continue to do so with no further intervention from the user.

Since the palette is an analog chip it requires a clean power supply – DRAMs are very noisy. To reduce noise along the supply line an inductor, L1, is used. TR4 and TR5 are used to provide a constant current source for the D/As.

Phase-locked loops

A phase-locked loop (PLL) is a very useful building block whose basic concept is illustrated in Figure 7.7. As can be seen, an input waveform of frequency $f_{in}(t)$ is fed into a *phase-sensitive detector* (PSD) and its phase is compared to that of the output frequency divided down by a factor N, or $f_{out}(t)/N$. Notice the dependence on t in these two functions, for the input and output frequencies can vary with time. The PSD produces a voltage proportional to the phase difference between the two signals. This voltage passes into a low-pass filter (LPF), the output of which goes to the control input of a *voltage-controlled oscillator* or VCO. This produces the output waveform at the frequency f_{out}. The whole circuit acts as a control loop with negative feedback. The difference between this and an op-amp feedback circuit is that the latter feeds back a voltage and uses that to control another voltage, whereas here we measure a phase difference and use that to adjust frequency.

Before discussing in detail the components that make up a phase locked loop it is worth making a few qualitative remarks. Firstly, the loop will be in a stable state when the output waveform divided by N has a constant phase relationship to the input waveform and the two frequencies match. Thus at equilibrium $f_{in} = f_{out}/N$. This immediately reveals one application of a PLL: if we make N a programmable divider then by changing N we can make the output frequency move up or down at will, in other words we have a frequency synthesizer. Secondly, the LPF means that the loop will not notice the odd missing or surplus input pulse, nor will it respond to noise. Hence if you feed a noisy signal into a PLL you can get a clean signal out.

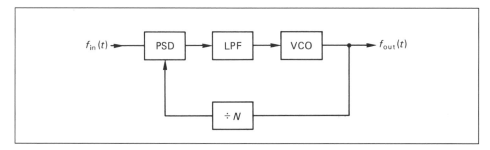

Figure 7.7 *A block diagram of a phase-locked loop*

PLL components

Phase detectors

The phase-sensitive detector is available in two common forms, known as type I and type II. Each produces an output voltage related to the phase difference input, $\Delta\phi$, by $V = K_p.\Delta\phi$. The type I is just an EX-OR gate; it has high immunity to input noise but the disadvantage of requiring a 50/50 duty cycle input to function correctly. It can also lock to a harmonic of the input waveform. Another drawback is that at lock the input and output signals are 90° out of phase.

For these reasons a type II phase detector is often a better choice. A type II detector consists of a state machine which examines the edges of the two incoming signals to decide what state to make its output. The use of edges means that a type II is more sensitive to noise than a type I. However, it has the advantage that it locks with the two signals exactly in phase, and it produces a logic level (HI or LO) when there is a phase error, otherwise the output goes into a high-impedance state. Thus, at lock a type II detector does not drive the LPF and hence the PLL remains precisely in lock.

An example of a PLL chip is the CMOS 4046, which contains both types of phase detector and operates up to a few megahertz. If you need to work at higher frequencies then the MC4044 is available; note that this is not a CMOS device despite the similarity of its number.

The low-pass filter

For the LPF two arrangements are commonly used, see Figure 7.8. The first, known as a lead-lag filter, can be used where the VCO input has a very high input impedance (for example, the VCO section of the 4046). The second is an op-amp filter ($C1 \approx 0.1C$ is there to make the gain fall off rapidly at high frequencies to smooth the digital pulses that come out of the phase detector). Note the minus sign in the op-amp's transfer function. This means that the input terminals to the PSD should be switched to give an overall positive loop gain. Their responses are (ignoring C') as follows.

Response of lead-lag filter:

$$L(\omega) = \frac{1 + sT_2}{1 + s(T_1 + T_2)}$$

Response of op-amp filter:

$$L(\omega) = -\frac{1 + sT_2}{sT_1}$$

where $T_1 = R_1C$, $T_2 = R_2C$ and $s = j\omega$.

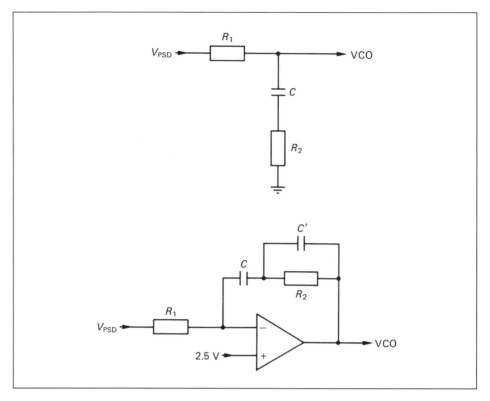

Figure 7.8 *Low-pass filters used in a PLL: top, lead-lag; bottom, using an op-amp*

Voltage-controlled oscillators

The third stage of the loop is the voltage-controlled oscillator. A VCO is a device which converts an input voltage into an output frequency, ideally linearly so that the frequency is proportional to the input voltage, given by $\omega_{\text{out}} = K_{\text{V}}.V_{\text{in}}$. For frequencies less than a few megahertz the VCO section of a 4046 can be used. At higher frequencies the 74S124 is a good choice (note, however, that its frequency–voltage curve becomes non-linear above about 25 MHz, so be sure to plot its characteristic before using above this frequency).

Using phase-locked loops

Phase-locked loops have a reputation of being somewhat difficult to use, the reason for this being probably because they are a mixture of digital and analog techniques. Nevertheless, with an understanding of how they function you should be able to get them to work satisfactorily.

The aim of the loop is to produce an output signal which is locked to the input. The key factor is how quickly the loop can respond to changes in the input signal – the input frequency might vary or the signal might

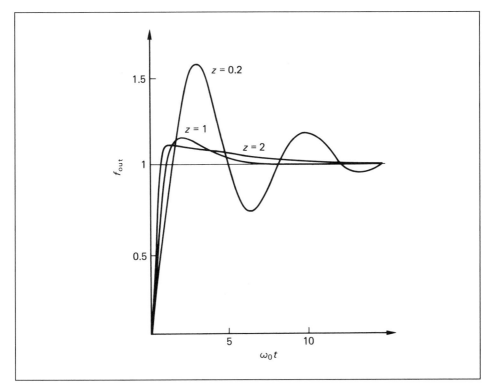

Figure 7.9 *The transient response of a PLL*

disappear entirely for a short period. In both cases we want the PLL to reacquire lock as quickly as possible. The time taken to relock depends on two parameters, ω_0 and z, called the natural loop frequency and damping coefficient respectively. Figure 7.9 shows how quickly the PLL acquires lock for various values of z. If z is much less than one the output frequency oscillates around the target frequency for a long time, and if z is much greater than one the output only responds slowly to changes in the input. For $z = 1$ the loop acquires lock in the minimum time and this is the value a functioning PLL should use. The values of ω_0 and z are given by the following formulae.

For the op-amp filter:

$$\omega_0 = \left(\frac{K_V K_P}{N T_1} \right)^{1/2}$$

$$z = 1/2 \; \omega_0 T_2$$

For the lead-lag filter:

$$\omega_0 = \left(\frac{K_V K_P}{N(T_1 + T_2)} \right)^{1/2}$$

$$z = 1/2 \left(\omega_0 T_2 + \frac{1}{\omega_0(T_1 + T_2)} \right)$$

K_V is measured in rad/s/V and K_P in V/rad ($5/2\pi$ for a 4046 operating off 5 V). Mathematically inclined readers may like to try to derive these formulae (Hint: analyse the loop in the Laplace transform or s-plane).

The loop frequency, ω_0, determines what sort of variations in the input signal the loop tracks. For example, you might store digital data on audio or video tape. To decode the data you derive a clock and feed it into a PLL; if ω_0 is set low enough, say 100 rad/s, the loop will ignore noise and high-frequency tape jitter, so the recovered clock will remain correct. If, however, the tape speed slowly varies the PLL will track the variation, provided ω_0 is greater than the speed of the variation.

Genlock – an example of a phase-locked loop

In video applications it is often desirable to superpose a test pattern or graphics onto a video or television picture. This allows you to output subtitles or timing information onto a screen which is displaying a picture of something else. A circuit which achieves this function is known as a *genlock*. To perform such a task two circuits are required. Firstly, a mixer to combine the two video pictures, and secondly a synchronizer to 'lock' together the two video screens. Since a synchronizer can be designed with a PLL we discuss it here.

We want to arrange that the video signals (the syncs to be precise) coming out of a computer graphics board exactly match those of an external video source, such as a television camera. If we can achieve this then by mixing the two signals we can overlay graphics and text generated by the graphics board onto the output of the video camera. Since we have two sets of frequencies (the horizontal and vertical syncs) from two video sources, we can use a PLL to compare their frequencies and phases and bring them into lock.

We are going to synchronize the SG84 video board's signals to an external video source. The board that does this is called the SG84X, see Figure 7.10. Since we cannot control the external video source its signals must be fed to the input of our phase-locked loop. To achieve lock we proceed as follows. First we compare the two vertical syncs in a PLL. We use a VCO on the SG84X to replace the 25 MHz oscillator on the SG84 (there is a hardware link for this purpose). Since the input frequency to the loop is the vertical sync frequency (50 Hz) this means that the division factor for the loop is $N = 25 \times 10^6/50 = 5 \times 10^5$. The divider is contained within the SG84 itself – the ACRTC is programmed to divide down its clock to produce the SG84's vertical syncs. The PLL compares the SG84's vertical sync frequency with that of the external video source's vertical sync frequency, and then varies the VCO frequency to bring the two into lock. With such a circuit the two video signals synchronize to an accuracy of about one line (around $100/625 = 0.2\%$). In other words, if we mixed the two video signals together the screen would show two superimposed images which would be positioned correctly up and down the screen, but because of the one-line inaccuracy the SG84 picture would be displaced either right or left of centre. In any case, if we leave things as they are then the pictures will continually wobble as the PLL attempts to correct for the residual error.

The next stage is to lock the horizontal sync signals together and so achieve lock to about a pixel. Again we feed the external sync signal into the PLL and compare it with the SG84's horizontal sync, using the difference to control the VCO and hence bring the SG84 signal into lock. The divide ratio in this loop is $25 \times 10^6/15.625 \times 10^3 = 1600$. In order to combine two PLLs into one we use an analog switch to change over the time constants of the low-pass filter in the two locking modes (vertical and horizontal).

Circuit implementation

ICs 7 and 8 on Figure 7.10(a) are the two phase detectors, one for the horizontal and one for the vertical loop. IC11 is the analog switch that selects between the two modes of operation. IC13 is the op-amp in the low-pass filter. Diode D13 is there to prevent the op-amp's output exceeding 5 V when the VCO (IC14 74S124) would be damaged. REG1 keeps the non-inverting input of the op-amp midway between the logic swings of the phase detectors. At equilibrium the voltage control pin of the VCO is set to be 1.8 V (using the variable capacitor VC1) giving a 25 MHz output. This means that at lock D13 is reverse biased with about 0.7 V across it. The resulting reverse leakage current produces an error voltage across R43 and R44 which leads to a phase error at lock. To compensate for this an additional diode D9 is used to produce an equal and opposite leakage current to D13.

Also shown on Figure 7.10(a) are IC15 (LM1881) which takes in the composite video from the external source and produces vertical sync (VSY) and composite sync (CSY) outputs, and IC6 (a non-retriggerable monostable) which strips out the equalization pulses from the composite sync waveform.

Referring to Figure 7.10(b), the section which decides whether to switch over into the horizontal locking mode is the comparator IC5a. If the phase pulse signal, PPV, is larger than a certain amount then the comparator output goes HI and the PAL IC3 asserts /VLOCK to say it is in the vertical locking mode. If it is locked to within a line then /VLOCK is not asserted and the yellow LED is lit.

Video mixer circuit

Figure 7.10(c) shows the video mixer circuit. It is a good example of the ideas of Chapters 2 and 3. TR3 and TR4 are used as emitter followers and VR4 strips off the sync pulses from the incoming video stream. TR3 buffers out the signal, unless D6 is pulled low by IC2b, in which case the transistor is switched off so none of the video data gets through – this is used in superposing one video signal on top of the other. TR2 mixes the RGB signals from the SG84 into monochrome. The final mixing of the

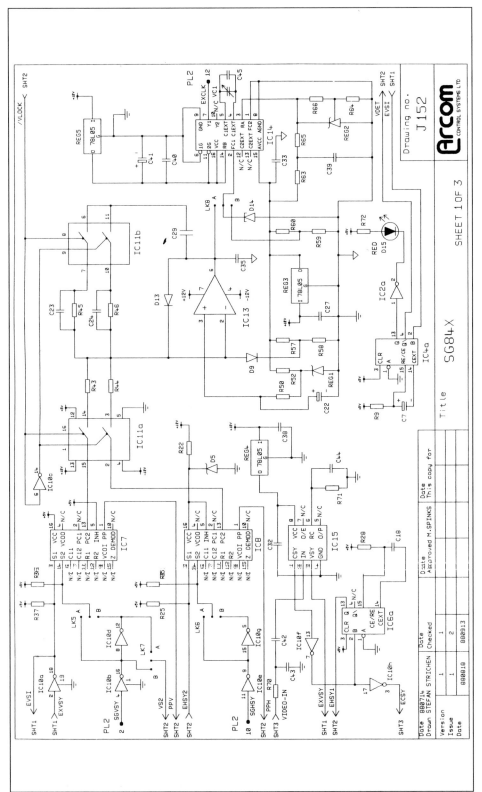

Figure 7.10(a) *The SG84X genlock circuit*

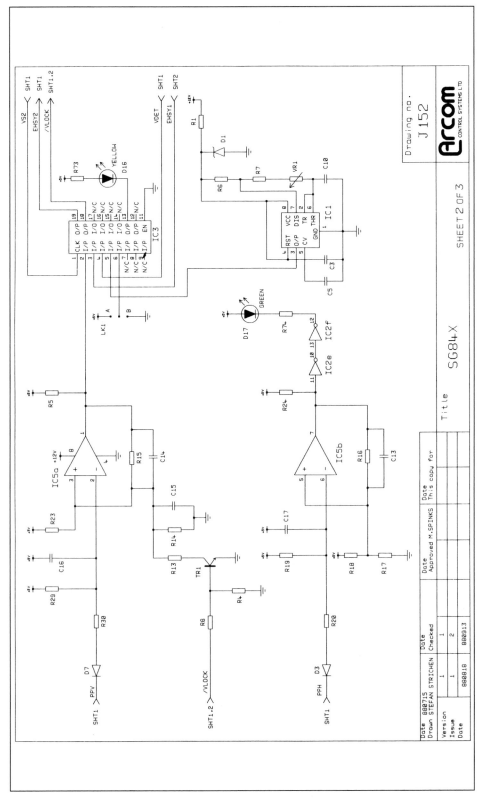

Figure 7.10(b) *SG84X sheet 2*

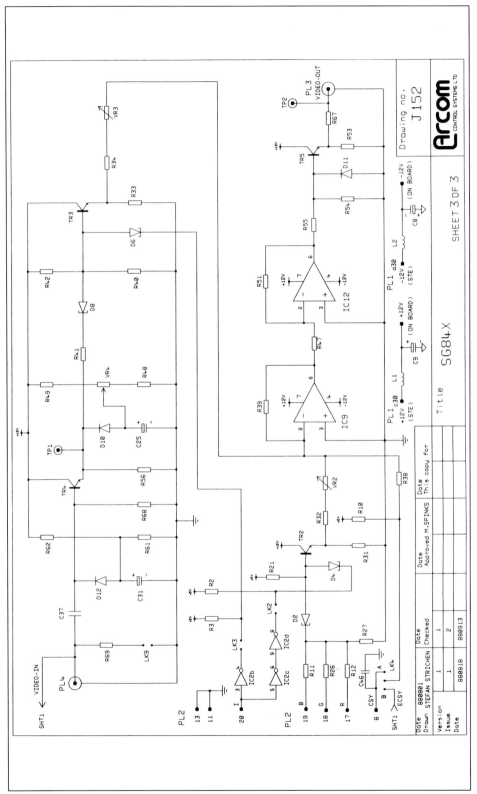

Figure 7.10(c) *SG84X sheet 3*

two video signals is done by the op-amp IC9 which adds together the composite sync and the two signals from the video sources. Finally TR5 buffers the video signal out.

8 Practical techniques

This chapter looks at some of the practical methods used in taking an idea and converting it into a finished microprocessor board. All engineers have their own ways of working, so some of the contents of this chapter are rather more subjective than those of the rest of this book. Nevertheless, it is hoped that readers (especially the less experienced) will find food for thought here to supplement their individual methods.

Designing

The art of designing microprocessor boards is best acquired by experience and learning from one's previous mistakes. However, by adopting a structured approach designs can be produced more quickly and with greater probability of success. For a small board, like the 6809 one in Chapter 5, such an approach is unnecessary – all you really need to do is understand the chips and connect them together; but for something like a VMEbus CPU board with around 80 ICs and 20 PALs some planning is essential.

The first stage in any design is to produce a board specification which should be short and indicate the minimum requirements, so giving the engineer room for manoeuvre when producing the design. The engineer then has to assimilate the various data sheets and commence the design itself. The method we recommend is similar to a software programmer's 'top-down' approach. First, produce an overall block diagram of the board. This should split up the design into manageable sections, showing the signals entering and leaving each part. In terms of the software approach the overall diagram corresponds to the main program and each section to a subroutine, the idea being that the subroutines can be individually written and debugged. The main difference with a hardware design is that you may find timing constraints mean that some global signals have to be modified, which necessitates redesigning sections which use those signals. Having produced an overall block diagram it may be necessary to rethink the specification; if not, the individual sections can be designed in detail – selecting parts, creating PAL equations and analysing timing diagrams.

As an example of this methodology we shall examine how to design a 68000 board; this will also give the reader an insight into a more powerful CPU than the 6809.

As our specification we'll take the following:

1 68000 CPU
2 6840 and 6850 peripherals
3 64K EPROM, 512K DRAM
4 8-bit expansion bus interface
5 64K SRAM dual-ported to bus
6 16 bits parallel I/O.

We have chosen an 8-bit expansion bus (possibly STE) so as to illustrate how to interface a 16-bit processor to an 8-bit bus.

The first stage in the design is to understand the 68000's control lines so that we can draw up an overall conceptual diagram. Its signals are as follows.

A1–23, D0–15	address and data buses
FC0–2	function code lines
CLK	clock input (we'll use 10 MHz version)
/AS	address strobe, indicates A1–23 valid
/LDS, /UDS	data strobes: /LDS LO if D0–7 valid
	/UDS LO if D8–15 valid
R/W	read/write signal
/DTACK	signal to terminate bus cycle
/BERR, /HALT	terminate bus cycle in unusual cases
/IPL0–2	encode interrupt pending level
/BR, /BG, /BGACK	signals to request 68000's buses
E, /VPA, /VMA	signals to interface to 68xx peripherals

A 68000 cycle consists of many clock periods, so /AS, /LDS and /UDS are used to indicate when A1–23 and D0–15 are valid. A cycle only terminates when one or more of /DTACK, /BERR or /HALT are asserted. /BR BG and /BGACK are the bus grant and request signals, which are used by the dual-port RAM interface. E, /VPA and /VMA let the 68000 interface to 68xx peripherals. When the peripheral is accessed /VPA is asserted and the 68000 then waits for E to become synchronized before asserting /VMA to access the peripheral. FC0–2 indicate the type of access the 68000 is making – interrupt acknowledge, supervisor or user. When the processor is in the user state certain instructions are illegal and FC0–2 can be decoded to stop access to supervisor areas of memory; thus user programs can be prevented from interfering with the operating system. We can now draw an overall block diagram of the board, see Figure 8.1. To do this note that we only need to know what the signals do rather than exactly how they work.

We group the EPROM, SRAM and parallel I/O logic in one block since they require similar signals. The expansion bus interface shows how to connect a 16-bit CPU to an 8-bit one, if the 68000 performs a byte transfer (just one of /LDS or /UDS asserted) then we have an 8-bit cycle with the appropriate byte multiplexed onto the bus. With a 16-bit (word) trans-

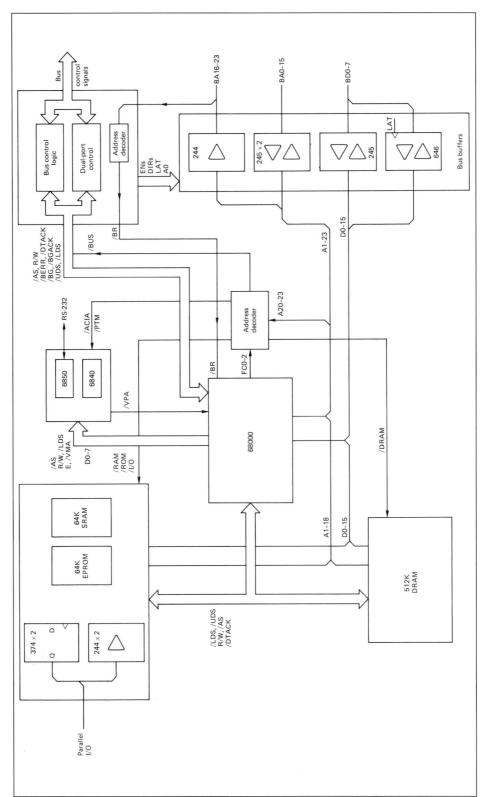

Figure 8.1 *A block diagram of a 68000 board*

fer we perform two 8-bit bus cycles but only give one /DTACK to the 68000. We therefore use a 646 transceiver latch (a 24 pin IC which acts like either a 245 or 374 under control of a logic input) to hold the data byte read in the first cycle. The dual-port RAM interface works like this: when the address comparator finds a match it asserts /BR to request the 68000's buses; if the 68000 is trying to make an expansion bus access (/BUS LO) then there is a deadlock condition and the dual-port logic asserts /BERR and /HALT causing the 68000 to terminate its cycle and rerun it when it regains control of its bus. The exception to this is if the 68000 drives the expansion bus with the address of its own dual-port RAM, which is not permitted (the 68000 will keep terminating and rerunning in an infinite loop), so we do not assert /BR but just let the cycle timeout causing a /BERR. Once the 68000 has tri-stated its buses it asserts /BG and the dual-port interface can then transfer data.

We now have a good idea of how the sections of the board interrelate and how each will work, and we have achieved it without getting bogged down in complicated timing diagrams. We can now produce detailed designs of each section, possibly prototyping them as we go along. As with the overall design, a systematic step-by-step approach is best. To illustrate this we shall look at one section, the DRAM interface, since this will be of interest to readers designing a variety of computer boards.

The DRAM interface

The first stage in any interface is to draw timing diagrams for the two devices, here a 256K $\times$ 4 DRAM and the 68000, but only to include important parameters. This makes the diagrams easier to understand; for example, the 68000 read cycle timing diagram has in the data sheet over 30 parameters, only a few of which are critical for a DRAM interface, the rest being easily satisfied. Figures 8.2 and 8.3 show the appropriate timing diagrams. As we have a high-frequency clock it is logical to use this to produce /RAS and /CAS and so design a synchronous system. It is important to choose the clock edge that optimizes setup and hold times. Here we do not have a choice: since /AS can go LO up to 55 ns after the rising edge of S2, it therefore is not guaranteed to be valid on the clock's falling edge, so it must be sampled on the rising edge. /AS indicates that A1–23 are valid, so we use this plus a /DRAM signal from the address decoder to determine when to start a DRAM cycle. We then draw a new timing diagram showing how /RAS and /CAS are derived from the 10 MHz clock edges, see Figure 8.4. Data is not valid early enough before the falling edge of S6 so we assert /DTACK on the rising edge of S6, and thus the 68000 samples D0–15 on the falling edge of S8. Notice that we hold /CAS one cycle after negating /RAS, which ensures that a second DRAM cycle does not start on the rising edge of S9 (/AS could still be LO at this point), and also keeps D0–15 valid on a read cycle till after /AS has gone HI to satisfy the 68000's timing diagram.

Once we have a timing diagram we can write down the corresponding PAL equations; these will need to be modified, but as with a complicated

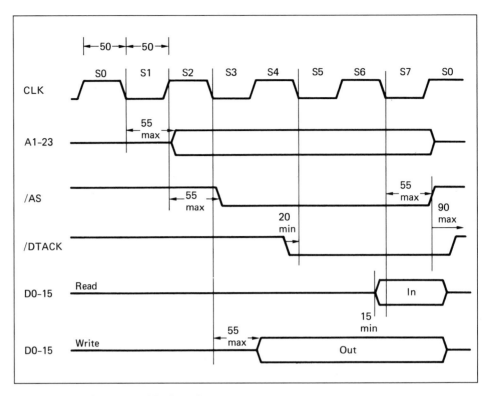

Figure 8.2 *A 68000 CPU cycle*

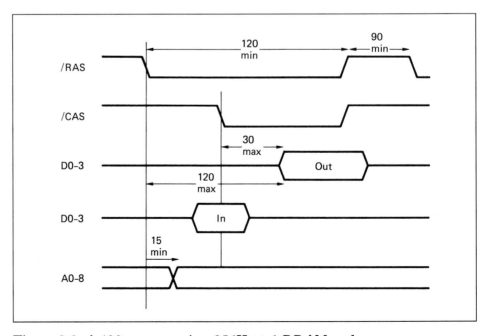

Figure 8.3 *A 120 ns access time 256K × 4 DRAM cycle*

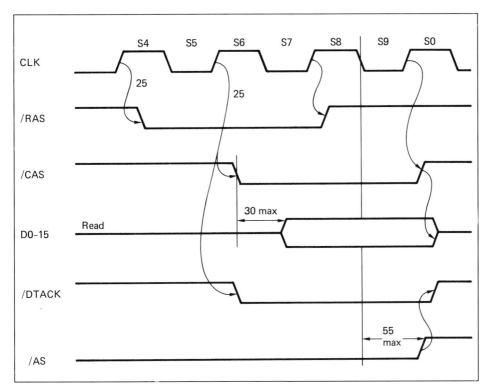

Figure 8.4 *A composite timing diagram showing /RAS and /CAS derived from the 68000's 10 MHz clock*

board a complex PAL should also be designed in stages. As with all registered designs we encode the state of the signals before the clock edge that precedes the states with the PAL's output LO. This gives:

/RAS.D   = /DRAM & /AS & RAS & CAS
                 + /RAS & CAS;
/CAS.D   = /RAS;
/DTACK.D   = /RAS;
DTACK.OE = /AS & /DRAM;

Notice that we qualify /DRAM with /AS in this PAL rather than in the address decoder. This avoids a decoder propagation delay (up to 25 ns for an 'A' series PAL) added to the 55 ns uncertainty already present in AS.

The next stage is to implement the DRAM's refresh cycles. Since the 68000 does not generate refresh addresses we shall use the /CAS before /RAS refresh mode. The 256K × 4 DRAM requires 512 refreshes every 8 ms (a rate of 64 kHz, which is 10 MHz/156). We therefore divide the 10 MHz clock by 128, and use the counter output to clock a D flip-flop which drives the refresh request input of our PAL. We use a synchronous 163 counter rather than a ripple type to ensure the PAL's setup time is satisfied. Figure 8.5 shows a refresh cycle, where /RCYC is generated by the PAL to indicate the type of cycle in progress. When /CAS and /RAS are both HI the PAL is in an 'idle' state and can choose whether to do a

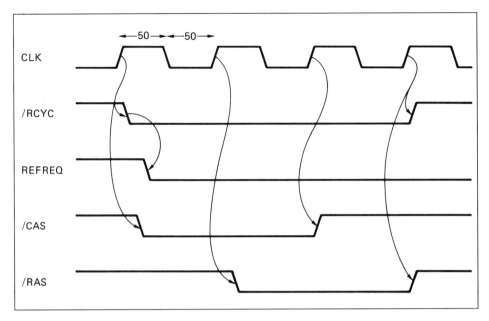

Figure 8.5 *A DRAM refresh cycle*

normal cycle or a refresh, if either is requested. We give refreshes priority
so the PAL equations relating to refreshes become:

```
/RCYC.D  = RFREQ & CAS & RAS
         + /RCYC & /CAS;
/CAS.D   = RFREQ & CAS & RAS
         + /RCYC & /CAS & RAS;
/RAS.D   = /RCYC & /CAS;
```

We now combine these equations with the originals, using RFREQ and
RCYC to select between the two modes of operation:

```
/RAS.D      = /AS & /DRAM & RAS & CAS & /RFREQ
            + /RAS & CAS & RCYC
            + /RCYC & /CAS;
/CAS.D      = /RAS & RCYC
            + RFREQ & CAS & RAS
            + /RCYC & /CAS & RAS;
/RCYC.D     = RFREQ & CAS & RAS
            + /RCYC & /CAS;
/DTACK.D    = /RAS & RCYC;
DTACK.OE    = /AS & /DRAM;
```

If we were using an 8-bit microprocessor the design would now be
complete, but the 68000 has a 16-bit data bus and uses /LDS and /UDs
to indicate whether it is accessing an odd or even byte of memory respectively. This means that when the 68000 writes a byte to, say, location $105
we only want to access the 'odd' DRAM and not the 'even' one too. Using
256K × 4 DRAMs, there are two ways round this problem: firstly generate two sets of /OE and /WE signals (see the SG84 circuit in Chapter 7),

or secondly use /CAS as an enable signal. Since many DRAMs (for example, 1 M × 1) do not have /OE pins we shall use the second method. We therefore want to produce two /CAS strobes, /CAS0 and /CAS1, to enable the two DRAMs; if a DRAM receives a /RAS but no /CAS then it will perform a /RAS-only refresh cycle instead of a read or write. Thus /CAS0 should only be asserted if /LDS is LO, and similarly for CAS1. The equations become:

$$
\begin{aligned}
\text{/RAS.D} \quad &= \text{/AS \& /DRAM \& RAS \& CAS0 \& CAS1 \& /RFREQ} \\
&+ \text{/RAS \& DTACK \& RCYC} \\
&+ \text{/RCYC \& /CAS0 \& /CAS1;} \\
\text{/CAS0.D} \quad &= \text{/RAS \& RCYC \& /LDS} \\
&+ \text{RFREQ \& CAS0 \& CAS1 \& RAS} \\
&+ \text{/RCYC \& /CAS0 \& /CAS1 \& RAS;} \\
\text{/CAS1.D} \quad &= \text{/RAS \& RCYC \& /UDS} \\
&+ \text{RFREQ \& CAS0 \& CAS1 \& RAS} \\
&+ \text{/RCYC \& /CAS0 \& /CAS1 \& RAS;} \\
\text{/RCYC.D} \quad &= \text{RFREQ \& CAS0 \& CAS1 \& RAS} \\
&+ \text{/RCYC \& /CAS0 \& /CAS1;} \\
\text{/DTACK.D} \quad &= \text{/RAS \& RCYC;} \\
\text{DTACK.OE} \quad &= \text{/AS \& /DRAM;}
\end{aligned}
$$

The only equation we have had to change significantly is to use DTACK rather than CAS in the second RAS.D term; we cannot use CAS0 or 1

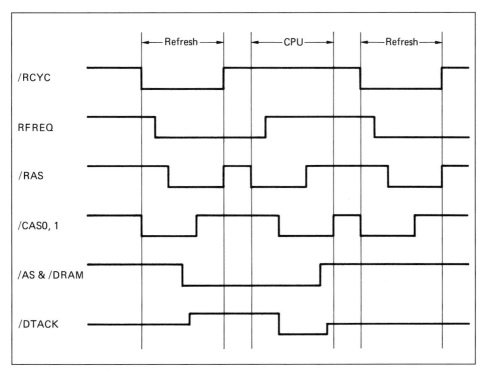

Figure 8.6 *A timing diagram for DRAM accesses, showing 'back-to-back' CPU and refresh cycles*

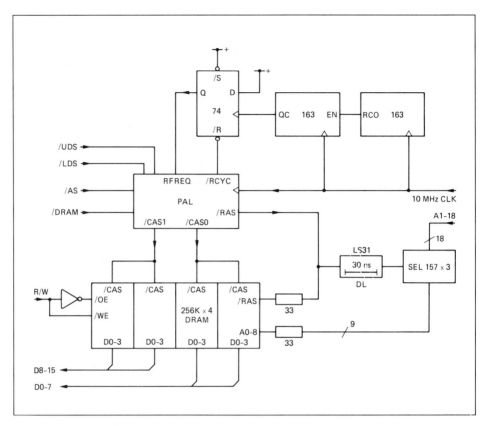

Figure 8.7 *The DRAM interface circuit diagram*

because either could stay HI throughout the cycle. Finally, we draw a timing diagram to check that nothing unusual happens if a refresh request occurs in the middle of a normal DRAM cycle and vice versa, see Figure 8.6. We can now produce a finished circuit diagram of this section of the project, see Figure 8.7. DL is a delay line which delays /RAS so that the multiplexers do not switch before the address hold time after /RAS is satisfied. An alternative here would be to clock /RAS into a D flip-flop on the clock's falling edge and use the flip-flop's output to switch the multiplexers.

You can see that although the final PAL equations are quite complex, each step has not been particularly difficult. This is the secret of a good designer – first break the whole project into separate chunks with the minimum of interaction between the sections, and then design each section in small easy stages.

Prototyping

Once you have a 'paper' design you have two choices, either to go straight to the PCB (printed circuit board) layout stage or else to construct a working prototype. For a straightforward design, especially if similar to a previous one, we would probably not waste time making a prototype, but for more complex circuits we prefer to build one.

A prototype lets you look for both timing faults and more serious logic errors, like misunderstanding the way an IC works in some of its modes. The errors that are essential to detect are those that would result in more chips being added to the board. Once you have a PCB such an error can mean a substantial re-lay costing a lot of time and effort. It is also easier to correct wiring and small logic faults on a prototype – you just disconnect and reconnect the wires – whereas with a PCB you have to cut tracks, which can be difficult on multi-layer boards.

Solderless breadboard

We shall now discuss some prototyping techniques, see Figure 8.8, going from (in our opinion) least to most useful. The first technique is that of

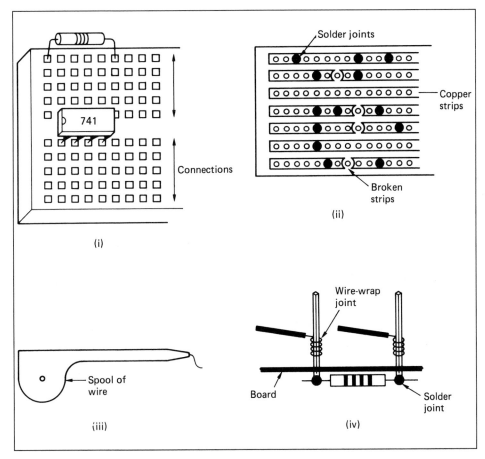

Figure 8.8 *Some prototyping methods: (i) solderless breadboard; (ii) stripboard; (iii) a wiring pen; (iv) wire-wrap – for analog components like the resistor shown the component must be soldered to wire-wrap pillars*

solderless breadboard. Here, the legs of components push into a matrix of holes which are electrically connected in the vertical direction. No soldering is required, but this means the prototype lacks rigidity, and certainly could not be used as a final product. This method is best used for quick tests of small parts of circuits, especially where you want to experiment using many different component values. Its other main use is in teaching electronics.

Solder prototypes

The next prototyping method is to make the connections with solder. For small analog circuits a stripboard (a board with a grid of 0.1 inch spaced holes) with copper strips on one side is an option. The strips make connections in the horizontal direction and wire is used to make the vertical connections on the other (component) side of the board. To stop the strips connecting unwanted parts of the circuit they are broken with either a drill or special cutter. This approach is good for analog circuits but is hard to alter, and the component layout must be carefully thought out before building the circuit. It is not particularly suitable for digital prototypes – there are too many connections and ICs cannot 'jump' over strips by changing their lead spacing like resistors and capacitors can. The resultant prototype is mechanically sturdy and so can be used as a finished one-off product, especially for small designs.

For soldering a digital prototype we recommend using a 'prototyping pen', which is a wire dispenser in the shape of a pen. The wire is very thin (30 swg) and can be wound round the pins of an IC socket. Once you have made all the connections a soldering iron is used to melt the wire's insulating plastic coating and so make electrical contact to the IC pins. The insulation means the wire can go anywhere across the board without shorting lines out, so you do not have to think out the layout before you start. Provided you avoid solder shorts between adjacent IC pins this prototyping method is quite good, and at high frequencies will give better performance than a wire-wrap board (see below). The thinness of the wire does, however, mean that the prototype is rather fragile, so you probably would not use it as a finished product, especially in a harsh environment.

Wire-wrap

The other method of prototyping a digital circuit is with *wire-wrap* which is our favourite. A wire-wrap IC socket has long legs with a square cross-section, and a wire-wrap 'gun' is used to wrap a wire tightly around the leg, forming cold welds and making a very good electrical connection. The other end of the wire is then joined to another point in the circuit. Wire-wrap wires are available pre-stripped in various lengths; it is less efficient to use a reel of wire, strip the insulator off and cut it to the right length as you go along. The advantages of wire-wrap are that it is quick, there are no dry solder joints or shorts, mistakes can be corrected by removing the wire with an unwrapping tool, and the prototype is sufficiently robust. It can easily be used as the final board if the project is a one-off. Its only disadvantage is that it is more prone to noise than a soldered board, because each wrap acts like a small inductor so reflections can occur on logic signals. This is only really a problem at quite high frequencies, for example we have successfully wire-wrapped a 25 MHz processor board. The best way to minimize noise problems is to have good ground and power lines, and use thicker tinned copper wire instead of wire-wrap wire for these connections.

Whichever prototyping method you use you have to decide whether to build the whole circuit or just part of it at a time. We recommend the latter; if you prototype just the bare minimum to get the board working then you do not have to worry about wiring faults in another part of the board preventing it from working. Secondly, as you add circuitry and the board ceases to function then you know it is the additional components that have caused the problem, and you can remove them one by one till the board starts to work again thus speeding up debugging.

Debugging

Once you have a prototype (or a PCB if you have omitted the prototyping stage) it is necessary to test and debug it. There are three basic types of error to be located and cured. Firstly, wiring or tracking faults; these are usually easy to find and simple to fix. Secondly, timing errors; these can range from mistakes which prevent a circuit from functioning at all to occasional metastability problems that cause the board to 'crash' at, say, 10 minute intervals or longer. Ironically, the worse the timing error the easier it is to find and correct. Most timing faults can be fixed by changing the logic inside a PAL or by clocking flip-flops and registered PALs on the other clock edge – only rarely is it necessary to redesign many chip interconnections. Thirdly, you may have misunderstood how a device works; this problem is usually easy to find, but often means redesigning part of the circuit, which if it is at the PCB stage can cost a lot of time and money.

How then should one debug a circuit to arrive at a working prototype? We shall look at a typical CPU board and some of the test equipment available to debug it.

Test equipment

We have a prototype with a CPU, UART, memory and some miscellaneous logic. We switch the power on, and unless we are very lucky no characters will be output to the terminal. To find out why the board has done 'nothing' we employ various pieces of test equipment, such as logic probes, logic pulsers, pulse generators, oscilloscopes and logic analysers.

225

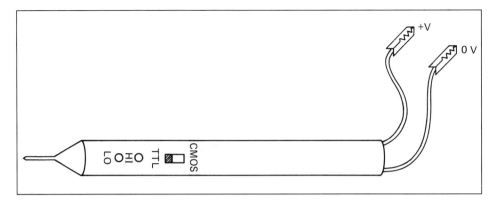

Figure 8.9 *A logic probe*

Logic probes and pulsers

A logic probe is a simple but essential piece of test equipment for debugging digital circuits. It comes in various forms but each gives a visual indication of the logic state of a point in a circuit. At one end of the probe is a metal tip which you touch to the point of the circuit under test, and at the other end two wires joined to clips which connect to the supply rails of the circuit, see Figure 8.9. The state of the logic line is indicated by up to three LEDs. We prefer the two-LED variety – if the green LED is lit the signal is LO, if the red it is HI, if neither the line is tri-state or open circuit, and if both the line is pulsing between the two states. If the line is in one state but there is a pulse in the opposite direction then the probe will lengthen the pulse and the other LED will flash. Sometimes a third (yellow) LED is present which lights if the line is pulsing, or can be used in a 'memory' mode where it remembers a short pulse and stays lit till a switch resets it. We have even seen one with a single LED – on equals HI, off equals LO and blinking means tri-state or open circuit.

Logic probes are designed for CMOS or TTL circuits (often they have a switch and so can be used for either). Make sure yours has over-voltage and reverse-voltage protection on both its tip and power connectors – sooner or later you are bound to connect up its power connectors backwards or touch the tip onto an RS-232 ±12 V signal! Check how short a pulse it can detect and stretch; if you are using TTL you need to be able to detect pulses of around 25 ns, ideally 10 ns. Finally, select a probe that is physically robust, because with some probes the tip can come loose if they are dropped.

A logic pulser looks very similar to a logic probe. However, whereas the aim of a probe is to indicate the state of a circuit without interfering with it, a pulser is designed to inject a short pulse into it. A typical pulser drives the line HI then LO for a short duration (around 10 μs), and can sink or source around 100 mA, thus overcoming the output drive of the gate attached to the line. The short duration of the pulse minimizes the chance of damage to the gate. Usually, the pulse rate can be either about 0.5 Hz or 500 Hz, selected by a switch. The former lets you apply one pulse at a time and use a logic probe to trace its effect through a clocked circuit. The latter can be used with an oscilloscope to observe how a circuit responds to a series of pulses.

The pulse generator

A pulse generator either produces square waves at a given frequency and duty cycle or single 'one-shot' pulses at the press of a button. This piece of equipment is not essential for debugging boards but can be helpful. It is most useful for supplying asynchronous signals, like bus requests and interrupts. By changing the rate and duty cycle of the pulses you can rapidly observe whether there are any hidden metastability problems or other timing faults which would only occasionally show up if such signals were generated by another processor producing them more slowly under software control.

Make sure that the generator has a TTL-compatible output; if not you must ensure its peak-to-peak voltage is correct and that the pulses use 0 V as their baseline rather than being centred on it – check with an oscilloscope before connecting the generator to your circuit. If you expect to do analog as well as digital work then get a generator with both square and sine wave outputs. Also, one with an automatic frequency sweep can be useful, especially for phase locked loop work.

Since commercial pulse generators are moderately expensive you may consider building a simple one out of discrete components, Figure 8.10 shows such a circuit. VRl sets the pulse width and VR2 their repetition rate, and the flip-flop by switch SWl is a 'debouncer' – when you make the switch it connects many times over a period of about a millisecond – and ensures that the monostable receives only one edge.

The oscilloscope

An oscilloscope is essential for analog work, but is less suited for microprocessor work – indeed if you possess a logic analyser you will rarely use an oscilloscope. Nevertheless, since oscilloscopes are more widely available and cheaper than logic analysers we shall look at some ways of using them to debug a microprocessor circuit.

Figure 8.11 illustrates the controls of a typical dual-beam oscilloscope. The oscilloscope displays the voltage of the two input signals in the Y-direction and time in the X-direction. The timebase control determines the speed at which the beams cross the screen, in other words how long each division (normally a centimetre) represents, for example 1 μs/div. The timebase usually has a ×10 mode which lets you magnify the display in the X-direction, at the expense of it being fainter.

The trigger control selects which voltage source to trigger on. When the oscilloscope detects the trigger input reach its threshold, it starts the beams off on their next pass across the screen. This explains why oscilloscopes are not entirely suited for debugging microprocessor circuits – they are

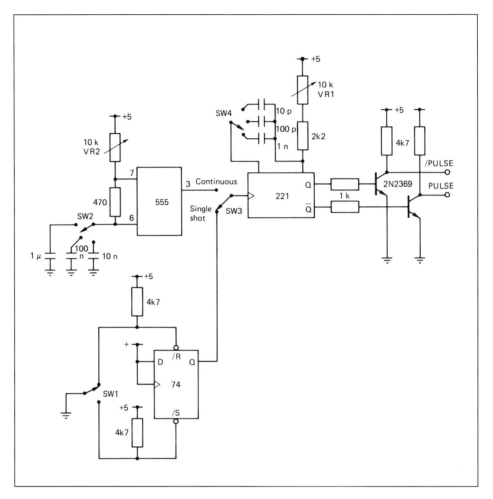

Figure 8.10 *A pulse generator circuit*

designed to be used for repetitive signals. Each time a trigger occurs the beams cross the screen at the timebase rate, so for the eye to see a clear picture the traces must superpose on where they were the previous pass. Unfortunately, a microprocessor circuit is not repetitive; data on the data bus does not repeat (consecutive op-codes are rarely the same) and read and write cycles do not occur at a constant rate (different instructions need different numbers of CPU cycles).

The a.c. and d.c. switches determine how the oscilloscope is connected to the input signals. With d.c. coupling the signal is fed directly into the oscilloscope (often attenuated by a factor of 10 by a ×10 probe); hence the display can be used to measure absolute voltages with respect to a 0 V level. With a.c. coupling a capacitor is put in series with the oscilloscope probes so the signal is centred on 0 V. This mode lets you observe a small signal riding on a large d.c. voltage; for example, to measure the noise on a 5 V digital power line switch to a.c. and a vertical amplitude of about 20 mV/div.

228

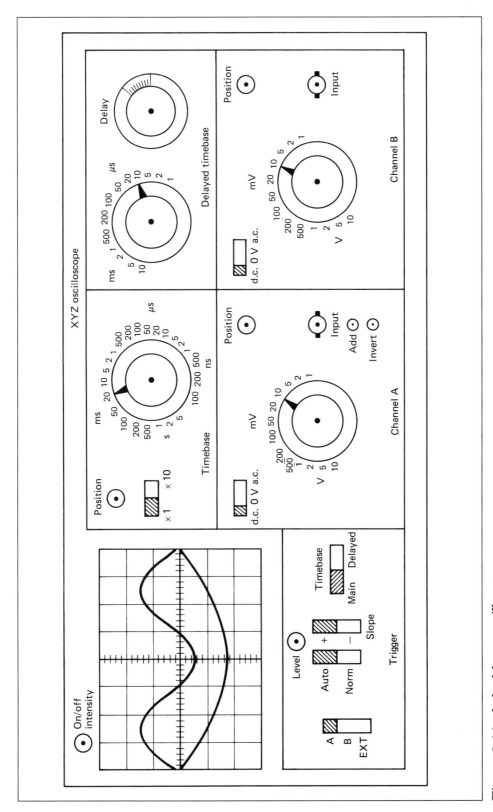

Figure 8.11 *A dual-beam oscilloscope*

An oscilloscope with a delayed timebase is useful for video work. Such a timebase lets you trigger the oscilloscope on one waveform (say the 50 Hz vertical sync) and zoom in on just a small part of the display, for example to examine just one line (64 µs); if you triggered on the horizontal line sync using the normal timebase you would superimpose all the lines and would be unable to examine them individually.

Two features useful for digital work are 'Add' and 'Invert'. The Add switch adds the two input signals together, which lets you see if two signals are active simultaneously. For example, if you have a /READ and a /WRITE strobe then they should not be asserted simultaneously. Although these strobes are not repetitive so you cannot display them clearly, by adding them you can see if they are asserted together – the display will consist of three instead of just two levels. Likewise Invert, which changes the polarity of the input, can be used with Add to detect whether an active-HI signal is asserted at the same time as an active-LO signal.

The logic analyser

The logic analyser is a tool for displaying changing logic levels. Figure 8.12 illustrates a typical analyser. Coming out of the analyser are a set of wires with clips which can be connected to individual parts of the circuit under test, either directly or, if you remove the clips, the wires push onto a wire-wrap leg or an IC test clip. The analyser samples the points under test at a selectable rate (up to 100 MHz for a fast analyser) and determines whether they are HI or LO. When the analyser detects a trigger condition, for example a certain line going LO, it displays the states of the lines both before and after the trigger – typically 256 sample periods might be displayed. You can then examine the waveforms to see if they are behaving as expected. The most important differences between an analyser and an oscilloscope are that an analyser takes a snapshot of the waveforms whereas an oscilloscope needs a repetitive signal; an analyser samples lots of signals at once (typically 30 or 40) whereas an oscilloscope is limited to just a few; and an analyser is a purely digital device – you cannot use it to examine the output of a D/A.

To use an analyser there are a number of operating parameters to set up. Firstly, the logic threshold: usually you select the standard TTL setting, though if you think noise might be a problem in your circuit you can change this so that the analyser detects signals which are only just out of specification. Secondly, you choose which lines to display and whether their values are to be shown in binary, hex or ASCII. You can examine every line but the display only has space for around 10, so you have to 'page' through your selections. Thirdly, the mode of sampling must be selected. This can be either asynchronous – sampling is continuous at a chosen rate – or synchronous – the analyser samples on a rising or falling edge of one of its designated clock lines. Asynchronous is used to look for general timing faults, and synchronous for examining signals which are supposed to be valid on a clock edge. Thus if you connect lines to the address and data pins of an EPROM and clock the analyser synchronously

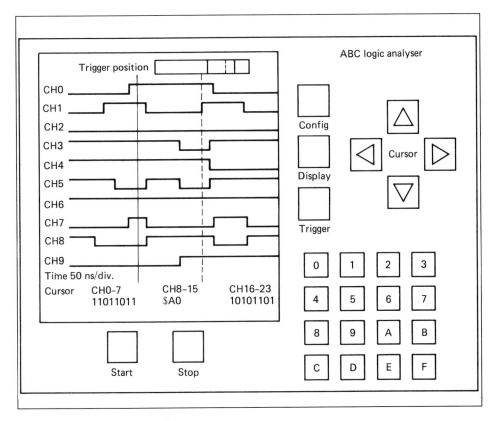

Figure 8.12 *A logic analyser*

on the rising edge of /OE it will display a list of address and data values which can be compared with a program listing. Finally, you have to set the trigger condition. This can be a simple 'one-level' condition like 'TRIGGER IF XX001XX0' – the analyser triggers if the eight lines (you might have more) reach this state, where X means don't care. Usually you can build more complicated trigger conditions using statements like JUMP IF, JUMP IF NOT, RESET IF, DELAY and WAIT FOR. For example, if you suspect that a strobe is occasionally being asserted for up to 150 ns instead of 100 ns, a possible trigger condition would be:

WAIT FOR	XXXXXXX0
DELAY	12
TRIGGER IF	XXXXXXX0
ELSE RESET	

The analyser waits for the strobe line (Bit 0) to go LO (0), counts 12 clock periods (120 ns, for 10 ns sampling), then triggers if the line is still LO or else goes back to the start of the trigger sequence. This simple example illustrates the power of a logic analyser. The fault might only occur once every few seconds (perhaps once in a million strobes if it was a DRAM /CAS signal) yet the analyser can trap that one event, together with the state of other signals before it happens, which should allow you to work out why it happened – with an oscilloscope you would not have a chance.

Analysers differ in their complexity, but the functions described above are probably the minimum for a useful machine. An add-on that can be helpful is a *disassembler* package. This monitors the microprocessor's buses and translates the data bytes into assembler mnemonics. You can thus see very quickly what the processor is doing without needing to refer to an up-to-date program listing. With a powerful CPU make sure its *cache* is disabled when using a disassembler – a cache is memory internal to the CPU which stores the last few instructions executed; then if the program loops the CPU can retrieve instructions from the high-speed cache rather than slower external memory, and thus with the cache enabled repeated instructions will not appear on the buses and will not be disassembled. For hardware development a disassembler is not essential – you are usually only running small pieces of code repetitively to exercise the various devices and interfaces – but for large software projects one can be very helpful.

Debugging a CPU board

The most important stage to reach with any new microprocessor board is to get it to talk to a terminal and run a program called a *monitor*. A monitor lets you read and write (*peek* and *poke*) bytes to specified memory locations. Once you have this capability you can use the processor itself as a debugging aid for the rest of the board. There is a small 'bootstrap' problem here – if you haven't got a working board (it might even use a new processor with a new instruction set) how do you produce the code for a monitor? The answer is to use a *cross-assembler*, which is a piece of software that runs on one microprocessor but assembles code for another. This lets you write programs for the new board using an existing computer, although you cannot run or test them – the development machine does not have the same instruction set.

To reach the monitor stage the following steps should be taken. Firstly, power up the board without any chips in it, and check with a logic probe that each IC socket has power correctly applied and that its signal pins are not connected to the power rails. Next, insert all but the expensive chips – switch off the power first! Check that the output pins of the micro-processor socket are not being driven by logic now present in the circuit (this check isn't foolproof – the lines could be tri-stated and might only be driven when the processor is present). Finally insert the processor and commence debugging.

We can now use some or all of the above test gear to debug our CPU board. The equipment should be used systematically to trace through the circuit in both the forward and reverse directions. Thus, if no characters are output to the terminal a logic probe should be used firstly to check whether the UART is outputting RS-232 data on its T×D pin, whether the UART is receiving chip selects, if the control logic is producing read and write strobes, whether the EPROM's /CS and /OE are activated and lastly whether the CPU's address and data lines are being driven correctly. In all cases check that the input signal to a chip behaves the same as the output from the chip that is producing it; this will quickly locate many wiring faults. The rationale behind working backwards through the circuit is that generally the further you go from the processor the less complex the circuit and the easier it is to see if it is behaving correctly. Having found the area at fault you have to fix it and then trace through the circuit in the forward direction. Using a systematic two-way approach like this can significantly reduce debugging time.

For the quickest location of timing and logic faults you need a logic analyser – if the circuit doesn't work you can immediately attach the analyser to the address, data buses and control logic of the board, and determine whether each chip is producing correct outputs in response to its inputs. You can thus rapidly discover if any PALs are incorrectly designed or if there are other timing problems.

With an oscilloscope instead of a logic analyser things are trickier. Since the processor signals are not normally repetitive you cannot use an oscilloscope to examine how the CPU executes a random piece of code. Instead you should produce a test EPROM with a tight loop in it. For example, to look at memory cycles use code like the following:

```
      LDA #$55
      STA RAM
LOOP: ROL RAM   ;read RAM, rotate left, write RAM
      BRA LOOP
```

A 68B09 takes 5 μs to go round this loop, and each time it reads and writes to a RAM location and changes its contents. Since the cycles repeat we can use an oscilloscope to observe the RAM's /OE, /WR and /CS strobes (or /RAS and /CAS for a DRAM) and see if there are any timing faults. Should this code fail to run then try removing the RAM chip(s). It may be that the RAM is being enabled at the same time as the EPROM, and removing the chips means that you can observe the control signals (though not the data). Removing ICs from a prototype is often a good way of locating faults, so prototypes and initial PCBs should use IC sockets even if the final product will not.

Should the above code still not run then the processor–EPROM interface is probably at fault. We can check whether the processor address lines are working (or wired up) correctly as follows. We could use a tight loop (doubling X each time round the loop and using STA ,X), but this assumes that the CPU's address lines are reaching the EPROM correctly. A better way is to fill the whole EPROM with an instruction that does nothing, for example NOP or CLRA. Then as the CPU runs through the EPROM its program counter and address bus will increment by one per instruction. Viewed with an oscilloscope the address lines will be square waves each having half the frequency of the previous one (1 MHz for A0, 500 kHz for A1, etc. for the 68B09). To get the CPU to loop round the EPROM it must be selected at all addresses, so we either need to produce a modified address decoder PAL, or hard-wire the EPROM's /CS LO and remove any other devices attached to the data bus to avoid contention.

The second method has the advantage that we can use the oscilloscope to check that other chip selects are active at the correct addresses.

Should the board pass these two tests (functioning addresses and able to read and write to RAM) then it is basically working, so it should be able to execute simple programs and initialize a UART. Should the UART fail to program then the problem could be either in the software or in the UART interface. To test for the latter put the CPU in a tight loop accessing the UART and observe the signals with an oscilloscope (or observe directly with an analyser). Once you have a working UART you can use a monitor to peek and poke bytes to memory and bus locations and use a logic probe or analyser to observe the results – such as a chip select going LO if and only if you access a device.

PCB layout

Given a circuit diagram which is believed to be correct the final stage in a product's development is to produce a printed circuit board (PCB), which is a laminated board with copper tracks on each side to make the electrical connections. PCBs can be fabricated in quantity and since they are identical wiring faults are eliminated. The track patterns are produced by a draughtsperson who takes the circuit diagram and creates the PCB layout. There are two ways of tracking a PCB, by hand or with CAD (computer-aided design). With the former coloured tape is placed on plastic film to show tracks and black rings plated through holes (where connections are made between layers of the board). This method is quick for simple circuits but for complex boards you really need to use a modern CAD system. With a typical CAD system the draughtsperson first enters the circuit diagram into the computer. To do so the names and physical positions of the ICs' pins must first be entered – a decent CAD package will have a library of standard TTL and CMOS devices, so this chore is minimized. The designer then verifies the computer's circuit diagram against the original. The draughtsperson then produces a component placement, positioning each component on the board. A 'rat's nest' is now run – the computer compares the circuit diagram with the placement and draws straight lines on the screen to connect the devices' pins together. The draughtsperson then tracks the board, selecting a line at a time and routeing it onto one or more layers of the board, changing its colour once done so that it no longer looks to be part of the untracked 'rat's nest'.

Tracking a highly complex PCB requires skill and the art can only be learnt by experience. Here therefore we shall look at how the designer and draughtsperson should interact to obtain an optimum layout, bearing in mind that the latter may have only minimal knowledge of electronics.

With a purely digital circuit the precise way a board is laid out is not usually important. An exception is arrays of DRAMs which must have good decoupling and wide power and ground tracks – it is best to use a multi-layer board with the inner layers dedicated to 0 and 5 V. Also, traces from ICs connected to expansion buses should be kept as short as possible to minimize capacitive loading of the backplane (STE and VME stipulate connections may be no more than 2 inches long). Otherwise tracks can, and frequently do, take long detours to reach their destinations (if you are working at very high frequencies, for example 100 MHz ECL logic, then more care is required). The main difficulty with tracking a digital board is actually making the myriad of connections, especially fitting the last few in. To speed up this process the designer should point out which connections can be interchanged. Thus, gates in one IC may often be swapped for gates in another; by rewriting PAL pin lists input and output pins can be rearranged; and with comparators 'P' pins can be interchanged provided the same 'Q' pins are. Finally, with RAMs you can connect up the address and data pins any way you want – thus the fact that you write $28 to address $52 but the RAM thinks it is $82 to address $25 does not matter; when you next read $52 the RAM will read $82 from location $25 which will appear to you as $28. Note that this trick does not work with EPROMs – the data is already in the EPROM so CPU and EPROM must agree on the ordering of the address and data buses. These tricks should be used as a last resort when it is otherwise impossible to complete the tracking of a complex layout.

With a board that contains a mixture of analog and digital electronics more care is required. Analog and digital tracks should be kept separate to prevent small analog signals picking up high frequency digital signals by capacitive coupling, and power and ground lines should be separated to stop currents in the power rails from affecting the analog circuit through the digital logic. Figure 8.13 shows how not to arrange things: currents

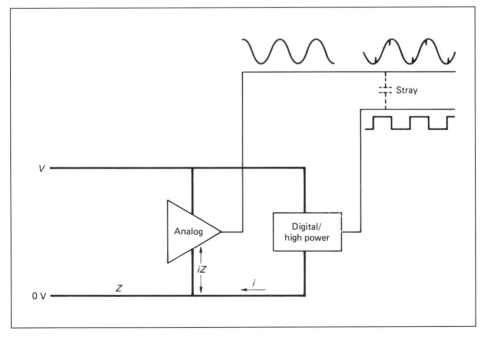

Figure 8.13 *Incorrect layout of an analog and digital circuit*

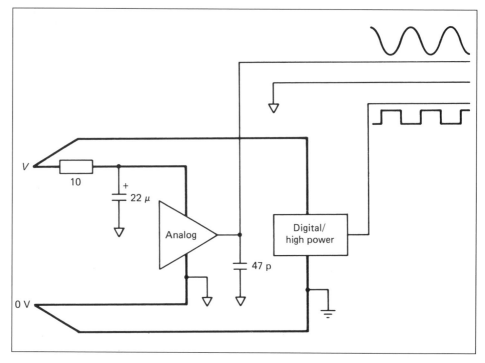

Figure 8.14 *Correct layout of an analog and digital circuit. The RC filter is only needed for noisy supplies and the 47 pF capacitor if the analog output goes near digital signal tracks*

powering the digital logic flow back to the power supply via the analog circuit imposing fluctuating iZ drops on the analog power rails. To avoid this, use separate power and ground connections for the analog and digital circuits and connect them at one point only, see Figure 8.14. It is best to use a low-impedance ground plane for the analog circuitry, and with a 5 V analog circuit on a very noisy board it is preferable to use a voltage regulator to generate the analog 5 V from an independent 12 V supply. You can also add an *RC* or *LC* low-pass filter to prevent high frequency digital noise travelling down the power rail and into the analog circuitry (for examples see the SADC12/16H and SG84 circuits in Chapter 7). The best way to avoid capacitive pick-up is to place a ground track between the analog and digital signals. If this is not possible then a small (say 47 pF) capacitor connected between the analog output and ground will reduce coupling but at the expense of degrading slew rate.

Test code writing

What happens after you have a working PCB depends on how many boards you require. If you only need one then you are finished and can use it in your system. If, however, large numbers are to be produced, perhaps for retail, then a means of quick testing is required. Test routines need to be written that enable a test engineer to locate faulty ICs and PCBs. Ideally these routines should be written by someone other than the board's designer, for a 'test development engineer' will have a more objective view of what may go wrong with a board than its designer. Here we shall point out some of the things to look for when writing programs to test CPU and peripheral boards.

CPU boards

One of the difficulties with production testing CPU boards is that the test program (in an EPROM) has to run on the board under test. This means it is inadvisable to write the test code in a high-level language such as BASIC, C or PASCAL. The problem is that for such a language to run most of the CPU board must be already functioning, for example it needs large amounts of working EPROM and RAM. Thus, if there is a fault the board will just appear dead and with no feedback will be difficult to fix. It is therefore better to write an assembler routine to test the rudimentary parts of the board, and use a high-level language to perform more extensive testing once the board is basically working. Possibly, the test engineer might only resort to the assembler program as a back-up if the high-level one failed to boot.

How should the assembler routine be structured? After fetching the reset vector, the first thing the CPU should do is to light the board's diagnostic LED (if it has one); if it has no such LED it should write to a memory location not used by the rest of the program. This write cycle can be looked for with a logic probe; if found you know that the CPU has read an instruction from the EPROM and executed it – you have some feedback with the very first instruction whereas with BASIC you would need working RAM, UART and hundreds of instructions to be successfully executed. Next the routine should initialize the UART and output a message to a terminal. Note that the program should not use any RAM to do this – it has not been tested yet – so do not use subroutines or interrupts which both save registers in RAM. The routine should now enter a polling loop waiting for a character from the terminal. This means that if no message appears on the screen, the test engineer can ascertain whether the fault lies with the UART/RS-232 interface or with the processor – if the serial interface is at fault the UART's chip select will be being pulsed, if it isn't then the CPU has probably 'crashed' so the fault lies with it or the EPROM interface.

The routine should now test the board's RAM by writing bytes to locations and displaying what it wrote and what it read back. The memory test should check that each location is independent. For example, if in a 64K block of RAM A15 is open circuit (a track break) then the bottom 32K will be duplicated into the top 32K. A simple test for this is to load each pair of memory locations with their address (so locations $5566–7 are loaded with $55 and $66) and then to read them back after filling the whole 64K. The other likely problem is a faulty memory chip with a data bit stuck at zero or one. This can be checked for with a 'walking bit test' – fill the memory with zeros and then set one bit at a time. This is somewhat slow and a quicker (but less rigorous) test is to fill the memory first with $55 and then with $AA which puts every bit into its two states with no adjacent bits being the same. With working RAM the board can use subroutines and interrupts and these should now be tested. The routine can now either test other interfaces (for example, parallel I/O or external buses), or else end and let these be tested by a high-level language program.

Peripheral boards

Peripheral boards are much easier to test than CPU boards. Partly this is because they are less complex than CPU boards, but mainly because the test program runs on a separate CPU board which transmits bytes to the peripheral. Since the CPU board is known to work the test program can (and should) be written in a high-level language. It is best to use BASIC, because a test engineer can easily modify this if it becomes necessary for a particular board, perhaps to halt the program at some point or to make it perform a certain action repeatedly. The program should try to establish that the bus interface is working by reading and writing bytes, but since the registers in many peripheral chips are not read/write this may not always be possible. If possible disable the CPU board's bus timeout circuitry, and then if the peripheral fails to respond (by giving a /DATACK) the address and data will 'hang' on the bus and a logic probe can quickly establish whether the peripheral is decoding the bus address correctly.

The CPU should then cause the peripheral to output data: if it is a parallel I/O board via its parallel I/O ports, or if a serial board via its serial ports, etc. The outputs should be connected into another board, perhaps the CPU board if it has an appropriate interface, and the data read back from it. The test code should exercise the peripheral over all its states, so for a parallel I/O board you would write $00, $01, $02, $04, ..., $80 and their inverses to each port, thus checking for track shorts; for user-friendliness the program should indicate which chip or signal is faulty. If the board can produce interrupts these should be tested – use a different maskable interrupt line to the rest of the CPU's system so that if the peripheral fails to clear its interrupt the CPU won't 'crash' but can just mask off that interrupt line.

As far as the board's outputs are concerned it is best not to cable them back onto the board itself. This is because if there is a fault on the board then since it is to some extent testing itself it may not show up. For example, suppose you have a serial board and you cable port A into port B. You run a test program that makes port A transmit characters to port B and the CPU successfully reads them back. You then hook port A up to a terminal but only gibberish comes out! What went wrong? Answer: the clock frequency was incorrect (perhaps the wrong crystal was fitted), so the UART was transmitting at an illegal baud rate, but since the same board received the RS-232 signal it decoded it correctly. Thus it is best to connect the outputs into another board in the bus.

Glossary

A/D or ADC Analog-to-digital converter. A device which takes an analog signal and converts it to a digital number for reading by a microprocessor.

ALU Arithmetic Logic Unit. The section of a microprocessor which performs arithmetic operations.

Amp Short for ampere – the unit of electrical current.

Anode The 'positive' end of a diode.

Arbiter A device which decides which master has control of a bus at any given instant.

Assembler A low-level programming language for a microprocessor.

Assertion Putting a signal into its active or TRUE state; thus asserting /WR causes that line to go LO. Compare with negation.

Backplane A printed circuit board that provides the hardware connections for a bus-based computer system.

Baud rate The bit rate of a serial transfer device.

Bit The smallest piece of information in a digital system, it can have the value 0 or 1; the least significant bit is Bit 0.

Boot The start-up code for a microprocessor.

Branch An instruction which changes the flow of control in a microprocessor program. Branches are often conditional – the branch is taken if a certain condition is satisfied.

Buffer A device which takes an input signal and transmits it unchanged, possibly with different drive capability or with tri-state or open-collector output. In software a buffer is an area of memory used for storing input or output data.

Bus A backplane and protocol definition which enables computer boards to communicate with one another.

Byte Eight bits of information, capable of storing numbers from 0–255 (0–$FF in hex).

Capacitor A device for storing charge. Capacitance is measured in farads, and is defined as charge per volt.

Cathode The 'negative' end of a diode.

CMOS Complementary Metal Oxide Semiconductor. A low-power logic family.

Comparator Device for determining whether an analog signal is above or below a certain level.

Coulomb The unit of electrical charge (symbol C), related to current which is the rate of flow of charge.

Counter A digital device which counts up or down, in binary or binary-coded decimal.

CPU Central Processing Unit. Synonymous with microprocessor.

D/A or DAC Digital-to-analog Converter. A device which takes in a digital number and produces an analog output voltage.

Decibel A measure of the ratio of two voltages. If the voltages are V_1 and V_2 then their ratio in decibels (symbol dB) is given by 20 log V_1/V_2.

Decoder A digital device which accepts a number of inputs and depending on their values selects one output to assert.

Decoupling Putting capacitors across the power supply rails to reduce noise in a digital circuit.

Development system A computer system used for producing code to run on a target system.

Diode A semiconductor device which only permits current to flow in one direction – from anode to cathode.

DMA Direct Memory Access. A technique whereby a microprocessor gives up control of its bus, and a separate device (the DMA controller) rapidly moves data between memory and a peripheral.

DRAM Dynamic RAM. Read/write memory which must be periodically refreshed to prevent it from losing its contents.

EEPROM Electrically Erasable Programmable ROM.

Emitter follower A transistor circuit in which the emitter voltage follows the base voltage minus one diode drop (0.6 V).

EPLD Erasable Programmable Logic Device. A device which is more flexible than a PAL and can also be erased by UV light.

EPROM Electrically Programmable Read-only Memory. A device that can store data, which is held even when there is no power present; the data can be erased by exposing the EPROM to UV light.

Fanout The number of logic inputs that a given chip can drive.

Farad The unit of capacitance (symbol F), defined as charge per volt.

FIFO A digital storage device which operates on the First In First Out principle.

Flip-flop A digital device which when clocked transfers data on an input pin to an output line.

Henry The unit of inductance (symbol H).

Hex or Hexadecimal The base 16 counting system. The counts go from 0 to 9 and A to F, A being 10 through to F being 15. To distinguish hex from decimal a '$' may be added before a number or an 'H' after it, for example $5A or 5AH.

Inductor A component which has inductance (measured in henrys) and acts to oppose a change in the flow of current through it.

Interrupt A means by which a microprocessor can be made to suspend the running of its program and execute a separate piece of code instead.

Inverter A logic gate which changes the polarity of the input signal.

Kilobyte Equivalent to 1024 bytes of information, often given the symbol K or Kb.

Latch A digital device which when clocked stores data.

LIFO Last In First Out. A term describing the action of a microprocessor stack.

Master A board which can assume control of a bus.

Metastability An unwanted state which can occur in a flip-flop when its setup time is violated.

MMU Memory Management Unit. A device which remaps a processor's memory space into different locations.

Monostable A device which produces an output pulse of a given duration in response to a clock edge.

Multiplexer A device which uses select pins to choose between one of a number of inputs which is then sent to an output.

Multi-tasking A system whereby a microprocessor executes more than one program at once. The operating system shares the processor's time between tasks so giving the appearance that they run simultaneously.

Negation Putting a signal into its inactive state. Thus negating /RD means driving the line HI.

Negative feedback A circuit where part of the output is fed back to the input and subtracted from it.

Ohm The unit of electrical resistance (symbol Ω) related to current and voltage by Ohm's law, which states that $V = IR$.

Op-amp Operational amplifier – a circuit block used to manipulate analog signals.

Open-collector A type of output such that the chip, or transistor, can drive the line LO but can only 'float' HI.

Operating system Software responsible for low-level control of a microprocessor system. Typically it is responsible for swapping tasks in a multi-tasking system, basic I/O and interrupt handling.

Opto-isolation A way of conveying signals without the need for an electrical connection – the signals are sent via a beam of light.

PAL Programmable Array Logic. A logic family that can be tailored to particular logical requirements.

Parity An extra bit added to a binary number so that the total number of ones is either even or odd. Parity allows single-bit transmission errors to be detected.

PLL Phase-locked loop.

Positive feedback Feedback where part of the output signal is added to the input signal. Used in comparator circuits to give Schmitt trigger characteristics.

PISO Parallel In Serial Out. Applied to shift registers, data enters in parallel format (for example, byte wide) and is shifted out 1 bit at at time (serially).

Polling Reading peripheral status registers to determine if data is available or if the peripheral has caused an interrupt.

Potential Synonymous with voltage.

PSD Phase-sensitive Detector. A device which converts the phase difference between two signals into a voltage.

RAM Random Access Memory. Memory which can be both read from and written to.

Refresh cycle A type of access to a DRAM chip which causes the DRAM to retain its memory contents.

Resistor A device that impedes the flow of electrical current; its value is measured in ohms (symbol Ω).

ROM Read-only Memory. Memory used for storing microprocessor programs. Usually the cheaper EPROMs are used instead.

RS-232 A defined protocol for serial data transmission.

Schmitt trigger A type of input circuit, the switching threshold depends on whether the input signal is increasing or decreasing.

Shift register Digital device in which on a clock edge the output data shifts one place left or right.

Sink A device sinks current when the current flows into the device.

SIPO Serial In Parallel Out. Applied to shift registers, the input is 1 bit at a time and the output is a parallel word.

Slave A board, interfaced to a bus, which can take or provide data but which cannot itself control the bus.

Slew rate The speed at which an op-amp's output can swing, measured in V/µs.

Source A device sources current when the current flows out of the device (compare with sink).

Stack A storage area used by a microprocessor, especially when executing a subroutine or interrupt.

STEbus A bus designed predominantly for 8-bit processors, also called IEEE-1000.

Subroutine A section of code which may be run, after which control returns to the main program.

Target system A computer system which controls or monitors equipment, often a stripped-down version of a development system.

Timing diagram A diagram which shows the relationships between signals in a logic design.

Transistor A semiconductor device with three terminals (base, emitter and collector).

Tri-state A logic state (labelled Z) which neither loads nor drives the line.

Truth table A table which shows the output states of a logic circuit as a function of the input states.

TTL Transistor-Transistor Logic. A logic family which comes in various types, such as Standard, LS, S, ALS, F.

Two's complement. A binary counting scheme which allows for negative numbers.

UART Universal Asynchronous Receive and Transmit. A device for sending and receiving serial data transmissions.

VCO Voltage-controlled Oscillator. A device that produces a waveform of a frequency which depends on an input voltage.

Vector A pointer to somewhere in memory; for example, the reset vector tells a microprocessor where to begin commencement of its program.

Vectored interrupt A way of responding to an interrupt; the processor performs a vector acknowledge cycle and the interrupting device provides a vector.

VMEbus A bus designed for 16- and 32-bit processors, also labelled IEEE-1014.

Volt The unit of voltage or potential difference (symbol V).

Zener diode A diode which when operated in the reverse bias condition breaks down and conducts current at a fixed voltage, V_Z.

Further reading

Listed below are some books that may be of interest to readers who desire to broaden their knowledge of topics covered in this book.

Dowding B. (1988). *Principles of Electronics.* Prentice-Hall, Hemel Hempstead. Easy to read coverage of analog electronics and digital logic.

Holdsworth B. (1987). *Microprocessor Engineering.* Butterworth-Heinemann, Oxford. General book on microprocessor techniques and interfacing, examines the 8085 CPU.

Horowitz P. and Hill W. (1989). *The Art of Electronics* 2nd ed. Cambridge University Press. The best general electronics textbook around. Very practically orientated and non-mathematical. Looks at the 68008 processor.

Millman J. and Halkias C.C. (1972). *Integrated Electronics.* McGraw-Hill, Tokyo. Advanced text on transistors and amplifiers.

Tooley M. (1988). *Bus-based Industrial Process Control.* Butterworth-Heinemann, Oxford. In-depth coverage of microprocessor control and the STEbus.

Zaks R. and Labiak W. (1982). *Programming the 6809.* Sybex, Berkeley. A good entry into the world of assembler programming techniques.

Index

Index

246